ʻIlm:

Science, Religion and Art in Islam

ʿIlm:
Science, Religion and Art in Islam

Edited by Samer Akkach

THE UNIVERSITY
of ADELAIDE

UNIVERSITY OF
ADELAIDE PRESS

Published in Adelaide by
University of Adelaide Press
Barr Smith Library
The University of Adelaide
South Australia 5005
press@adelaide.edu.au
www.adelaide.edu.au/press

The University of Adelaide Press publishes peer-reviewed scholarly books. It aims to maximise access to the best research by publishing works through the internet as free downloads and for sale as high-quality printed volumes.

For the full Cataloguing-in-Publication data please contact the National Library of Australia: cip@nla.gov.au.

ISBN (paperback) 978-1-925261-75-2
ISBN (ebook: pdf) 978-1-925261-76-9

Senior Editor: Rebecca Burton
Cover design: Emma Spoehr
Typesetting: Midland Typesetters

Cover image:
20072A13(a-c)
Celestial globe, 19th century, Lucknow, Uttar Pradesh, silver, 15.5 cm (diam);
Gift of Barrie and Judith Heaven 2007, Art Gallery of South Australia, Adelaide

CONTENTS

PREFACE

Conceptions of 'knowledge' (*ʿilm* in Arabic) — its virtue, necessity, and socio-religious function — have played a central role in Muslims' life throughout Islamic history. The two sacred sources of Islam, the Quran (words of God) and the Hadiths (words of the Prophet), placed a strong emphasis on *ʿilm*, considering knowledge acquisition to be mandatory for all Muslims, the act of knowing to be essential to all aspects of cultural production, and knowledge in its highest state to be akin to prophecy. Discriminating between knowledge and ignorance, the Quran asks, 'Are those who know and those who do not know equal?' (39:9), and goes on to assure Muslims that God will raise believers and possessors of knowledge above others (58:11). The Prophet Muhammad adds further import to the Quranic view by declaring that 'seeking knowledge is obligatory on every Muslim', and that 'the *ʿulamāʾ* (possessors of knowledge) are the inheritors of the prophets'.

It is little wonder that *ʿilm* framed Muslims' high aspirations, determined their social status, and paved their ways to paradise. The high significance Muslims accord to *ʿilm* is evident in the numerous sources (in Arabic, Persian, and Ottoman Turkish) devoted to articulating the nature, virtue, and function of the three related aspects of knowing: *ʿilm* (possession of knowledge), *taʿlīm* (dissemination of knowledge, through teaching, education, and moral upbringing), and *tuʿallum* (acquisition of knowledge, through learning, training, and making). There are also numerous biographical reference books on the life and works of the *ʿulamāʾ*— that is, the individuals who had devoted their lives to the pursuit of knowledge. These sources show the enduring preoccupation with *ʿilm*'s epistemological, moral, and socio-religious values. Indeed, the large body of literature available on various aspects of knowledge testifies to the fact that the concept of *ʿilm* has dominated Islam to such an extent that one can safely say it has given Islamic civilisation its distinctive shape and complexion today.

This edited volume of chapters resulted from an international conference held at the University of Adelaide in July 2016 under the same title to explore the multifaceted concept of *ʿilm* in Islam — its agency and manifestations in the connected realms of science, religion, and the arts. *ʿIlm* is normally rendered into English in a straightforward manner as 'knowledge'. This unnuanced translation tends to conceal the complexity and multivalent nature of the Arabic expression, which is at once simple and complex. It is simple in its transparent and intuitively recognisable meaning, yet complex in its many derivations, connotations, and associations, which link it to diverse aspects of knowing, such as comprehension, conception, perception, feeling, and familiarity, as well as different modes of knowledge acquisition, production, and dissemination, including teaching and learning, education, and morality (*tarbiya*).[1] Mediaeval Arabic lexicographers relate *ʿālam*, 'world', also to *ʿilm*, thereby signifying that the divine creative act was fundamentally an act of knowing and that the created world was a product of knowledge.[2] Muslim mystics (Sufis) customarily report a holy tradition in which God identifies the main reason behind creating the world as being 'his desire to be known', thus rendering *knowledge* as the ultimate aim of the religious pursuit.

The conference presented an opportunity, at national and international levels, to examine the concept of *ʿilm* in pre-, early, and postmodern Islamic cultures in order to better understand its role in social, cultural, and intellectual developments. Over four days, the conference brought together a broad group of scholars, artists, designers, curators, conservators, and higher-degree researchers across the fields of Islamic intellectual history, history and theory of Islamic art and architecture, history of Islamic science, and Islamic studies to address key issues of concern and to highlight points of intersection between science, religion, and the arts. Presenters and participants discussed how *ʿilm* is understood, engaged with, and experienced by Muslim communities today; what practices, territories, and histories of *ʿilm* are in need of better understanding; and how *ʿilm* continues to shape Islam's past, present, and future within the Muslim world and beyond.

In conjunction with the conference the Art Gallery of South Australia (AGSA) staged, in collaboration with the University of Adelaide's Centre for Asian and Middle Eastern Architecture (CAMEA), an Islamic art exhibition titled *ʿIlm: Art and Knowledge in Islam*. On display at AGSA were 45 works of art from Iran, Egypt, Turkey, India, and Indonesia dated from the 10th century to the contemporary era. A rare cultural feast in Australia, the displayed objects showed the rich diversity of Islamic art, and, most important for this occasion, they showed how knowledge formed a constant basis and framework for artistic expression in the Islamic tradition. Both the conference and the exhibition provided intellectually stimulating and thought-provoking occasions for contemplating the contributions Islam had made, and has continued to make, to humanity and global civilisation.

The conference was generously supported by two grants, a Discovery Project grant from the Australian Research Council (ARC), and a culture and art grant from the Council for Australian-Arab Relations (CAAR). I wish to thank both organisations for their support, without which neither the conference nor this edited volume would have been possible. I also wish to extend special thanks to the Art Gallery of South Australia (AGSA) for accepting my invitation to set up the exhibition, and the curator of Islamic art, James Bennett, for assuming the responsibility of designing and setting up the exhibition and turning it into such an attractive and informative event. I am thankful to the four keynote speakers, Professors James Piscatori, Nidhal Guessoum, Peter Harrison, and Stefano Carboni, for enriching the conference through valuable lectures and stimulating discussions; to the University of Adelaide and School of Architecture and Built Environment (SABE) for providing the facilities and administrative support for the event; and to the conference secretary and my research assistant, Perri Sparnon, for her tireless organisational and research efforts from inception to end; without her much appreciated assistance the *ʿilm* project would not have reached its current state. Finally, special thanks go to the conference participants whose works are published here in chapter form, and to John Emerson and Rebecca Burton of the University of Adelaide Press for their support and assistance in the production of this volume.

NOTES

1 In many Arab countries today, the ministry for education is called *wizārat al-tarbiya wa -l-taʿlīm*, placing 'moral upbringing' (*trabiya*) before 'teaching' (*taʿlīm*, from *ʿilm*). This shows the enduring bond between knowledge dissemination and moral upbringing in the collective Arab imagination to this day.

2 Ibn Manẓūr, *Lisān al-ʿarab al-muḥīt*, *ʿ-l-m*.

NOTES TO THE READER

In various chapters, authors have used primary sources in different Islamic languages (Arabic, Ottoman Turkish, Farsi, and Urdu), and thus transliterations may vary according to the systems used by each author. Attempts have been made to unify them as much as practically possible.

The following Arabic terms and names are commonly known in English and are therefore used without diacritics: Quran, Hadith, sheikh, sultan, Muhammad, Ahmad, Mustafa, Abdullah.

Names of certain figures (scholars or sultans) or places are written differently in different original sources (for example, Murat in Ottoman, Murad in Arabic). Attempts have been made to keep transliterations consistent within each chapter according to its author's preferences. One form of the name is kept in the bibliography where possible.

Translated citations from the Quran and the Hadiths vary in different chapters according to the choices of the authors.

The Glossary lists words frequently used throughout this book; note that the spelling in an individual chapter may vary from the spelling given in the Glossary for the reasons mentioned above.

Sources used in the chapters are combined in one bibliography placed at the end.

All dates are given in the Gregorian calendar (BCE/CE), unless otherwise stated.

The abbreviations 'sing.' (for 'singular') and 'pl.' (for 'plural') are used throughout this volume.

Every effort has been made to contact copyright holders to obtain permission for the usage of the illustrations reproduced in this book. Should you have any concerns regarding copyright of any of these illustrations, please contact press@adelaide.edu.au.

GLOSSARY

Akhlāq: Literally 'ethics', or 'disposition'; a term referring to the practice of virtue, morality, and manners in Islamic theology and philosophy.

ʿAql: Literally 'intellect' and 'reason'; a term used in Islamic theology and philosophy for the intellect or the rational faculty of the soul or mind.

Batik: Late 19th-century term, from Javanese, literally 'painted'. A method (originally used in Java) of producing coloured designs on textiles by dyeing them, having first applied wax to the parts to be left undyed.

Ceplokan: Also Ceplok, describes a category of patterns used in Indonesian batik (see above) including geometric forms and motifs of circles, squares, rectangles, ovals, stars, and animals.

Dīn: Literally 'religion' or 'creed'; in the Quran it means the way of life which righteous Muslims must adopt in order to comply with divine law (as defined by the Quran and *sunna*).

Falsafa: Literally 'philosophy'; it designates the pursuit of philosophy in Islam, including reflections on problems connected with life, the universe, ethics, society, and so on, as inherited by Islam from the Greek intellectual tradition in the 8th century CE.

Fann: Literally 'art' (pl. *funūn*); originally, *fann* meant 'kind', 'sort', 'branch', or 'species', and later 'ornament'.

Fiqh: Literally 'understanding' or 'knowing'. It is the technical term for 'jurisprudence' in the Islamic sciences of religious law. *Faqīh* (pl. *fuqahāʾ*), 'jurist', is one who professes or practises the science of Islamic law.

Hadith: Literally 'speech', 'saying', and 'talk'. In Islamic religious sciences, it refers to the reported sayings of the Prophet Muhammad. *ʿIlm al-ḥadīth* is the 'science of Prophetic traditions' that deals with the authentication of the reported accounts of what the Prophet said or did.

Ḥajj: Literally 'pilgrimage'; from *al-ḥajj*, 'targeted destination'. It refers to the greater Muslim pilgrimage to Mecca, which takes place in the last month of the Muslim calendar and which all Muslims are expected to make at least once during their lifetime if they can afford to do so. It is one of the Five Pillars of Islam.

Ḥaqīqa: Literally 'truth' or 'reality'; from *ḥaqq*, 'right' and 'true'. *Ḥaqq*, the 'Real', one of God's 99 most beautiful Names identified in the Quran and Hadiths. It is commonly used in mystical writing in contrast to *sharīʿa*, 'divine law'.

Ḥikma: Literally 'wisdom', 'philosophy', 'rationale', or 'underlying reason'; a concept used in Islamic philosophy and law.

ʿIbāda: Literally 'worship'; from ʿabd, 'slave', and ʿubūdiyya, 'slavery' and 'servitude'; worship in this sense is an expression of one's utter servitude to God.

ʿIlm: Literally 'knowledge' or 'science' (pl. *ʿulūm*); later, 'modern science' and 'natural science', as in the duality of science versus religion.

Kaʿba: The large cube-shaped building dressed in black cloth inside the al-Masjid al-Ḥaram mosque in Mecca, considered by Muslims to be the holiest place on earth.

Kalām: Literally 'speech', abbreviated form of *'ilm al-kalām,* meaning 'science of discourse'; an Islamic form of theology sometimes referred to as 'Islamic scholastic theology'. A scholar of *kalām* is referred to as a *mutakallim* (pl. *mutakallimūn*).

Khiyāmiyya: Literally 'tentmakers'; a type of decorative applique textile historically used to decorate tents across the Middle East, but most famous in Egypt.

Madrasa: Literally 'school' or 'college', from the Arabic verb *darasa,* 'to study', and *darrasa,* 'to teach'. It is commonly recognised today as a college for Islamic education.

Quran: Literally 'recitation', from the verb *qara'a,* to 'read' or 'recite'. The Islamic sacred book, believed to be the word of God as dictated by the archangel Gabriel and written down in Arabic. It consists of 114 chapters (*sūra,* pl. *suwar*) of varying length.

Sharī'a: Literally 'law'; in the Islamic context, 'divine law'. It is the system of rules, injunctions, and prohibitions that is derived from the Quran and Hadiths.

Sheikh: Also spelt 'shaykh', literally 'old man'; normally a leader in a Muslim community or organisation, often the (male) chief or head of an Arab tribe, family, or village. It also refers to a religious cleric; *sheikh al-Islām* was the top religious cleric during Ottoman times.

Shī'i: A follower of the *Shī'a* sect that emerged in the formative period of Islam after a political dispute involving 'Alī, the Prophet's son-in-law. The *Shī'a* is the dominant sect in Iran.

Shikār: A Persian term meaning 'to hunt', which also refers to 'game/prey'. It was used throughout the Persian-speaking countries and in Mughal India.

Ṣinā'a: Literally 'craft', 'practical knowledge', or 'skill'; today it also means 'industry', and traditionally it referred to 'art'.

Sunna: Literally 'form', 'way', 'course', or 'rule', referring specifically to the Prophet Muhammad's way of life as expressed through his words or acts, which are recorded, authenticated, and transmitted from one generation to another. The Quran and the Sunna together form the two authoritative pillars of Islamic orthodoxy.

Sunni: A follower of the *sunna,* the Prophet's way of life that came to represent orthodox Islam. The *Sunnis,* the orthodox Muslims, are the dominant sect in Islam.

Sufi: Literally 'one wearing woollen garment', from *ṣūf,* 'wool'. It refers to a 'mystic', or a follower of the mystical path. Historically, Sufis have had an uneasy relationship with mainstream Islam.

Ṭarīqa: Literally 'way' or 'technique'; in mystical literature, the 'pathway' of spirituality, often coupled with *ḥaqīqa*, 'truth', the destination of the spiritual journey.

Tafsīr: Literally 'interpretation'; it is the Arabic term for 'exegesis', usually of the Quran, involving the explanation of Quranic verses and the provision of contextual information, as well as giving different views and opinions of scholars on the verse. An author of *tafsīr* is a *mufassir* (pl. *mufassirūn*).

Tawḥīd: Literally 'unity' or 'oneness' of God; it refers to the concept of monotheism in Islam.

'Ulamā': Literally 'those who know'. It is used to identify both religious authorities and scientists, the 'possessors of knowledge', since the root *'ilm* in Arabic means 'science' and 'knowledge'. In pre-modern Islam it referred generally to the 'jurists', a powerful group of clerics who represented religious authority.

Umma: Literally 'people', or 'community'. The whole community of Muslims bound together by ties of religion.

LIST OF CONTRIBUTORS

Samer Akkach is professor of architectural history and theory and Founding Director of the Centre for Asian and Middle Eastern Architecture (CAMEA) at the University of Adelaide. His main areas of expertise are in the fields of Islamic art and architecture, Islamic mysticism (Sufism), and Islamic intellectual history, and his interdisciplinary research interests extend to socio-urban and cultural history of the Levant and history of Islamic science in the early modern period. He has held several Australian Research Council (ARC) Discovery grants and was a recipient of the ARC Discovery Outstanding Researcher Award (DORA). His major publications include the landmark *Cosmology and Architecture in Premodern Islam* (2005), *Islam and the Enlightenment* (2007), *Letters of a Sufi Scholar* (2010), *Intimate Invocations* (2012), *Damascene Diaries* (2015), and, most recently, *Istanbul Observatory* (2017).

Katharine Bartsch is a senior lecturer at the University of Adelaide. Katharine trained as an architect and practised in Adelaide and India before commencing her academic career. Her interdisciplinary research examines the production and transformation of the predominantly hybrid architecture of Muslim communities in the context of human mobility. She is currently part of a research team, funded by the Australian Research Council (2013-16), which examines 'The Architecture of Australia's Muslim Pioneers'. This project surveys the remnant architecture of Australia's Muslim cameleers who played a vital role in the discovery, exploration, and settlement of Australia.

James Bennett is curator of Asian Art at the Art Gallery of South Australia. His major exhibitions and catalogue publications include *Crescent Moon: Islamic Art and Civilisation of Southeast Asia* (2005), *Golden Journey: Japanese Art from Australian Collections* (2009), *Beneath the Winds: Masterpieces of Southeast Asian Art* (2011), *Realms of Wonder: Jain, Hindu and Islamic Art of India* (2013), and *Treasure Ships: Art in the Age of Spices* (2014). He is currently undertaking doctoral research at the University of Adelaide examining the definitive elements appearing in the development of an Islamic aesthetic in Java, with specific reference to the art of the *pesisir* period dating from the 16th to the 18th century.

Sam Bowker is a senior lecturer in art history and visual culture at Charles Sturt University (CSU) in Wagga Wagga, New South Wales. He is the curator of regional and international exhibitions on the theme of 'Khayamiya', or Egyptian Tentmaker Applique, and developed 'ART240: Introduction to Islamic Art and Design' as Australia's first distance-education undergraduate subject in Islamic art from contemporary perspectives. Prior to joining CSU he lectured in art and design theory for the Australian National University (ANU), where he completed his PhD. He has also developed education programs for the National Portrait Gallery, National Library of Australia, and National Museum of Australia.

Syed Mehboob Bukhari is a lecturer in philosophy at the University of Karachi, Pakistan, where he completed his doctoral study. His research interests include critical theory, postcolonialism, and South Asian Islam. His most recently published paper is 'Social Sciences in South Asian Islam: Some Lessons for the Muslim World'.

Faris Hajamaideen is director of the School of Architecture and the Built Environment at the Singapore Polytechnic, where he has been teaching history and theory of ideas since 2002. He completed his master's degree at McGill University's School of Architecture and his PhD at the University of Adelaide's Centre for Asian and Middle Eastern Architecture (CAMEA). His main research interest has been the study of the human body as a site for architectural imaginings, with a special focus on, first, the relationship between Vitruvius' *De Architectura* and Platonic philosophy, and, second, the understanding of the body in the works of the 12th-century Muslim illuminationist (*ishrāqī*) Shihāb al-Dīn al-Surawardī. He has written, taught, and presented invited talks on this topic.

Virginia Hooker is emeritus professor at the Australian National University and a fellow of the Australian Academy of the Humanities. She was formerly professor of Indonesian and Malay and is now a fellow in the Department of Political and Social Change, College of Asia and the Pacific. Her current research concerns Islam-themed art in Southeast Asia. Among her publications are *Writing a New Society: Social Change through the Novel in Malay* (2000), 'Art for Allah's Sake' (*Inside Indonesia 101:* Jul-Sept 2010), 'Reflections of the Soul' (*Inside Indonesia* 112: Apr-Jun 2013), and 'Mindful of Allah: Islam and the Visual Arts in Indonesia and Malaysia' (*Artlink*, 33(1) March 2013).

Selen Morkoç is visiting research fellow at the University of Adelaide's Centre for Asian and Middle Eastern Architecture (CAMEA), where she completed her PhD on early modern Ottoman architecture. She has taught art and architectural history in Turkey and Australia. She is the author of *Ottoman Narratives on Architecture: Text, Context and Hermeneutics* (2010), and co-author of *The Elements of Modern Architecture: Understanding Contemporary Buildings* (2014).

Shaha Parpia is a PhD candidate at the University of Adelaide's Centre for Asian and Middle Eastern Architecture (CAMEA). She holds a master's degree in the history of Islamic art and architecture from the School of Oriental and African Studies (SOAS), University of London. Her recent publications include 'Mughal Hunting Grounds: Landscape Manipulation and "Garden" Association' (2016), 'Reordering Nature: Power Politics in the Mughal Shikargah', and 'Hunting Ground, Agricultural Land and the Forest: Sustainable Interdependency in Mughal India 1526-1707' (2018).

Susan Scollay is a Melbourne-based, independent art historian specialising in the study of the art and architecture of Islam, with a focus on the Ottoman Empire. She was guest curator of the exhibition *Love and Devotion: From Persia and Beyond* at the State Library of Victoria, Melbourne, in 2012 and at the Bodleian Library, University of Oxford, in 2012-13. Susan edited the exhibition publication, named by the *Art Newspaper* in London and New York as one of the best art books of 2013. She is a fellow of the Royal Asiatic Society of Great Britain and Ireland.

Peter Scriver is an associate professor and a founding member of the Centre for Asian and Middle Eastern Architecture at the University of Adelaide (CAMEA). He is a leading authority on the colonial and modern architectural histories of South Asia and has published several pioneering books in that field over the past quarter century, most recently *India: Modern Architectures in History* (2015), with co-author Amit Srivastava. With Katharine Bartsch and partners in the South Australian Museum and International Islamic University of Malaysia he is currently leading an ARC Linkage Project which examines the impact of Afghan and Indian cameleers on the settlement history of colonial Australia.

Perri Sparnon is an emerging researcher and curator whose work focuses on the history of science and art in pre- and early modern Islam. Perri joined the University of Adelaide in 2015 to complete her honours thesis, 'Revelation and Reason: The Development of Islamic Cosmology, 7th-18th centuries', under the supervision of Professor Samer Akkach. Previously, she completed a bachelor of arts majoring in art history at the University of Melbourne, where she is currently pursuing a diploma of Arabic Language. She has held research positions at the University of Adelaide and Art Gallery of Western Australia.

LIST OF ILLUSTRATIONS

Figure 2.1 Illustration of the visual system in Ibn al-Haytham's *Kitāb al-manāẓir.* Süleymaniye Library, Istanbul, MS Fatih 3212, fol. 81b.

Figure 2.2 Illustration of the visual system in Kamāl al-Dīn al-Fārisī's *Tanqīḥ al-Manāẓir.* Topkapi Palace Museum, Istanbul, Ahmed III Library, MS 3340, folio 16a.

Figure 2.3 Diagram of the eye in Kamal al-Din al-Fārisī''s *Tanqiḥ al-Manāẓir.* Topkapi Palace Museum, Istanbul, Ahmed III Library, MS 3340, folio 25b.

Figure 2.4 Illustration of the visual system in Taqī al-Dīn's *Nūr ḥadaqat al-ibṣār.* Dār al-Kutub al-Miṣriyya, Cairo, 'Ulūm Riyāḍiyya MS 893, folio 8a.

Figure 2.5 'De humani corporis fabrica (Of the Structure of the Human Body)' by Andreas Vesalius (Flemish, Brussels 1514-1564 Zakynthos, Greece), John of Calcar (John Stephen Calcar) (Netherlandish, Calcar, Cleves 1499-1546/50 Naples, Italy). Published by Johann Oporinus (publisher 1536-1567), Basel, 1555. Woodcut, 39.5 × 26.7 × 8.3 cm. The Metropolitan Museum of Art, New York, Acc. 53.682. (Licensed under CC0 1.0.)

Figure 2.6 *Kitāb ṣuwar al-kawākib al-thābita* (Book of the Images of the Fixed Stars) of al-Ṣūfī by 'Abd al-Raḥmān al-Ṣūfī (Iranian, Rey 903-986 Shiraz). 18th century, Iran. Ink, opaque watercolour, and gold on paper 24.9 × 19.4 × 2.4 cm. The Metropolitan Museum of Art, Acc. 1975.192.2. (Licensed under CC0 1.0.)

Figure 2.7 Illustration of the anatomy of the eye in Friedrich Risner's *Opticae Thesaurus*, 1572. ETH-Bibliothek Zürich, VD16 H 693, p. 6. (Licensed under Public Domain Mark 1.0.)

Figure 2.8 A plate from Johannes Kepler's *Ad Vitellionem Paralipomena, quibus Astronomiae Pars Optica*. Published by A Apud Claudium Marnium & Haeredes Ioannis Aubrii in 1604, page 177. Reproduced from http://www.hps.cam.ac.uk/starry/keplerbooks.html. (Licensed under Creative Commons via Wikimedia Commons.)

Figure 2.9 Illustration of the eye in René Descartes' *Optics: Discourse on Methods*. (Licensed under Creative Commons CC BY 4.0 via Wellcome Images.)

Figure 3.1 Rhinoceros, *Vaki'at-i Baburi.* Or. 3714 vol. 4 fol. 379, British Library, London. © British Library Board (Or. 3714).

Figure 3.2 Dipper/*Saj,* album leaf painted by Mansūr. Acc. 55.121.10.16, The Metropolitan Museum of Art, New York. (Licensed under CC0 1.0.)

Figure 3.3 Akbar hunts with cheetahs in a *qamarghā* ring in Lahore in 1567, painted by Miskīna with Mansūr and Sarwān, *Akbarnāma.* Reproduced from the Victoria and Albert Museum, London. Permission granted © Victoria and Albert Museum, London.

Figure 3.4 Akbar hunting black buck with trained cheetahs in 1527, painted by La'l and Kēsav Khord, Akbarnama. Reproduced from the Victoria and Albert Museum, London. Permission granted © Victoria and Albert Museum, London.

Figure 9.3 Detail: Rose gives Nightingale a handkerchief as a keepsake. From a manuscript of Badīʾ al-Dīn Manūchihr al-Tajirī al-Tabrīzī, *Dilsuznāmah*, dated 860/1455-56, Edirne. The Bodleian Libraries, The University of Oxford, MS. Ouseley 133, fols 49r, 62r.

Figure 9.4 Detail: Architectural reconstruction of the Saʿdabad Pavilion at the Edirne Palace drawn by Orhan Çakmakçıoğlu (1923-2003). Photograph by S Scollay, 2007.

Figure 9.5 Saʿdabad Palace, engraving by WH Bartlett (1809-54), c. 1836. From Miss Pardoe, *Beauties of the Bosphorus: Views of Constantinople and its Environs*, 1839, plate facing page 6. Reproduced from *Travelogues*, http://eng.travelogues.gr. Courtesy of Aikaterini Laskaridis Foundation Library, Greece.

Figure 10.1 *Kain panjang* (long hip cloth), printed on cotton. White and blue with *pagi-sore* and *ceplok* patterning, 104 × 250 cm. Indramayu, North Coast Java, 20th century AD/14th century AH. Reproduced from Anne Dunham Collection, © Islamic Arts Museum Malaysia.

Figure 10.2 Carved stone panels based on textile patterns, found at Candi Sewu temple, Central Java, erected c. 782 CE, documented in 1865 photograph (1403-3792-25). © Museum Volkenkunde.

Figure 10.3 Length of cloth, ceremonial textile and sacred heirloom, c. 1690, Gujarat, India; found in Tanah Toraja, South Sulawesi. Cotton, natural mordant dyes, batik and block print, 420.0 × 77.0 cm. Gift of Michael and Mary Abbott 1996. Gift of Michael and Mary Abbott 1996 to the Art Gallery of South Australia, Adelaide. Courtesy of the Art Gallery of South Australia, Adelaide.

Figure 10.4 Shoulder cloth or wrap garment, with rhombic design. Late 19th century, Jambi, Sumatra. Cotton, natural dyes, hand batik. 104.0 × 240.0 cm. Gift of Michael and Mary Abbott through the Art Gallery of South Australia Foundation. Courtesy of the Art Gallery of South Australia, Adelaide, 2003.

Figure 10.5 Portrait of Sultan Abu'l Ḥasan Quṭb Shāh

wearing a skirt cloth featuring a Coromandel coast design, c. 1675, Golkonda, Telangana, India, opaque watercolour and gold on paper, 22.1 × 14.2 cm; San Diego Museum of Art, Edwin Binney 3rd Collection, San Diego (1990.491) © San Diego Museum of Art.

Figure 10.6 Ceremonial cloth and sacred heirloom early 18th century. Handspun cotton, natural dyes, mordants, 405 × 115 cm. Gift of Michael and Mary Abbott 1988, conserved with the assistance of Brian O'Keeffe AO and Bridget O'Keeffe AM. © National Gallery of Australia.

Figure 10.7 Ceremonial cloth with gold leaf (*kain prada*), with *truntum* design. Late 19th century, probably north coast of Java, gold applied in Bali. Cotton, hand cap batik, indigo dye, gold. 80.0 × 191.0 cm. Gift of Michael Abbott AO QC through the Art Gallery of South Australia Foundation, 2013. Donated through the Australian Government's Cultural Gifts Program. Courtesy of the Art Gallery of South Australia, Adelaide.

Figure 10.8 Wrap cloth (*kain panjang*), with 'creating tranquillity' (*ciptoning*) design detail. Late 20th century, Yogyakarta, Central Java. Cotton, dyes, hand batik. 122.0 × 206.0 cm. The Abbott Gift Year 2000. Courtesy of the Art Gallery of South Australia, Adelaide.

INTRODUCTION

In 2007, Franz Rosenthal's (1914-2003) seminal work, *Knowledge Triumphant: The Concept of Knowledge in Medieval Islam,* was posthumously published.[1] This massive work by the renowned Islamic historian stands as one of the most comprehensive and significant books on the concept of 'knowledge' (*ʿilm,* in Arabic) in mediaeval Islam, and indeed as a remarkable testimony to Rosenthal's distinguished career and outstanding scholarship. In this work Rosenthal proposed that '[c]ivilizations tend to revolve around meaningful concepts of an abstract nature which more than anything else give them their distinctive character'[2], and that in the Islamic civilisation, as the title of his book suggests, the concept of *ʿilm* triumphed above all as its most conspicuous definer.[3] Such was the level of importance Islamic civilisation had accorded the idea of *ʿilm,* Rosenthal adds, it was 'unparalleled in other civilisations'.[4] He went so far as to identify Islam with *ʿilm,* stating unambiguously that '*ʿilm* is Islam', because there was in his view 'no branch of Muslim intellectual life, of Muslim religious and political life, and of the daily life of the average Muslim that has remained untouched by the all-pervasive attitude toward "knowledge" as something of supreme value for Muslim being'.[5] Rosenthal's exhaustive discussions leave little room for doubt about the central role knowledge had played, and has continued to play, in the shaping of Muslims' collective imagination and social reality.

The proposition that it is possible and appropriate to identify a whole civilisation with a singular concept or idea, no matter how significant and central it might have been, is certainly reductive and problematic. Yet, contestable as this thesis may be, Rosenthal's masterful coverage and forceful arguments remain admirably insightful and enlightening, presenting a multifaceted, rich understanding of the notion of *ʿilm* from the religious, mystical, philosophical, and literary perspectives. As an abstract concept, *knowledge* is often contrasted with *ignorance,* and is regarded as a virtue, a good thing to have, yet the nature and content of knowledge vary not only across cultural boundaries but also within the same cultural context. Muslim mystics, jurists, and philosophers, for example, would agree on the centrality of the Quran and Hadiths as two indispensable and incontestable sources of knowledge in Islam, yet they would significantly (and even vehemently) differ over the appropriate method of using and interpreting these sources to attain certainty and truthful knowledge. Revelatory and rational approaches to knowledge differ markedly in Islam, and many religious scholars consider philosophical knowledge to be corruptive and pernicious.

While inspired by Rosenthal's study in certain ways, the focus on the concept of *ʿilm* in this publication is not driven by a desire to support, advance, or contest Rosenthal's thesis, but rather by the necessity to use it as a launching ground. The aim of this volume is to explore the Islamic civilisational responses to major shifts in the concept of 'knowledge' that took place in the post-mediaeval period, and especially within the context of the 'early modern'. The Western historiography of the rise of the so-called early modern science and the consequent demarcation of the 'early modern' in European history have posed insurmountable challenges to the writing of both Islamic intellectual history and the history of Islamic science (*ʿilm*). The challenges lie in how and where to position the Islamic world in a global history shaped by the critical episodes of the early modern which appear to be entirely Eurocentric. Many perplexing questions have arisen from these challenges and have so far remained without satisfactory answers — for example, how to account for the Copernican revolution and subsequent surge of intellectual curiosity in Europe from an Islamic perspective? How to construct and maintain an Islamic relevance to the new 'scientific' developments of early modernity? And how and where to position Islam in the profound intellectual changes that took place during the Enlightenment? The responses to these challenges have been many and varied; however, most positions (and especially those from the Islamic world) have revolved around the issues of Eurocentrism and Western hegemony, and can be generally characterised by defensiveness and disengagement.[6] The theory of civilisational rise and decline has weighted heavily in the field, leaving only a limited space for negotiating a positive outlook.

In focusing specifically on mediaeval Islam, Rosenthal was able to present a more or less static and stable understanding of *ʿilm*, which allowed him to shuttle freely between numerous sources (Islamic and non-Islamic) spanning over a millennium. He carefully avoided the difficult questions concerning the Islamic civilisational response to the early modern shifts in the understanding and pursuits of knowledge. If knowledge was the core preoccupation of the Islamic civilisation, how can we explain its apathetic attitude toward the revolutionary shifts that took place in Europe? Although he did not delve into this area, Rosenthal's response can be gleaned from the following statement, which he made in the last paragraph of his book:

> Its insistence upon 'knowledge' has no doubt made medieval Muslim civilization one of great scholarly and scientific productivity, and through it, Muslim civilization made its most lasting contribution to mankind. 'Knowledge' as its center also hardened Muslim civilization and made it impervious to anything that did not fall within its view of what constituted acceptable knowledge.[7]

With reference to the concept of *ʿilm*, Rosenthal thus presents a clue to a possible new reading of Islamic intellectual history in the post-mediaeval period, which proposes that it was the Islamic civilisation's stubborn preoccupation with its own knowledge that prevented it from developing openness towards the new developments in European knowledge. Recent studies in the field tend to support this proposition.[8] Plausible as this may appear at first glance, the proposition involves several contradictions. First, one of the supposed key features of the Islamic attitude that led it to be of 'great scholarly and scientific productivity' was both its openness towards the achievements of other civilisations (Greeks, Persians, and Indians) and its dynamic nature, which enabled Muslims to absorb existing knowledge and create new knowledge throughout the mediaeval period. To assume that 'knowledge' itself suddenly turned into an 'inertia' that rendered Islamic civilisation 'impervious' to external influences seems contrary to its supposed fundamentally receptive and productive nature in the first place. Second, following the popular civilisational rise and decline theory, many have assumed that the state of knowledge creation and production in the Islamic world had indeed reached a level of inertia that made it impervious to European influences; however, recent studies have shown that the dynamic and productive characteristics of Islam have continued, though along traditional lines, but Muslim scholars have remained uninterested in new scientific developments. Thus, the main issue was not internal inertia and stagnation in Islamic societies but something else, which is yet to be identified.

Third, at a certain point in their early modern history Muslims realised that they needed to change their traditional stance on knowledge, and that the new pursuits of knowledge advanced by the Europeans were indeed *better* than their own. This moment of collective realisation is highly significant, and the change of heart that followed raises the perplexing question of the timing of this sudden awakening — why did it not happen two centuries earlier? From Rosenthal's perspective, the answer lies in the unflinching confidence in the validity and truthfulness of its own internal system of knowledge, which prolonged the life of the Islamic belief system and delayed its eventual collapse — which later, ironically, took place under the mounting pressure of a new form of *ʿilm* (as modern science).

To the unflinching confidence in their own system of knowledge, Rosenthal would add the Muslims' attitude toward doubt (*shakk*), which he discussed at some length in his book. 'Doubt in whichever way indicated', he wrote,

> became the true pariah and outcast of Muslim civilization. It stands for all that is to be shunned like the plague. No worse fate can befall man than being tossed into the sea of doubts and left there to flounder and possibly to drown. Doubt in itself is a sufficient manifestation of ignorance.[9]

Indeed, doubt is paired with certainty, faith, and belief in antinomies that present it as the soul's most perilous disease, a satanic tool devised to deviate people from the right path of religion. Yet again, one cannot ignore the great works of Muslim scholars in which they raised — in true scientific spirit — doubts about the works of leading Greek figures, such as Ibn al-Haytham's *al-Shukūk ʿalā Baṭlīmyus* (Doubts on Ptolemy) and *al-Shukūk ʿalā Iqlīdis* (Doubts on Euclid), and al-Rāzī's *al-Shukūk ʿalā Jalīnūs* (Doubts on Galen). If doubt in scientific studies was an accepted methodology in the Islamic knowledge system, and some would credit Muslim 'scientists' with introducing it, why were Muslim scholars not interested in doubt when it became an established methodology of knowledge acquisition and verification in early modern scientific developments? One can understand the Muslims' rejection of doubt in matters of faith and belief, but not in science, especially when they themselves used it and presented fine examples of its efficacy. The answer to this perplexing question lies in the complex polarity of religion and science, the intertwined history of which is one of the main themes of this volume.

In discussing the intertwined relationship between science, religion, and art in Islam under the embracing theme of *ʿilm*, this book aims to show how the unflinching confidence in the validity and truthfulness of the Islamic system of belief manifested itself through various enduring cultural practices, erratic events, and challenging new encounters during the early modern and modern periods. The chapters, which have been selected from papers originally presented at the *ʿIlm: Science, Religion, and Art in Islam* Conference 2016 in Adelaide, Australia, take multiple positions on the Islamic approach to knowledge, viewing *ʿilm* not as a static and stable enterprise, but rather as a dynamic understanding and engagement that can represent different and changing notions and values. The scientific and intellectual developments that took place in early modern Europe, which changed its whole civilisational outlook concerning the types of knowledge that should be pursued and the kind of education that must be cultivated and delivered, have undermined the stability and consistency that the Islamic notion of *ʿilm* was struggling to maintain. This moment of critical shift in understanding clearly shows that the knowledge strongly desired and pursued by Muslims meant ignorance and stagnation to early modern Europeans.[10]

The chapters in this volume bring into focus three related complex issues. First, through the concept of *ʿilm* Islam was able to maintain — in the face of the divided epistemology that Western modernity introduced after the Enlightenment — an undivided approach to knowledge until the early 20th century. The rise of modern science introduced an unprecedented rift into the traditional approaches of knowledge by establishing a self-propelled mode of knowing completely independent of the moral values of religion. In this new mode of knowing the purpose, validity, and merit of knowledge are determined by science itself, thereby creating two systems of belief, one guided by religious values and principle, and one not. This divided approach was, and still is, alien to Islamic tradition.

In the introduction to his monumental catalogue of Islamic sciences (*ʿulūm*, pl. of *ʿilm*), *Kashf al-ẓunūn* (Dispelling Doubts), the renowned 17th-century Ottoman scholar Kātip Çelebi expressed this unitary understanding of knowledge when he referred to *ʿilm* as being 'one in meaning and in truth' (*maʿnā wāḥid wa ḥaqīqa wāḥida*).[11] This statement reflects the broader Islamic understanding of the undivided and unpolarised nature of knowledge, which was a major reason why Islamic culture neither experienced a divisive split between 'science' and 'religion' as two distinct modes of knowledge nor witnessed a liberating divorce of art from the religious/scientific concerns until the wide infiltration of European influence in the 20th century. Throughout the pre- and early modern periods in the Arab-Islamic world, *ʿilm* was used to denote one, undivided mode of knowing, and the terms *ʿālim* (sing.) and *ʿulamāʾ* (pl.) were used for both 'scientists' and 'clerics' — that is, for scholars concerned with and having expert knowledge in worldly matters, as well as for scholars concerned with and having expert knowledge in other-worldly matters. Primary Arabic sources show how *ʿilm* has always been one in nature, but different in purposes. This is to say that the belief system guiding the processes of knowing is the same, and the ultimate goal is one (knowledge of God), but meanwhile the purposes and approaches in various branches of knowledge are different. Accordingly, a literary scholar, a religious scholar, a philosopher, an astronomer, and a medical practitioner all share the titles *ʿālim* and *ʿallāma* (one with an exceptionally high level of knowledge), although the purposes and pathways of their pursuit of knowledge are different. All branches of Islamic religious sciences involve rational reflections and most philosophers, mathematicians, and natural scientists either were religious scholars or shared with religious scholars the same set of religious beliefs. This has continued to the present time, albeit with a sharper definition of the two realms of expertise.

The second complex issue derives from the first, and concerns the unitary understanding of *ʿilm* and the enduring dilemma this unified approach to knowledge creates, as it can be evaluated from two contrasting positions. From the modern scientific perspective, the stubbornly unified approach can be blamed for having impeded the development of the new mode of knowing called 'science', which consciously and deliberately divorced itself from the traditional approach during the early modern period. Historically, there has been no specific Arabic word for 'science' (other than *ʿilm*), understood in the modern sense as 'the intellectual and practical activity encompassing the systematic study of the structure and behaviour of the physical and natural world through observation and experiment'.[12] Early modern and modern Arab intellectuals, linguists, reformers, and 'scientists' did not coin a new term for this to help delineate the territories of modern science from that of traditional *ʿilm* in Arabic thought. The Arabic term *ʿilm* (pl. *ʿulūm*) has continued to be used to describe both religious and non-religious pursuits of knowledge — that is, the term comprises the devotional and intellectual engagements with the divine revelation as well as the rational and empirical study of nature. For critics of the science-religion split, who see modern scientific enterprise as having been divorced from the questions of morality and religious beliefs, the unified Islamic approach appears as a positive trait of resistance. For those who consider the liberation of science from the dictates of religion as a key factor in its modern success and advancement, however, the Islamic position appears as a negative expression of traditional inertia. Today, as the chapters in this volume show, the Islamic world is certainly torn by this dilemma: Muslims want to be progressive owners and producers of scientific knowledge, yet they also want to remain traditional and 'Islamic'.

The third complex issue raised in this volume concerns the relationship between art and knowledge. The modern demarcation of scientific and religious epistemologies has been predicated on a deeper division of objective and subjective modes of knowing. Modernity privileged the objective over the subjective mode, which has been relegated to the realm of the individual. This is where religion and art now belong. Art in particular has become a self-focused enterprise concerned more with subjective emotions, feelings, and personal experiences than with objective knowledge production and acquisition. This is alien to Islamic cultures, which equate beauty with truth and goodness and neither reduce the transcendental dimension of beauty to aesthetics nor confine it to the eye of the beholder. Despite the exquisite beauty of Islamic art, Muslim craftsmen and scholars are not recognised for having produced a coherent theory of aesthetics. Rather, art was always at the service of religious, literary, scientific, or everyday life's needs. Whether it be a scientific instrument, a calligraphic inscription, a miniature in a manuscript, or an everyday object, Muslim craftsmen produced objects that appeal to the taste of diverse communities that have one thing in common: privileging the mind over the soul, and knowledge over feeling. Acting as a unifying cultural force, *ʿilm* informed art (*ṣanʿa*), imagination (*khayāl*), and artistic creativity (*ibdāʿ*), thereby bringing together science and religion to form the common foundation of artistic production. A master craftsman was referred to as *muʿallim* (from *ʿilm*), which is the same term used today for 'teacher'. From this perspective, the traditional concept of *ʿilm* was able to, on the one hand, fuse science and religion together into an indissoluble whole, and, on the other, make art an act of knowledge before being an expression of feeling.

The structure of this volume follows that of the conference, which explored the agency of *ʿilm* in the three related realms of science, religion, and art. Viable as this structure may appear, the intertwined nature of these three realms of knowledge within the unifying perspective of *ʿilm* makes the tripartite division often seem contrived, superficial, and indeed problematic. Discussions could not be segregated neatly into these three conceptual spaces without some inconsistency, especially since most chapters focus on the early modern context within which the term's unifying epistemological scope was still wielding significant force. Yet it is this complex synthesis of ideas and connections buried within the folds of *ʿilm's* multidimensional conceptual scope that this volume is attempting to unravel.

Part I, '*ʿIlm* as Science', features four chapters examining the conceptualisation of *ʿilm* as science and the different modes of engagements with the 'scientific' study of the natural world. Two of the chapters focus on the Arab-Ottoman context and two focus on the Indian-Mughal context. My own opening chapter, on the polarisation of the unitary scope of *ʿilm* into science and religion, which took place in the second half of the 19th century, discusses the role that the influential works of JW Draper (1811-82) and AD White (1832-1918) played in raising an awareness of the polarity among Arab scholars and intellectuals as well as the general public. The irony of such an awareness lay in the way Draper's and White's theory had led Arabs to see the conflictual relationship between science and religion as having resulted from the repressive practices of the Church and, accordingly, being expressive of the internal affairs of Christendom. Islam by contrast was seen, thanks to Draper in particular, as a religion of science. The study discusses how the conflict thesis then re-emerged in the second half of the 20th century in a historical narrative that attempted to explain the destruction of the Istanbul Observatory by Sultan Murād III (r. 1574-95) as an event that expresses the triumph of religious fanaticism over rational sciences. This attempt mapped the modern polarity of science and religion over the traditional distinction between rational (*'aqlī*) and religious (*naqlī*) knowledge, thus extending Draper's and White's conflict theory into the Islamic religion. Showing how such mapping is inconsistent with early modern sources, the study argues that the questions the polarity of science and religion has raised in the Arab-Islamic context have not been concerned with issues of historiography and the lost moral guidance of the scientific enterprise, but rather with Islam's compatibility with modernity and its secular-scientific foundations.

In Chapter 2, Perri Sparnon's study, 'Science and Art', focuses on anatomical illustration in early Islamic optics through examining the agency of the image as a bearer of scientific knowledge in Islamic culture. Sparnon examines the oldest surviving image of the optical system, initially found in the *Kitāb al-manāẓir* (Book of Optics) by the celebrated mediaeval scholar Ibn al-Haytham (d. 1040), so as to trace its function in this landmark study and its reproductions as an expression of anatomical knowledge in subsequent commentaries. The main question underlying Sparnon's study concerns the role of art in the advancement of scientific knowledge as developed in early modern Europe. She critically examines the proposition that the Islamic religion's prohibition of the mutilation of the human body was responsible for the limited use of anatomical dissection and illustrations and consequent impediment of scientific developments. Shaha Parpia's study, meanwhile, in Chapter 3, of the imperial Mughal hunt as a pursuit of knowledge shifts the focus to early modern Mughal India to introduce a new reading of the cultural practice of hunting, showing its agency and efficacy in technological advancements and the understanding of the natural system. Customarily understood as a leisure activity, hunting was rarely considered a 'scientific' activity that involves investigations, experimentation, and analyses of natural phenomena encountered on the field, as well as systematic recording of findings with emphasis on anatomy, taxonomy, and animal psychology. Parpia's study shows, on the one hand, how science, ethics, and religion were interrelated concepts in Mughal cultural contexts, and, on the other, how the documentations of scientific activities were closely linked to art.

Part I concludes with Katharine Bartsch's and Peter Scriver's study of the ill-fated modern astronomical observatory, *Tarewali Kothi* (House of Stars), which was established in Lucknow during the reign of Nawab Naṣīruddīn Ḥaidar (r. 1827-37). The erratic closure of this state-of-the-art scientific institution in 1849 by the last Nawab of Awadh, Wajīd 'Alī Shāh (r. 1847-56), recalls the puzzling destruction of the Istanbul Observatory, discussed in Chapter 1, showing that after more than two and a half centuries the state of the science of astronomy was still shrouded with ambiguity with regard to its legality and religious merit. The politics of destruction always comes to the fore when explanations of such baffling events are sought, yet one cannot but ponder the apathy Muslim cultures have shown towards *'ilm* as 'modern science', the lack of immunity against the rulers' whimsical desires, and the absence of other indispensable legal tools for ensuring the survival of the new institutions of early modern science.

Part II, '*'Ilm* as Religion', features four chapters concerned with the centrality of religion in the production, dissemination, and authentication of knowledge in Islamic society. They explain, albeit in different ways, Rosenthal's emphatic statement that '*ʿilm* is Islam', with Islam understood here primarily as a faith or system of belief and not as cultural potency and dynamism. Virginia Hooker opens with a study of the way in which Quranic calligraphy is used as a vehicle for spreading *ʿilm*, as 'religious knowledge', in contemporary Indonesia, and conversely how Islamic religious knowledge provides the foundation and impetus for artistic creativity, production, and refinements. Didin Sirojuddin's school of Quranic calligraphy, which Hooker presents in detail, is a remarkable example of how a modern aesthetic sensibility is profoundly shaped by religious knowledge in the world's largest Muslim majority nation. It shows how knowledge and not feeling remains a strong driving force of artistic expression. There are many other forms of subjective and emotional artistic expressions in Indonesia; however, in the continuing struggle between tradition and modernity and the search for cultural identity, the self-conscious appeal to the religious source for inspiration has never been greater.

This anxious search for an Islamic identity in an increasingly globalised world is further elucidated in Chapter 6, in which Syed Mehboob Bukhari focuses on the preoccupation with the Islamisation of modern science that goes back to Islam's early encounters with modern Europe in the 19th century. Bukhari examines the intellectual campaign of two leading Muslim scholars, Seyyed Hossein Nasr and Ziauddin Sardar, who have called for the Islamisation of *ʿilm* — that is, the remarrying of modern science, which deliberately divorced itself from religion, with the religious and moral principles of Islam, so as to show the contradictions and shortcomings of their project in today's globalised society. Nasr and Sardar view modern science as a product of the Western secular system, which generated an uncontrolled, reductive, and destructive approach to knowledge, in contrast to which their utopian 'Islamic science' presents not only a potent progressive project, but one that is also inherently ethical and environmentally friendly. Bukhari's study questions the validity and relevance of such religiously driven, utopian visions to find simple answers to the maladies of the increasingly globalised, technologised, and spiritless modern world.

Selen Morkoç's chapter, 'In Between the Mind and the Heart', follows by showing that the conscious preoccupation with differentiating between Islamic and foreign sciences, which Nasr and Sardar have dramatised, was not new to the Islamic system of knowledge. This duality emerged early with Islam's wide exposure to Greek knowledge, and took on various forms, one of which has been the distinction between the rational (*ʿaqlī*) and religious (*sharʿī*) sciences, which was conspicuously expressed in the works and personal quest for truthful knowledge of the celebrated Ottoman Scholar Kātip Çelebi (1609-57). Being among the first Ottoman scholars to present a positive attitude towards early modern sciences and to engage actively in introducing them to a Muslim audience, Çelebi occupies a special place in Islamic intellectual history. It is thus remarkable to see him oscillating between his mind and heart in his quest for the truth, and to hear the visionary dream that put an end to his perplexity, by settling the intellectual battle in favour of faith over reason. As Morkoç shows, Çelebi's dream might have represented a decisive moment that resolved his personal dilemma, yet his views can be taken to represent a prevailing trend among various intellectual circles in the Ottoman society at the time.

Finally, Faris Hajamaideen's '*ʿIlm* and the Human Body' concludes Part II by shedding fresh light from the Islamic perspective on the agency of the body in the conceptual relationship between knowledge (*ʿilm*) and light (*nūr*). Focusing on the work of the renowned 12th-century philosopher-mystic Shihāb al-Dīn al-Suhrawardī (d. 1191), Hajamaideen shows how conceptions of the relationship between knowledge, illumination, and the human body were constructed using two architectural metaphors: the temple (*haykal*) and the fortress (*ṣīṣiyya*). Focusing on Suhrawardī's two key works, *Hayākil al-nūr* (Temples of Light) and *Ḥikmat al-ishrāq* (The Philosophy of Illumination), Hajamaideen examines the cosmological significance of these architectural metaphors in order to show how the structure of the human body was conceived as playing a key cognitive-illuminative role in the process of transformation from being a fortress of darkness into becoming a temple of light. He discusses the process through which the body and the mind work as a unified 'structure' or 'temple', wherein 'form' and 'space' work together in an integral manner as 'architecture' to enable the infusion of light to dematerialise the body and erase its opacity.

Part III, '*ʿIlm* as Art', features three chapters concerned with the questions of Islamic aesthetics in the art and architecture of early modern and modern Turkey, Indonesia, and Egypt, and the challenges of staging Islamic art outside its cultural context in modern institutions of display. Susan Scollay opens with a study of the aesthetic context that shaped the unprecedented imperial palace built by the Ottoman sultan Murād II (r. 1421-51) at Edirne in Thrace. She draws attention to the lack of theoretical writings on art and architecture in pre-modern Islam, and the consequent absence of collective aesthetic theory that informs Islamic artistic imagination and guides modern interpretations. Mediaeval sources on Islamic sciences (*ʿulūm*) do not mention *ʿilm al-jamāl* (the science of beauty), which emerged in the 20th century to account for the existing Western discourse on the topic. In this rather ambiguous interpretive context, Scollay proposes that palaces of the imagination described in illustrated manuscripts, such as the Persian *Shāhnāma* (Book of Kings) and other Persianate poetic tales, were likely models for the Edirne Palace. She argues that through the agency of *ʿilm*, understood as knowledge of literature and cultural models from elsewhere in the Islamic world, appropriate poetic ideals of beauty were constructed and mobilised to play a large part in the artistic evolution of the House of Osman during the early modern period.

James Bennett's chapter, '*ʿIlm* or Fashion?', follows, showing how in the absence of established Islamic aesthetic theories, modern scholars fabricate their own theories to fill in the vacuum with constructed ideals of beauty that serve their religious ideologies and nationalistic tendencies. This is particularly the case, as Bennett shows, with the geometric batik motifs of Javanese textiles, generically known as *ceplokan*, which Southeast Asian scholars interpret as visual expressions of the Islamic concept of *tawḥīd* (divine unity). Tracing the long history of *ceplokan,* which is among the most popular category of designs, the origins of which date back to the pre-Islamic early classical period (c.700-900 CE) in Java, Bennett argues that the geometric motifs did not develop as a conscious response to the concept of *tawḥīd,* but came about through a natural process of cultural negotiation, by which older Hindu-Buddhist textile designs were reinterpreted in the context of the new dress fashions that emerged following the ascendency of Islam in Java in the 16th century. As *ceplokan* patterns became particularly admired in the Javanese sultanates, imported India textiles, featuring similar geometric designs, contributed to the development of the batik style, now closely identified with Javanese aesthetics, long before the introduction of the *tawḥīd* theory.

Sam Bowker's 'Curating *ʿIlm*' concludes Part III and the volume with a study of the agency of *ʿilm* in the process of curation, which tends to impose new, and often foreign, aesthetic frameworks to enable the visibility, appreciation, and understanding of works of art. In this process, several modes of knowledge come into an interactive play. Bowker distinguishes the mode of *ʿilm* involved in the act of curatorship from the haptic knowledge of the makers or tacit knowledge of the visitors and/or previous owners of the objects displayed. With reference to two Egyptian Tentmaker Applique exhibitions (*khiyāmiyya*) he curated in regional Australia and the Islamic Art Museum Malaysia (IAMM) in Kuala Lumpur, Bowker shows how the curation of exhibitions acknowledges and balances those forms of knowledge as a core component of the museum's and gallery's educational function. He further shows how each of his exhibitions enabled the creation and transmission of haptic, tacit, and explicit knowledge viewed as conceptual structures of *ʿilm*.

Rosenthal concluded his study with the following question: 'What does it mean for a civilization, and beyond it, for the history of mankind, if "knowledge" is made its central concern'? Important though the question seems, Rosenthal made it appear rather rhetorical with his admission that 'no one answer would seem possible ... and it is, perhaps, enough merely to have posed it'.[13] His difficulty with finding an answer seems to derive from the cultural relativity position he assumed, wherefrom the meaning and merit of knowledge can only be determined from within. From the perspective of this volume, as shown by the multiple perspectives of the authors, the true value of knowledge lies in its cross-civilisational reach, as when the development of knowledge in pre-modern Islam exerted profound changes onto the Europeans, whose resurgence in the early modern period has in turn forced massive changes onto the Islamic world view and its systems of knowledge. Now the landscape of knowledge has significantly changed, the Muslim mind, which has been historically calibrated to be particularly sensitive towards knowledge, can and should contribute to opening new horizons of knowing where science, religion, and art can meet again on freshly cultivated and intellectually fertile grounds.

NOTES

1 Franz Rosenthal, 2007, *Knowledge Triumphant: The Concept of Knowledge in Medieval Islam* (Leiden: Brill).
2 Rosenthal, 2007, 1.
3 Rosenthal, 2007, Introduction, 1-4.
4 Rosenthal, 2007, 334.
5 Rosenthal, 2007, 2.
6 See, for example, the heated debate between George Saliba and Toby Huff on the rise of modern science, which I discussed in my book on Istanbul Observatory. Samer Akkach, 2017, *Marṣad Istanbul: hadm al-raṣd wa raṣd al-hadm. Taṭawwr thaqāfat al-ʿulūm fī al-Islām baʿd Copernicus* (Doha: Arab Centre for Research and Policy Studies), Chapter 12.
7 Rosenthal, 2007, 340-1.
8 See Khaled El-Rouayheb, 2015, *Islamic Intellectual History in the Seventeenth Century: Scholarly Currents in the Ottoman Empire and the Maghreb* (Cambridge: Cambridge University Press).
9 Rosenthal, 2007, 300.
10 Rosenthal, 2007, 240.
11 Kātip Çelebi, 1835, *Kashf al-ẓunūn ʿan asāmī al-kutub wa l-funūn* (Beirut: Dār Ṣadir, rep. London: Bentley), vol. 1, 24-5.
12 Angus Stevenson (ed.), 2010, *Oxford English Dictionary*, 3rd ed. (Oxford: Oxford University Press).
13 Rosenthal, 2007, 340-1.

Part I

‘*Ilm* as Science

CHAPTER 1

POLARISING *ʿILM*: SCIENCE AND RELIGION IN EARLY MODERN ISLAM

SAMER AKKACH

ABSTRACT

The polarisation of the traditional concept of *ʿilm*, 'knowledge', into *ʿilm*, modern 'science' versus *dīn*, 'religion', has a short history in the Islamic tradition. Emerging awareness of the conflict between *ʿilm* and *dīn* can be traced back to the early decades of the 19th century; however, intense public debate of the polarity began later in the same century. Views about the conflict emerged after exposure to the European Enlightenment ideas generally, and the works of the fabricators of the 'conflict thesis', JW Draper and AD White, specifically. Arab and Turkish scholars celebrated Draper's view that, unlike Christianity, Islam nurtured and advanced science. Taking this as evidence of Islam's superiority over Christianity, they restricted the conflict thesis to Christendom and saw it as a result of the repressive practices of the Church. By the mid-20th century, new adaptations of the conflict thesis emerged, which mapped the polarity of science and religion over the traditional Islamic division of sciences into rational (*ʿaqlī*) and transmitted (*naqlī*). This chapter discusses the polarisation of *ʿilm* into science and religion, which occurred in the 19th century, in order to show, first, its inconsistency with pre-19th century Islamic sources on the classification of the rational and transmitted sciences, and, second, the distinct trajectory the polarity took in the Arab-Islamic context. It argues that the questions the polarity has raised in the Islamic context are concerned primarily not with historiography and the lost moral guidance of the scientific enterprise, but rather with Islam's schizophrenic approach to modernity and its humanistic foundations.

'THE RESTORATION OF SCIENCE IN THE SOUTH'

In the second half of the 19th century two American authors, scientist John William Draper (1811-82) and historian Andrew Dickson White (1832-1918), each wrote a well-received book that had an enduring influence on the ways in which the relationship between science and religion has since been viewed and understood. These books were Draper's *History of the Conflict between Religion and Science*, published in 1874, and White's *A History of the Warfare of Science with Theology in Christendom*, published in two volumes in 1896.[1] As the titles clearly indicate, the central thesis of these two works was that the history of science was not a mere record of groundbreaking discoveries, but primarily 'a narrative of the conflict of two contending powers, the expansive force of the human intellect on one side, and the compression arising from traditionary faith and human interests on the other'.[2] These two influential works are widely recognised today as being responsible for the fabrication and promotion of the idea of the intrinsic intellectual conflict between science and religion, which has become commonly known as the 'conflict thesis'. Still popular among many scientists and scholars, the conflict thesis came under strong attack in the second half of the 20th century and has since gradually lost its appeal among historians of science and religion in the West.[3] In his recent book *The Territories of Science and Religion*, historian Peter Harrison has captured the prevailing sentiment on this topic, forcefully arguing that while territorial distinction might have existed between science and religion in the past, their perceived conflictual relationship emerged only after Draper's and White's influential intervention.[4] While the critique of the conflict thesis might have been effective in changing prevailing perceptions of this sensitive topic, at least among historians, most Western studies concerned with the agency of these two texts have focused solely on their relevance to Christianity in the West and assumed that Draper's and White's generalisations extend to other religions. They overlooked or ignored Draper's lengthy and detailed discussions of Islam, which he viewed and presented in a completely different light.

Against the grim picture Draper painted of the oppressive, idolatrous, corrupt, and divisive history of the Catholic Church and its wicked clergy, he presented his unreserved admiration of Islam. He saw in the rise of the 'Arabian Empire' not only a shining beacon of enlightenment but indeed 'the salvation of Europe'.[5] In his highly personal reading of the character of Muhammad and rise of Islam, Draper stressed its distinction from Christianity by highlighting Islam's rationalism, scientific-mindedness, inventiveness, and great scientific achievements, which made it not just compatible with science, but the religion of science *par excellence*. True, all religions in his view were founded on fanatical beliefs; however, he did not hide his surprise at seeing 'how quickly the ferocious fanaticism of the Saracens was transformed into a passion for intellectual pursuits'.[6] The main cause for such rapid transformation, Draper explained, lies in the way Islam viewed and understood *progress* in contrast to Christianity. 'To the Christian', Draper wrote,

> the progress of the world was an exhibition of disconnected impulses, of sudden surprises. To the Mohammedan that progress presented a very different aspect. Every corporeal motion was due to some preceding motion; every thought to some preceding thought; every historical event was the offspring of some preceding event; every human action was the result of some foregone and accomplished action.[7]

In this sharp awareness of unfailing causality, Draper saw the essence of the Muslims' unique scientific-mindedness. 'In science', Draper explained,

> their great merit consists in this, that they cultivated it after the manner of the Alexandrian Greeks, not after the manner of the European Greeks. They perceived that it can never be advanced by mere speculation; its only sure progress is by the practical interrogation of Nature.[8]

Draper's view of Islam's scientific tradition, which he expounded in Chapter 4 of his book, 'The Restoration of Science in the South', shows clearly that in his conflict model 'religion' referred specifically to Christianity and its history in the West and not to all religions, or Islam in particular. This raises several hitherto undiscussed questions about how Muslims received and interpreted Draper's and White's works; how his conflict thesis has appeared from their perspectives; how they made use of it in their historical writings; and what issues it has provoked with regards to the relationship between science and religion. These are the main concerns of this chapter. To address them, this chapter will discuss awareness of the conflict model among Arabs and Ottomans through three historical phases. The first phase is in the 19th century prior to the Muslim's exposure to Draper's and White's work; the second phase is after the translation of, and wide exposure to, their works in the late 19th to the early 20th centuries; and the third phase is in the second half of the 20th century, when scholars were making an attempt to explain the destruction of the Istanbul Observatory in 1580.

The discussions will show that prior to the 19th century Arab and Ottoman exposure to European Enlightenment ideas in general and to the new theories of heliocentrism and evolutionism in particular, there was no perceived division between science and religion in the Muslim world, and that the 20th-century mapping of this modern polarity over the traditional distinction between rational (*ʿaqlī*) and transmitted (*naqlī*) knowledge is inconsistent with early modern Islamic sources. The chapter will also show that unlike the intellectual developments in Europe where it was the transformation in understanding of the already existing polarity of *religio* and *scientia* that provided the basis for the new polarity of religion and science, in the Islamic context it was the transformation of the understanding of the notion of *ʿilm,* from 'knowledge' to 'modern science', that led to the polarisation of *ʿilm*'s unitary scope in order to support the emerging differentiation of science from religion.[9] The chapter argues that the issues which the polarity of science and religion has raised in the Islamic context have not been concerned primarily with historiography and the lost moral guidance of the scientific enterprise, as is the case in Western studies, but rather with Islam's compatibility with modernity and its secular-scientific foundations.

'ENEMIES OF ENLIGHTENMENT'

Perceptions of the conflict between science and religion among both Arabs and Ottomans emerged in the early decades of the 19th century and were shaped by both external influences and internal intellectual developments. Journalists, intellectuals, and educated officials, using the powerful new mass media (journals and newspapers), actively engaged in the science and religion debates by questioning the validity of both religious beliefs and new scientific findings. Early awareness of the conflict can be found in the young Rifāʿa al-Ṭahṭāwī's (1801-73) memoirs of his educational trip to Paris. Describing the lack of faith among Parisians and their explicit contempt for religion, he referred to the public view of the religious clergy as 'enemies of enlightenment and knowledge' (*aʿdāʾ li-l-anwār wa-li-l-maʿārif*).[10] Even though he lamented the state of decline and backwardness Islam had reached during his time, Ṭahṭāwī never saw Muslim religious scholars as being enemies of enlightenment and knowledge. Being himself a religious cleric from the al-Azhar school in Cairo, he represented the religious establishment and its dedication to intellectual development and reform.[11] Yet, the long 19th century witnessed a growing awareness of the conflictual relationship between science and religion, which intensified in the second half of the century. Two important journals were instrumental in the promotion of the conflict model and the sharpening of public awareness of it, *al-Jinān* (The Gardens, 1870-86) and *al-Muqtaṭaf* (The Snippets, 1876-1952), which featured heated debates on science and religion, and focused specifically on heliocentrism and evolutionism.[12]

In 1875, a Syrian journalist living in Egypt named Salīm Ilyās al-Ḥamawī (1843-1913) published a book in Alexandria entitled *al-Barāhīn al-qaṭʿiyya ʿalā ʿadam dawarān al-kurā al-arḍiyya* (The Definitive Proofs against the Circular Motion of the Planet Earth).[13] Parts of the book were initially written as a response to a series of articles on new astronomy published in *al-Jinān* in 1872.[14]

Al-Ḥamawī first sent his response for publication to *al-Jinān*, but the editor seems to have ignored it.[15] In 1873, al-Ḥamawī founded a new journal called *al-Kawkab al-Sharqī* (The Oriental Plant) and began exposing his ideas gradually there, until the journal suddenly folded after the 14th issue.[16] Prompted by keen responses from his readers, who apparently were enthused by his ideas, as well as by encouragements from friends and colleagues, al-Ḥamawī decided to collect the fragments and publish them in a book.[17] In this book al-Ḥamawī presented a mixture of religious, historical, and scientific arguments against the motion of the earth, which then formed a core proposition of the new heliocentric astronomy. His polemics, which were anchored in the perception of conflict between religion and science, were shaped by the raging debate between proponents and opponents of heliocentrism, and his 'definitive proofs' against the motion of the earth included, first, religious citations and interpretations from the three sacred books, the Torah, the Bible, and the Quran, so as to show a united traditional front against the new science of heliocentrism; second, a historical overview tracing the origin of heliocentrism to Greek thinkers, in order to undermine the originality of the Copernican discovery; and third, technical arguments discrediting the motion of the earth on 'scientific' grounds.[18]

In the following year (1876), only a few months after the publication of al-Ḥamawī's book, Abdullah Fikrī (1834-90), a high-ranking government bureaucrat and poet from Mecca also living and working in Cairo, published a treatise in favour of the new astronomy entitled *Risāla fī muqārant baʿḍ mabāḥith al-hayʾa bi-l-wārid fī al-nuṣūṣ al-sharʿiyya* (A Treatise on Comparing some of the Arguments of Astronomy with what is Mentioned in the Religious Texts).[19] Fikrī's treatise was not prompted by al-Ḥamawī's book but rather by the growing awareness of the conflict between science and religion. Like al-Ḥamawī's text, it was first published in stages in a journal called *Wādī al-Nīl* (The Nile Valley) before it was republished as a treatise in response to popular demands. Unlike the monologue of al-Ḥamawī, however, Fikrī's treatise was presented in the form of a dialogue between an astronomer/scientist (*ṣāḥib al-hayʾa*) and a jurist (*faqīh*), which was reminiscent of Galileo's *Dialogo*. Fikrī's main aim was to subject the long-held conventional understanding of certain texts of the Quran and Hadiths to critical discussions from a new scientific perspective. The then prevailing religious position on the new astronomy was revealed in the first statement by the *faqīh*:

> I can see you now believing in this new astronomy (*al-hayʾa al-jadīda*) despite its being in contradiction with the lawful texts of the Book and the Tradition (*al-kitāb wa-l-sunna*). I have always thought you had certainty in your religion and insight in your affairs, so how did you choose for yourself the departure from religion and the exiting from the circle of the well-guided faithfuls?[20]

Fikrī's response shows that his dialogical arguments were not intended to undermine or discredit Islam and its religious tenets, but rather to show that fresh interpretations of certain texts were becoming necessary for the Islamic religion to remain relevant to the indisputable scientific evidence of the new astronomy.[21] These two books were only samples of a growing body of literature on the topic, which included monographs, translations, journal and newspaper articles, and school textbooks, resourcing a heated debate around the core propositions of the new heliocentric astronomy and the relationship between science and religion.[22] Popular journals and newspapers were highly effective in promoting the conflict thesis, wittingly and unwittingly, as they presented numerous articles about the new scientific findings in astronomy, geography, physics, medicine, and other fields (*al-ʿulūm al-jadīda*). Progressive intellectuals, such as Shiblī Shumayyil (1850-1917),

Salāma Mūsā (1887-1958), and Isma'īl Maẓhar (1891-1962), also vigorously engaged in the science and religion debates sparked by Darwin's then highly controversial theory of evolution. The most important aspect of this emerging discourse, as far as this study is concerned, is the new use of the term *'ilm* as 'modern science', which was now used in a contrasting polarity with religion (*dīn*). Still somewhat vague in its new scope, the new usage of *'ilm* was clearly different from the pre-19th century general meaning of the term as 'knowledge'.

The effect of this transformation in meaning was captured by a short article on 'Natural Sciences' (*al-'ulūm al-ṭabī'iyya*) published in January 1877 as an opening piece of the eighth issue of *al-Muqtaṭaf*, a monthly journal devoted specifically to dealing with matters related to science and industry (*'ilmiyya ṣina'iyya*).[23] The article was meant to highlight the importance of natural sciences for the development of modern society and to show their indisputable benefits. It began by identifying four prevailing attitudes, presumably among Arabs, towards natural sciences:

> Some people believe that natural sciences are harmful, for they lead to doubting what is revealed in the sacred books and thus they deny their benefits. Others believe that they do lead to doubts in religious matters; however, they admit that they are nonetheless beneficial. Yet others believe that they are truthful and beneficial and denounce revelation for their sake. Whereas the remaining group believe that they are the proofs of revelation, the delight of the minds, and the substance of prosperity, and those without doubt are the correct ones.[24]

Immediately after this opening piece on natural sciences, the editors of *al-Muqtaṭaf* published a lengthy correspondence sent to the journal by an archimandrite of the Antiochian Church, Gabriel Jbāra, who seemed to be a representative of the first group identified above. In his letter Jbāra presented his utter rejection of heliocentrism according to a host of evidence he cited from the Bible. He was prompted to write his rebuttal, as he explains, by an article published two months earlier in the sixth issue, which argued in favour of heliocentrism.[25] In other issues of this popular journal, readers referred to and discussed the works of al-Ḥamawī and Fikrī, mentioned earlier, and excerpts from Fikrī's treatise were republished to show the evolving Islamic position on new astronomy.[26]

The four different attitudes towards natural sciences identified in the above article revealed the immediate effect of the polarised understanding of *'ilm*, which gradually became associated with natural sciences. Any such understanding now required people to have an expressed position on how 'science' relates to religion. It is difficult to know who the dominant group was; however, considering the growing popularity of *al-Muqtaṭaf* and the increasing acceptance of the legitimacy and benefits of natural sciences, it is the fourth group endorsed by the journal that seems to have gradually become the dominant one. In contrast to the first three groups, who upheld the conflict model and took a position on it, the fourth group was the only one that maintained an understanding of the harmony between science and religion, even though science and religion now appear to have acquired a somewhat independent realm of their own.

DRAPER'S INTERVENTION

Draper emerged onto the Islamic intellectual scene when the eminent Ottoman journalist Aḥmed Midḥat (1844-1912) translated his text as *Nizā-i 'Ilm ü Dīn* (The Conflict between Science and Religion) and published it in four volumes between 1895 and 1900.[27] Midḥat was a prolific writer who owned a major printing house which also published a leading journal. Most important, however, Midḥat was close to Sultan ʿAbdülḥamīd II (r. 1876-1909) and thus had access to top social, political, and intellectual circles. The importance of Draper's work for Midḥat and for his wide network lay in his unambiguous testimony to the religious superiority of Islam over Christianity, especially on the ground of Islam's compatibility with science. Soon after the appearance of Draper's work in Ottoman Turkish, the Arabs welcomed Midḥat's translation and celebrated his findings, overlooking a critical point in Draper's narrative: that Islam's compatibility with science was a direct result of Muhammad's sustained exposure to the philosophical teachings of the Nestorians, which shaped his ideas and religious world view. This important point in Draper's argument was dropped in the three-part summary and review of Draper's book published in 1927 by an Egyptian author named ʿUmar ʿInāyat in the newly established journal *al-ʿUṣūr* (The Ages 1927-29), founded and edited by the eminent Egyptian Scholar Ismāʿīl Maẓhar. Prior to this introduction of Draper's work to Arabic readers, his ideas were indirectly introduced through a landmark debate between two leading Arab intellectuals that took place at the turn of the 20th century, shortly after the translation of Draper's work into Turkish.

Between 1902 and1903, a heated debate on science and religion unfolded on the pages of two popular Arabic journals, *al-Jāmiʿa* (The Gatherer, 1899-1910) and *al-Manār* (The Beacon, 1898-1935). The former was founded by Faraḥ Anṭūn (1874-1922), a Christian intellectual with liberal views, the latter by Muhammad Rashīd Riḍā (1865-1935), a Muslim reformer with a conservative outlook. The debate reflected the contrasting views of their founders, who were close colleagues of Syrian background living in Egypt.[28] The debate was not between Anṭūn and Riḍā, though, but between Anṭūn and the eminent Azhar cleric and reformer Muhammad ʿAbduh (1849-1905), who, prompted by Riḍā, wrote lengthy responses to Anṭūn's provocative remarks on the development of science in Islam. Anṭūn's remarks appeared in a series of articles he wrote on the intellectual career of the great Muslim philosopher Ibn Rushd (1126-98) and his struggle against the religious establishment. Pointing to the persecution and opposition he faced, Anṭūn regarded Christianity as having been more tolerant towards, and supportive of, philosophy and science than Islam, evidenced by the rise of the Enlightenment's anti-religious sentiment as well as the development of modern science. Riḍā disagreed with Anṭūn's reading of Islamic intellectual history, and accused him of being prejudiced and offensive. Thus, the debate took on a religiously acrimonious tone from the start, and ʿAbduh was bent on showing the superiority of Islam over Christianity by virtue of Islam's rationality, tolerance, and support of scientific creativity and philosophical thinking.[29] Both Anṭūn and Riḍā subsequently compiled and published their texts in separate volumes; however, it was Riḍā's book (of ʿAbduh's commentaries) that achieved greater success, appearing in several editions, circulating widely, and remaining to this day a popular reference on science and religion in the Arab world. Entitled *al-Islam wa-l-naṣrāniyya maʿ al-ʿilm wa-l-madaniyya* (Islam and Christianity in Relation to Science and Civilisation), ʿAbduh's passionate response to Anṭūn's rational critique has endured in the Muslim collective imagination ever since, and has become the standard position on Islam's relationship to science.[30]

In the exchange, both Anṭūn and ʿAbduh showed remarkable familiarity with Draper's book, with the latter quoting from it directly to support his argument. Yet each used Draper's text in a different way. It is likely that both Anṭūn and ʿAbduh were introduced to Draper's text through Midḥat's translation, as they had limited knowledge of English. Ignoring what Draper had said about Islam, Anṭūn used the conflict model to write an intellectual history of Islam, reflecting Draper's, to show the suffering endured by Muslim philosophers and scientists at the hands of the religious authorities. In his replies, 'Abduh used Draper's argument literally to show the oppressive history of Christianity and the tolerant history of Islam, which was upheld by Draper himself as *the* true religion of science. It was easy and convenient for 'Abduh, armed with such strong testimony to Islam's compatibility with modern science from an eminent American scholar, to blame the political circumstances and corruption of Muslim leaders for the civilisational decline, and to present the return to the true spirit of the Islamic religion as a way for Islam to reclaim its leadership in science and, with that, its lost glory.[31]

With the wide circulation of the Anṭūn-'Abduh debate, the popularity of Draper's book among Arab readers rose in the early decades of the 20th century. 'Ināyat's three-part summary and review, already mentioned, appeared consecutively in the September, October, and December issues of *al-'Uṣūr.* Immediately after this introduction to Draper, in the fourth issue of January 1928, Maẓhar himself published a scathing review of 'Abduh's book, which Riḍā compiled and published, criticising 'Abduh's rehashing and representation of Draper's texts without a proper acknowledgment to Draper. He considered 'Abduh's commentaries as no more than a summary of Draper's book and disapproved of 'Abduh's uncritical adoption of Draper's arguments.[32] Not only were 'Abduh's sloppy scholarship and indeed plagiarism of grave concern to Maẓhar, but also his inconsistent position on Islam and Christianity, following Draper's misreading and misrepresentation of historical facts. Yet, Maẓhar remained committed to the scientific critique of institutional religions and their official theology. He seemed closer to White than Draper in his ideas. Differentiating between religion (*dīn*) and theology (*lāhūt*), Maẓhar argued that the struggle of science has been against theology, not religion, for science can accommodate the religious belief in the supra-rational.[33] Remarkably, he credited White with clarifying this point in his famous book, which Maẓhar translated liberally into Arabic and published as *Bayn al-'ilm wa-l-dīn: tārīkh al-ṣirā' baynahumā fī-l-qurūn al-wusṭā* (In between Religion and Science: The History of the Struggle between them in the Middle Ages).[34]

After the wide exposure to Draper's and White's works, the conflict model became accepted among Arab and Ottoman scholars, notwithstanding the different ways in which it was interpreted and represented. Because of his favourable views of Islam, Draper received more attention among Arabs and Ottomans than White and exerted stronger influence. Midḥat's and 'Abduh's readings of Draper became the most popular, intersecting at two points: first, that what Draper meant by the word 'religion' in his conflict thesis was 'Christianity', and, second, that there could be no such conflict between Islam and science as testified by the author himself. Thus, the conflict thesis became a useful reference to use in the Islam verses Christianity politics. It was particularly handy in the argument against the growing presence of Christian missionaries in the Ottoman Empire. Many conservative Muslim reformers and intellectuals were becoming increasingly concerned about the rising popularity of the Christian missionaries' schools among the Muslim population. They were worried that Christian education was corrupting the young students' minds and leading them to doubt the basic principles of the Islamic religion. By showing the inherent conflict between Christianity and science in contrast to the harmony and compatibility with science that Islam promotes, both Midḥat and 'Abduh were able to use Draper's text as a potent resource in both their fight against the infiltrations of the Christian missionaries and their campaign to raise public awareness of Christianity's dangerous influences.[35]

THE DEFEAT OF RATIONAL SCIENCES

By the mid-20th century, ʿAbduh's emotional, selective, and methodologically sloppy reading of the Islamic history of science began to give way to more self-critical and conceptually and methodologically rigorous approaches. The conflict thesis remained, though, forming an integral part of post-Enlightenment modern thinking. Progressive, modernist historians began to see the relevance of the Enlightenment's rational critique of religion to Islam, and interpretations began to swing towards Anṭūn's and Maẓhar's perspectives. In his famous *The Ottoman Empire: The Classical Age 1300-1600*, published in 1968 (English translation in 1973), the eminent Turkish historian Halil Inalcik (d. 2016) presented a widely shared reading of Ottoman history based on a new projection of the conflict thesis. In Chapter 18 of his book, which he devoted to what he called 'The Triumph of Fanaticism', Inalcik discussed the beginning of the decline of the Ottoman Empire, which he attributed to the defeat of 'rational sciences'.[36] The 'defeat' was represented by the declining interest in rational sciences, in contrast to the rising interest in these sciences in Europe that led to the scientific revolution. An evidence of this 'defeat', Inalcik argues, was the destruction of the Istanbul Observatory, which, in his view, marked a critical turning point in Ottoman history characterised by the triumph of religion over science.[37]

In his new historical reading, Inalcik used Draper's and White's conflict model, which by then had become a normative approach; however, unlike ʿAbduh and Riḍā he viewed Islam and Christianity as having shared the same repressive attitude towards science. Inalcik presented the Istanbul Observatory as having been the most advanced in the Islamic world at the time, and drew the readers' attention to how it was equipped with state-of-the-art observational instruments, which were strikingly similar to those in Tycho Brahe's (d. 1601) observatory, which was built and operated in Denmark around the same time.[38] As the destruction of the Istanbul Observatory took place in 1580, around the same time of the burning of Servetus (d. 1553) and Bruno (d. 1600), and the trial of Galileo (1633), the conflict model made good sense in Inalcik's narrative.

In his appropriation of the conflict thesis, Inalcik took a new tack: he mapped the modern polarity of science and religion over the tradition division of rational and transmitted sciences (*ʿaqlī* vs. *naqlī*). With this move, the conflict thesis acquired an Islamic history not unlike the largely Christian history presented by Draper and White. With the aid of this new theoretical lens, the destruction of the Istanbul Observatory became the outcome of a decisive confrontation between proponents of two long-entrenched and opposing approaches to Islamic knowledge, the rationalists and the traditionalists. The rationalists were advocates of *al-ʿulūm al-ʿaqliyya* (rational sciences), representing the philosophers, physicians, and scientists, while the traditionalists were advocates of *al-ʿulūm al-sharʿiyya* or *al-naqliyya* (religious or transmitted sciences), representing the jurists and religious scholars. With the observatory being viewed and represented as an advanced 'scientific' institution, its destruction could only signify the triumph of religion over science.

Inalcik's use of the conflict thesis with regard to the Istanbul Observatory resonates with Anṭūn's reading of Islamic intellectual history; it is an attempt to present a viable reason for the decline of Islamic science. Science triumphed in the West, whereas religion triumphed in the East. As with Galileo's trial and the burning of Bruno, the circumstances that led to the destruction of the Istanbul Observatory were far more complex and enigmatic than Inalcik's reading.[39] His explicit correlation between the rise of religious fanaticism and the waning of rational sciences has already been challenged and refuted in recent studies.[40] His implicit correlation between the modern polarity of science and religion and the pre-modern Islamic division of rational and transmitted sciences, however, has escaped critical examination. I shall discuss this briefly here.

To begin with, seeing the Istanbul Observatory as a 'scientific' institution and its director Taqī al-Dīn bin Maʿrūf (d. 1585) as a 'scientist' involves historical distortion, because the polarity of science and religion did not exist then. This can be seen in the way in which Taqī al-Dīn was depicted in historical sources. In his biographical dictionary *Sullam al-wuṣūl* (The Ladder of Reach), the eminent 17th-century scholar Kātip Çelebi (d. 1657) introduced Taqī al-Dīn as *al-Qāḍī al-ʿAllāma*, literally 'the judge, the most knowledgeable'.[41] The chosen terms identify Taqī al-Dīn's earlier and latter professional engagements — that is, first as a judge and then as an astronomer. While his professional identification as a *qāḍī* (judge) is clear, his identification as a *ʿallāma* ('most knowledgeable', a superlative adjective of *ʿālim*) is ambiguous. The Arabic title *ʿallāma* is normally used for individuals who possess a high or distinguished degree of knowledge, and it is most commonly used for religious scholars. Rarely, a distinguished literary figure (*adīb*) is called *ʿallāma* for his or her outstanding literary skills and knowledge. Accordingly, Çelebi's description of Taqī al-Dīn as *ʿallāma* shows his understanding of 'scientists' as individuals with a high degree of knowledge without distinction from religious scholars who carry the same title.[42]

The cognate Arabic terms *ʿilm/ʿālim/ʿallāma* blur the boundaries between science and religion, showing how all knowledge-oriented activities were embraced by the unifying perspective of *ʿilm*. This is not to say that there was no distinction between astronomy and jurisprudence as *ʿilm*, or between an astronomer and a judge as *ʿālim*, but rather that there were no inherent distinctions in the mode, method, and ultimate purpose of knowing that can render the astronomer as a 'scientist' in contrast to the judge as a 'religious scholar'. Taqī al-Dīn's works reflect the same intertwined scope of science and religion, although his main areas of study — astronomy, mathematics, mechanics, and optics — fall squarely within the purview of today's natural sciences and are not part of religious sciences. This intertwined relationship between science and religion in early modern Islam can also be seen in the popularity of a wide range of occult sciences at the time, which belonged to both realms of science and religion, and which are now completely disowned by both science and religion.[43] The lack of a clear conceptual distinction between science and religion casts doubt on the assumed identity of the observatory as a 'scientific institution' destroyed to put an end to its 'scientific' activities.

An examination of early modern Islamic sources sheds more light on the correspondence between the division of rational and transmitted sciences and the polarity of science and religion. Three key sources are identified: Ṭāshkubrīzāda's *Miftāḥ al-saʿāda* (16th century), Kātip Çelebi's *Kashf al-ẓunūn* (17th century), and al-Tahanawī's *Kashshāf* (18th century). These sources are concerned with the definition and classification of current and recorded sciences. The first two were by eminent Ottoman scholars who lived in Istanbul immediately before and after the destruction of the Istanbul Observatory, while the third was by an eminent scholar from Mughal India, thereby presenting a perspective external to the Ottoman cultural context. Each author's personality, individual experiences, and agency had certainly coloured his mode, style, and focus of writing; however, the texts themselves reflect the evolving perceptions of *ʿilm*, especially in response to the increasing exposure to the European scientific developments.

Ṭāshkubrīzāda (1495-1561) divides his *Miftāḥ* into two parts, each of which he calls *ṭaraf*, literally 'edge' or 'end'. The first 'edge' is concerned with the production and classification of knowledge, whereas the second 'edge' is concerned with the morality of knowing — that is, the religious conditions and implications of knowledge in practice. This main division maps over another division relating to modes of knowing: one is called *ṭarīq al-naẓar* (the way of reflection) and is concerned with knowledge acquired through reasoning or rational thinking, while the other is called *ṭarīq al-taṣfiya* (the way of purification) and is concerned with knowledge acquired through revelation or inner purification. This differentiation in the modes of knowledge acquisition does not, directly or indirectly, map over or translate into the division of science and religion, nor over the polarity of the rational versus transmitted knowledge. Under the approach of rational reflection (*ṭarīq al-naẓar*), all sciences are included: religious, psychological, and natural. By contrast, under the approach of inner purification (*ṭarīq taṣfiya*), only issues of morality are discussed, which Ṭāshkubrīzāda describes as the ways in which knowledge is put into practice — that is, how one conducts oneself according to the knowledge acquired (*thamarat al-ʿamal bi-l-ʿilm*).[44]

The *Miftāḥ* classifies sciences into seven categories, each of which is referred to as *dawḥa* (large tree). The first four *dawḥas* include sciences classified according to the philosophical division of modes of existence: textual, verbal, mental, and material. The fifth *dawḥa* includes sciences concerned with 'practical philosophy' (*al-ḥikma al-ʿamaliyya*) — that is, ethics, politics, economics, and management. The sixth *dowḥa* includes religious sciences (*ʿulūm sharʿiyya*), while the seventh *dawḥa* includes mystical sciences (*ʿulūm al-bāṭin*). It is in the fourth *dawḥa*, which includes sciences concerned with physical existents or the 'natural world', where we find what are conventionally designated today as 'rational sciences'. Yet the first branch of the fourth *dawḥa* is theology (*ʿilm ilāhī*), which includes a host of disciplines that fall squarely within the purview of religion from today's perspective. Despite this intertwining of scopes between natural and theological sciences, the *Miftāḥ* delineates religious sciences clearly in the sixth *dawḥa*, which is larger than the first five put together. But religious sciences are not presented in opposition to rational sciences because all sciences, as mentioned earlier, follow one of two approaches, either the way of reason or the way of the heart. And all religious sciences except the mystical involve rational thinking and follow the way of reason (*ṭarīq al-naẓar*). Thus Ṭāshkubrīzāda's classifications and discussions show how conceptually broad the established division of sciences into rational and transmitted (*ʿaqlī* and *naqlī*) was, and the absence of a recognised distinction between scientific and religious modes of knowing.

Kātip Çelebi (1609-57), the author of the second source, was a celebrated Ottoman bibliophile, whose concept of *ʿilm* was discussed in several of his works.[45] Çelebi wrote one of the most important sources on Islamic sciences in the early modern period, *Kashf al-ẓunūn ʿan asāmī al-kutub wa-l-funūn* (Dispelling Doubts Concerning the Names of Books and Branches of Science).[46] This bibliographic dictionary includes a long and sophisticated introduction on the conceptualisation of *ʿilm*, covering many aspects such as its meanings, essence, objects, divisions, nobility, status, morality, and origin. Çelebi refers to and quotes from Ṭāshkubrīzāda's *Miftāḥ*; however, he had a wider exposure to the emerging 'new sciences' of the Europeans and hence his conceptual approach was different from his predecessor.

Çelebi was a rational, scientifically inclined thinker; thus if we can describe Ṭāshkubrīzāda's approach to *ʿilm* as an attempt to confer legitimacy on rational sciences within the authoritative space of religious knowledge, then Çelebi's approach can be viewed as an attempt to confer legitimacy on religious sciences within the emerging new authoritative space of rational knowledge. With Çelebi's work, a tension between the traditionalists' and modernists' approaches to *ʿilm* can be seen to have begun to emerge in the Ottoman society. His openness to European sciences and critical view of the role of religion in constraining the pursuit of knowledge opened new horizons of thinking in the Ottoman context. In fact, his whole life and intellectual career were polarised by his oscillation between the rational and religious sciences. Yet he emphasised that, although *ʿilm* is divisible into many divisions according to different considerations, it remains 'one in meaning and in truth (*maʿnā waḥid wa ḥaqīqa wāḥida*)'.[47] The unity of the scope of *ʿilm* withstood the new challenges, with no vertical division appearing between science and religion during his time.

Çelebi refers to the rational and transmitted approaches to *ʿilm* as each being represented by a different type (*ṣinfayn*) of science: one is 'natural to man who is guided to it by his thought', while the other is 'transmitted and is taken from the one who established it'.[48] He called the first type the intellectual or philosophical sciences (*al-ʿulūm al-ḥikmiyya*), and the second type the transmitted and conventional sciences (*al-ʿulūm al-naqliyya al-waḍʿiyya*).[49] Thus Çelebi saw the rational versus transmitted approaches to *ʿilm* as *natural* versus *conventional* approaches. The rational sciences derive their validity and legitimacy from the universality of human nature, whereas the transmitted sciences derive their validity and legitimacy from the specificity of a community's religious conventions. 'These transmitted sciences', he wrote,

> are all specific to the Islamic community, even though every community must have similar sciences; thus all communities share in the need for religious sciences; however, the Islamic community's conventions are specifically different from those of all other communities.[50]

Çelebi's natural versus conventional polarity can be seen as an early form of the modern distinction between science and religion. This is further confirmed by his view that Islam's conventional sciences have already 'had its heydays (*nafqat aswāquha*) in the Muslim community with no new ascents, and that scholars' knowledge in those fields had already reached their limits with no leaps beyond'.[51]

Muhammad Aʿlā al-Tahānawī, the author of the third source, was both a philologist (especially a lexicologist) and a judge (*qāḍī*) who came from the town of Tohāna northwest of Delhi. We know little about his life, other than that he was from a family steeped in religious knowledge and was a contemporary of the Mughal Emperor Aurangzeb (d. 1707), who was known for his conservative religious attitude. Al-Tahānawī's main work, *Kashshāf iṣṭilāḥāt al-funūn wa-l-ʿulūm* (Dictionary of Technical and Scientific Terms), continues the tradition of defining and classifying knowledge, albeit in a different way. Tahānawī's *Kashshāf* is notably different from both Çelebi's *Kashf* and Ṭāshkubrīzāda's *Miftāḥ* in being conceived of as a necessary reference to important terminologies in the context of the changing and expanding scope of science. Tahānawī prefaces his dictionary with a lengthy introduction in which he discusses the definition and classification of sciences using a similar approach to those of Çelebi and Ṭāshkubrīzāda. This shows the consistent methodology in discussing the conceptual dimensions of *ʿilm* among Muslim scholars. A number of critical shifts appear to be emerging in Tahānawī's reference dictionary, however. The first is the growing awareness of the necessity of such reference works to avoid ambiguity and confusion in understanding the meanings of discipline-specific terms (*ishtibāh al-iṣṭilāḥ*); the second is the growing confidence in the utility and adequacy of books in fulfilling the epistemological needs of seekers of knowledge without dependency on teachers; and the third is the growing need for encyclopaedic references that bring together all sciences in an 'objective' manner.[52]

Despite his encyclopaedic perspective, Tahānawī follows the traditional divisions of sciences into the linguistic, the religious, and the rational. While the linguistic sciences of Arabic (*al-ʿulūm al-ʿarabiyya*) and the religious and transmitted science of Islam (*al-ʿulum al-sharʿiyya*) remained within the traditional perspective in terms of scope, definition, and branches, the rational science took on a new scope and definition as *al-ʿulūm al-ḥaqīqiyya*, literally 'real' or 'true sciences', which Tahānawī describe as 'those sciences which do not change by the change of sects and religions'.[53] They included, as listed by Tahānawī, logic, philosophy, theology, mathematical science, natural science, medicine (*ʿilm al-ṭibb*), veterinary science, physiognomy, dream interpretation, astrology (*ʿilm aḥkām al-nujūm*), magic, talismans, semiology, chemistry, agriculture, arithmetic, geometry, building construction, optics, science of mirrors, weight physics, surveying, water engineering, mechanical clocks, military machines, automata, astronomy, calendar and celestial conjunctions, time keeping, observation, the flattening of sphere, shadow machines, and heaven and the world.[54]

The expression 'true sciences' itself is not new, as indicated by Tahānawī himself in his reference to the celebrated 15th-century theologian al-Jurjānī (d. 1414); however, the way in which Tahānawī appropriated the expression to describe and classify rational sciences in opposition to religious sciences was certainly new. Theology remained consistently part of the rational sciences. To describe the rational sciences, which had been under sustained attack from religious authorities, as 'true' or 'real' imbues them with a new form of legitimacy and immunity. This does not automatically mean that religious sciences become untrue or less true, but a new distinction on the basis of the relativity and universality of *ʿilm* appears to have become necessary. By introducing this new distinction, Tahānawī did not seem to have been trying to create a new category for natural or empirical sciences alone, but a category that included the philosophical and religious rational sciences that were under attack, such as logic (*manṭiq*) and theology (*kalām*). The explanation he offers for the inclusion of theology is rather intriguing: 'for all prophets, peace be upon them, were in agreement concerning issues of beliefs [*muttafiqīn fī-l-iʿtiqādiyyāt*]', thus putting more emphasis on their common grounds rather than their differences.[55] Accordingly, Tahānawī's new ecumenical perspective is notably different from the one established by his predecessors and continued by many of his contemporaries.

The brief examination of these three early modern sources on the classification of sciences shows that, despite the texts' different scopes and approaches, they presented a consistent understanding of the concept of *ʿilm*, which remained stable across the threshold of the early modern period; it shows, too, that awareness of an intrinsic split and conflict between science and religion did not emerge until the early decades of the 19th century. The sources also reveal that it was by the mid-18th century that the need to differentiate a category for a universal kind of scientific undertaking independent of time, place, and religion began to emerge, as the early delineation of 'true sciences' (*ʿulūm haqīqiyya*) indicates.[56] Yet these, as well as other important sources of this period (16th-19th century), were of interest neither to Draper and White, nor to the Arab and Ottoman intellectuals who adopted and promoted Draper and White's views, such as Midḥat, ʿAbduh, Anṭūn, Riḍā, and Maẓhar. This was because the period did not carry any significance for any of them: it was the dark ages into which the Islamic civilisation had plunged after giving Europe her salvation and assisting her emancipation into the modern world.

'KNOWLEDGE IS POWER'

In Chapter 11 of his book, Draper focused on 'Science in Relation to Modern Civilization', in order to address a question that lies at the heart of his study: '[W]hat has science done for humanity?'[57] At the end of the chapter he asked: 'What has science done for the promotion of modern civilization[?]'; and '[W]hat has it done for the happiness, the well-being of society?'[58] After giving various examples of the remarkable intellectual, social, medical, and economic progress achieved with the aid of science, he concluded with two statements summing up the essential difference between religion and science: 'Ignorance is the mother of Devotion', while 'Knowledge is Power'.[59] Arab and Ottoman intellectuals and reformers, who were relentlessly searching for ways to catch up with the scientific advancement of the West, seem to have had Draper's postulation in their minds and hearts. *ʿIlm*, now standing for 'modern science', became the way to salvation. With the Arab and Ottoman polarisation of *ʿilm* into science and religion, Draper's ideas aided two contrasting understandings of the role of science in bringing about modern civilisation and its social prosperity and progress.

One group championed Draper's conflict thesis and sought to apply it to Islam on the ground of the inherent incompatibility between religious and scientific thinking. For those, *ʿilm* must triumph over *dīn* if society is to be modernised. They saw the new meaning of *ʿilm* (that is, as modern science) as having helped dissolve the creedal differences between Muslim and Christian Arabs, who began to share common views on the relationship between science and religion. Anṭūn, for example, dedicated his book on Ibn Rūsh's life and philosophy to 'the rational thinkers of the Orient from Islam, Christianity, and other Religions', whom he described as 'the new cultivation' (*al-nabt al-jadīd*). 'By 'new cultivation', he wrote,

> we mean those rational thinkers [*ʿuqalāʾ*] in every sect and religion in the Orient, who have realised the harms of mixing worldly affairs with religion in an age such as this, so they demanded putting their religion aside in a respectful, sacred place, in order to be able to achieve true unity among themselves, to be in line with the new trend of European civilisation, to compete with its people [that is, the Europeans], and to avoid being swept away by the new trend and turned into servants for others.[60]

In a manner similar to Draper, Anṭūn concluded his exposition with questions concerning the significance of science for modern civilisation, asking: Has '*ʿilm* achieved all the duties the human intellect has assigned to it? And has it succeeded in replacing religion permanently after that great intellectual war which unfolded in Europe between different nations and different philosophies?'[61] Acknowledging that *ʿilm* had thus far failed to meet all human expectations, Anṭūn wondered whether that was because of a weakness in *ʿilm* itself or in humanity which could not bear *ʿilm*'s tremendous power.[62]

Yet the other group saw the conflict as an internal affair of Christendom, celebrated the superiority of Islam in this regard, and emphasised the harmony between science and religion in the Islamic tradition. Draper's forceful testimony on Islam made it easy and convenient for them to blame the political circumstances and corruption of Muslim leaders for the civilisational decline, and to advocate for the centrality of religion in Muslim life. Today's popular slogan 'Islam is the solution' is a view that had its roots in the fallout of Draper's intervention, with which a utopian dream emerged to reclaim Islam's leadership in science and, with that, its lost glory. This view received wide support and established a strong trend that enabled puritanical and fundamentalist ideologies to prosper side by side with liberal thought. Speaking of the Quran, ʿAbduh described it in his reply to Anṭūn as

> that glorious book, which was followed by *ʿilm* wherever it went, east or west; its light will eventually re-appear to tear apart the veils of misguidedness, and return to its first home at the heart of all Muslims to reside there. *ʿIlm* will be following it as an intimate friend, in whom it finds solace and upon whom it depends.[63]

This approach was instrumental in protecting the religious establishment from being undermined by the growing authority of modern science. The domain of the sacred thus remained immune from critical encroachments, and strands of pre-modern religious thought, discourse, ideas, and practices, which were no longer in line with scientific thinking and findings, have survived in the Islamic world in a unique way side by side with advanced science and technology. In many ways, this can no longer be seen as an expression of harmony between science and religion, but rather a forced marriage of contradictions. This stands out today as a unique feature of Muslim modernity, which has been sustained, as Dan Diner has put it in *Lost in the Sacred*, by 'an unholy alliance between *premodern* conditions still prevalent in the Middle East and an apologetic *postmodern* discourse that has established itself in the West'.[64] Thus the questions that the polarisation of *'ilm* into science and religion has raised in the Islamic context are not concerned essentially with the lost moral guidance of the scientific endeavour or with how to conceptualise the polarity of science and religion and write their intertwined history, but rather with Islam's perplexing ability to sustain both pre- and postmodern modes of thinking and living in the present, and with its compatibility with modernity's non-sacred, humanistic orientation.

NOTES

1 See John William Draper, 1875, *History of the Conflict between Religion and Science* (New York: D Appleton and Company); and Andrew Dixon White, 1897/1910, *A History of the Warfare of Science with Theology in Christendom* (New York: D Appleton and Company, vol. I 1897, vol. II 1910).

2 Draper, 1875, vi. White described the central thesis of his book as follows: 'In all modern history, interference with science in the supposed interest of religion, no matter how conscientious such interference may have been, has resulted in the direst evils both to religion and to science, and invariably; and, on the other hand, all untrammelled scientific investigation, no matter how dangerous to religion some of its stages may have seemed for the time to be, has invariably resulted in the highest good both of religion and of science'. White, 1897, viii.

3 See David Lindberg and Ronald Numbers, 1986, *God and Nature: Historical Essays on the Encounter between Christianity and Science* (California: University of California Press); and David Wilson, 2002, 'The Historiography of Science and Religion', in Gary Ferngren, ed., 2002, *Science and Religion: A Historical Introduction* (Baltimore: Johns Hopkins University Press), 13-29.

4 See the following works by Peter Harrison: 2015, *The Territories of Science and Religion* (Chicago: Chicago University Press); and 2007, *The Fall of Man and the Foundations of Science* (Cambridge: Cambridge University Press). See also Harrison's edited volume, 2010, *The Cambridge Companion to Science and Religion* (Cambridge: Cambridge University Press).

5 Draper, 1875, 99.

6 Draper, 1875, 110.

7 Draper, 1875, 110.

8 Draper, 1875, 111-12.

9 See Harrison, 2015.

10 Rifā'a Al-Ṭahṭāwī, 2003, *Takhlīṣ al-Ibrīz fī talkhīṣ bārīz* (Beirut: Dār al-Anwār), 185. Unless otherwise stated all translations from Arabic sources are mine.

11 John Livingston, 1996, 'Western Science and Educational Reform in the Thought of Shaykh Rifa al-Tahtawi', *International Journal of Middle East Studies* 28(4): 543-64.

12 *Al-Jinān*, a bi-monthly journal, was founded by eminent Christian scholar Buṭrūs al-Bustānī (1819-83) and his son Salīm in Syria-Lebanon, covering political, literary, and scientific topics. *Al-Muqtaṭaf*, a monthly journal, was established by two Christian intellectuals, Ya'qūb Ṣarrūf and Fāris Nimr, first also in Syria-Lebanon before they moved it to Cairo; it was devoted to science and industry. It was the most popular and longest surviving early modern Arabic journal.

13 Salīm Ilyās al-Ḥamawī, 1875, *al-Barāhīn al-qaṭ'iyya 'alā 'adam dawarān al-kurā al-arḍiyya* (Alexandria: Maṭba'at al-Kawkab al-Sharqī). The author's surname associates the family with the Syrian city of Ḥamā; however, he indicates that he was 'Damascene by birth and Egyptian by residence': Al-Ḥamawī, 1875, 2.

14 *Al-Jinān* was published between 1870 and 1886. Al-Ḥamawī referred to the articles published in the 14th, 15th, and 16th issues of the journal in 1872.

15 As a leading figure of the Arab Awakening movement, the editor Buṭrus al-Bustānī was a strong advocate of modern science and a proponent of the new heliocentric astronomy, hence his disinterest in al-Ḥamawī's response.

16 Al-Ḥamawī, 1875, 2. He published his ideas in the 12th, 13th, and 14th issues.

17 Al-Ḥamawī, 1875, 4.

18 Al-Ḥamawī, 1875, 4.

19 Abdullah Fikrī, 1876, *Risala fī muqārant ba'ḍ mabāhith al-hay'a bi-l-wārid fī al-nuṣūs al-shar'iyya* (Cairo: Maṭba'at al-Madāris al-Malakiyya).

20 Fikrī, 1876, 12.

21 Although 19th-century Christian scholars were, generally speaking, more inclined to accept Western ideas and advocate for modern science, in this case it was the reverse: Fikrī was a Muslim while al-Ḥamawī was a Christian. This shows that the reaction to the radical ideas of modern science was not predetermined by one's religion. Lewis Sheikhū (1859-1927), for example, strongly criticised Shiblī Shumayyil's (1850-1917) zealous support for modern natural science and considered his ideas to be heretical. Both were Christians.

22 The debate of the heliocentric versus the geocentric systems intensified only in the second half of the 19th century. For a long time before that, religious scholars were debating whether the earth was round or flat. Even Rafā'a al-Ṭahṭāwī (1801-73), who was exposed to and fascinated by modern science and who was expected to have an explicit view on modern astronomy, was coy about heliocentrism and referred only to the round-or-flat-earth debate among Muslim scholars. See Ṭahṭāwī, 2003, 50.

23 It was the first year of this monthly newspaper, which was founded in Beirut in June 1876 by two Christian Syrian-Lebanese intellectuals, Ya'qūb Ṣarrūf and Fāris Nimr. Later the newspaper moved to Egypt.

24 *Al-Muqtaṭaf*, 1877a, 1(8): 169.

25 *Al-Muqtaṭaf*, 1877b, 1(8): 171-4.

26 *Al-Muqtaṭaf*, 1877c, 1(10): 217-20.

27 See Alper Yalcinkaya, 2011, 'Science as an Ally of Religion: A Muslim Appropriation of "the Conflict Thesis"', *The British Journal for the History of Science* 44(2): 161-81. Whereas Midḥat used the Arabic term *nizā'* for 'conflict', 'Ināyat and Maẓhar used *niḍāl*, literally 'struggle', 'resistance'. Today, *ṣirā'*, 'fight', is most commonly used.

28 See Faraḥ Anṭūn, 1903, *Ibn Rush wa falsafatuhu* (Alexandria: al-Jāmi'a); and Mohammad 'Abdu, n.d., *Al-islām wa-l-naṣrāniyya ma' al-'ilm wa-l-madaniyya* (Alexandria: al-Manār).

29 In their highly emotional responses, both 'Abduh and Riḍā clearly misread Anṭūn's rational critique of religion, which was presented in the true spirit of the Enlightenment; they accused Anṭūn of promoting misconceptions of Islam. The debate resulted in a bitter fallout between the once-close Christian and Muslim colleagues, who grew up in the same Syrian town of Ṭarāblus and travelled together on the same ship to Egypt to pursue their shared ambitions in journalism.

30 Rashīd Riḍā's compilation of 'Abduh's responses to Anṭūn are published under 'Abduh's name. See Muhammad 'Abduh, n.d., *Al-islām wa-l-naṣrāniyya ma' al-'ilm wa-l-madaniyya* (Alexandria: al-Manār).

31 'Abduh, n.d., 16-19.

32 Ismā'īl Maẓhar, 1928, *Al-'Uṣūr* 4: 125-6.

33 See the introduction to his Arabic translation of White's book: Ismā'īl Maẓhar, 2014, *Bayn al-'ilm wa-l-dīn: tārīhk al-ṣirā' baynahuma fī al-qurūn al-wusṭā* (Cairo: Hindāwī).

34 Maẓhar, 2014. Maẓhar's re-presentation of White's book in Arabic was liberal, interpretive, and selective rather than being a literal translation. It also has a different title to White's.

35 Yalcinkaya, 2011.

36 Halil Inalcık, 1973, *The Ottoman Empire: The Classical Age 1300-1600*, trans. Norman Itzkowitz and Colin Imber (London: Weidenfeld and Nicholson), 179-85.

37 Inalcık, 1973, 179.
38 See Sevim Tekili, 1980, 'The Observational Instruments of Istanbul Observatory,' in M Dizer, ed., *Proceedings of the International Symposium on the Observatories in Islam* (Istanbul), 33-43.
39 My Arabic book on the Istanbul Observatory examines the events and significance of the destruction in greater details, focusing on the development of the ethos of science in the Arab-Ottoman context in the post-Copernican period. See Samer Akkach, 2017, *Marṣad Istanbul: hadm al-raṣd wa raṣd al-hadm. Taṭawwr thaqāfat al-ʿulūm fī al-Islām baʿd Copernicus* (Doha: Arab Centre for Research and Policy Studies).
40 See Khaled El-Rouayheb, 2015, *Islamic Intellectual History in the Seventeenth Century: Scholarly Currents in the Ottoman Empire and the Maghreb* (Cambridge: Cambridge University Press); and 2008, 'The Myth of "The Triumph of Fanaticism" in the Seventeenth-Century Ottoman Empire', *Die Welt des Islams* 48(2): 196-221.
41 Kātip Çelebi, 2010, *Sullam al-Wuṣūl ilā Ṭabaqāt al-Fuḥūl*, Ekmeleddin Ehsanoğlu, ed. (Istanbul: Research Centre for Islamic History, Art and Culture).
42 From today's perspective, however, *ʿallāma* can mean 'highly distinguished scientist'.
43 Tunç Şen, 2017, 'Practicing Astral Magic in Sixteenth-Century Ottoman Istanbul: A Treatise on Talismans Attributed to Ibn Kemāl (d. 1534)', *Magic, Ritual, and Witchcraft* 12(1): 66-88.
44 Ṭāshkubrīzāda (Ahmad bin Mustafa), 2002, *Miftāḥ al-saʿāda wa miṣbāḥ al-siyāda fī mawḍūʿāt al-ʿulūm*, vol. 1 (Beirut: Dār al-Kutub al-ʿIlmiyy), 3-70. The two parts of the treatise, which was published in three volumes, are prefaced by a lengthy four-part introduction: the first part presents knowledge as a virtue; the second discusses the learner's or student's moral attributes; the third discusses the teacher's moral attributes; and the fourth compares two modes of acquiring knowledge, through active thinking and passive self-refinement.
45 See Chapter 7 of this volume for more details.
46 Kātip Çelebi, 1835, *Kashf al-ẓunūn ʿan asāmī al-kutub wa l-funūn* (Beirut: Dār Ṣadir, rep. London: Bentley ed).
47 Çelebi, 1835, vol. 1: 24-5.
48 Çelebi, 1835, vol. 1: 94-5.
49 Çelebi, 1835, vol. 1: 94-5.
50 Çelebi, 1835, vol. 1: 96.
51 Çelebi, 1835, vol. 1: 96.
52 After mastering the Arabic language and religious sciences with the help of his father, al-Tahānawī writes, he studied philosophy, divine sciences, and natural sciences, including mathematics, geometry, astronomy, the astrolabe, and other subjects, all on his own through available books and glosses. This is how he managed to achieve the wide encyclopaedic scope of his dictionary, which embraces all sciences. See Muhammad Aʿlā al-Tahānawī, 1996, *Kashshāf al-iṣṭilāḥāt al-ʿulūm wa-l-funūn* (Beirut: Maktabat Lubnān Nāshirūn).
53 Al-Tahānawī, 1996, 43.
54 Al-Tahānawī, 1996, 43-65. Two sciences were mentioned twice in the published edition, medicine (*ʿilm al-ṭibb*) and astrology (*ʿilm al-nujūm*). The repetition was omitted in the list provided here.
55 Al-Tahānawī, 1996, 43.
56 Al-Tahānawī, 1996, 43.
57 Draper, 1875, Chapter XI, 286.
58 Draper, 1875, 325.
59 Draper, 1875, 326.
60 Anṭūn, 1903, dedication page.
61 Anṭūn, 1903, 84.
62 Although many Christians belonged in this camp, the positions that Christian intellectuals assumed varied remarkably. The liberal-minded — like Fikrī, Antūn, and Maẓhar, for example — promoted this view, whereas conservative figures — like al-Hamawī, ʿAbduh, and Riḍā — sided with each other to mount a united religious front against the doubtful findings of new science.
63 ʿAbduh, n.d., 176.
64 Dan Diner, 2009, *Lost in the Sacred: Why the Muslim World Stood Still*, trans. Steven Rendall (Princeton: Princeton University Press), 3, emphases in the original.

Chapter 2

Science and art: Anatomical illustration in early Islamic optics

Perri Sparnon

ABSTRACT

This chapter aims to address an often-overlooked aspect of the history of Islamic science and art: the role and development of anatomical illustrations in early Islamic scientific activities. Focusing on early Islamic optical science (*ʿilm al-manāẓir*), the chapter examines two key designs for the visual system developed by Muslim opticians from the 10th to 16th centuries. The first design originated in Ibn al-Haytham's (d. 1040) monumental 11th-century treatise on optics, the *Kitāb al-manāẓir*, and can be found in Kamāl al-Dīn al-Fārisī's (d. c. 1318) early 14th-century commentary *Tanqīḥ al-manāẓir*. The second design can be found in Taqī al-Dīn ibn Maʿrūf's (d. 1558) *Kitāb nūr ḥadaqat al-ibṣār*. The chapter questions whether practices of dissection and the knowledge of anatomy (*ʿilm al-tashrīḥ*) informed the development of these drawings, arguing that this is the case with the first design for the visual system and Ibn al-Haytham's and al-Fārisī's accompanying chapters on the anatomy of the eyes. At the same time, the chapter argues that although Muslim opticians achieved a high level of development in the field of optics and contributed to early scientific activities, descriptive anatomical illustrations were never significant carriers of knowledge in the *ʿilm al-manāẓir* tradition and only ever occupied a marginal place in the opticians' writings. The chapter closes with an assessment of what this means for the relationship between science and art in pre- and early modern Islam, and compares this to the situation in early modern Europe. It suggests that in both Islam and Europe the role and development of illustrations were complex, and the significance of illustrations as bearers of knowledge varied between different branches of science.

INTRODUCTION

The oldest surviving image of the visual system (Figure 2.1) can be found in an early copy of the *Kitāb al-manāẓir* (Book of Optics), a monumental seven-volume treatise on optics written by the Muslim polymath Ibn al-Haytham (d. 1040) in the 11th century.[1] The illustration appears in the first book of the treatise at the end of Chapter Five, 'On the Structure of the Eye', before the start of Chapter Six, 'On the Manner of Vision', and displays a multifocal view of the human head showing a horizontal cross-section of the two eyes and optic chiasma, merged with a frontal view of the nose.[2] A simple statement in Arabic at the top of the illustration reads: 'And here is a picture of the two eyes' (*wa-hādhihi ṣūratu-l-ʿaynayn*), while the numerous other Arabic labels describe the basic parts of the visual system as understood at the time, including the lens, cornea, pupil, and vitreous humour.[3]

Despite being the oldest surviving image of its kind, the *Manāẓir* illustration has not attracted sustained scholarly attention until recent years.[4] In a 2007 article, the leading historian of Islamic science and medicine, Emilie Savage-Smith, references this drawing as part of her overarching assessment of the production of anatomical illustrations in Arabic and Persian medical encyclopaedias and compendia of the 10th to 16th centuries. Her core proposition is that early anatomical illustrations, although varied, were characteristically geometric, being 'almost entirely defined by triangles, circles, and other geometric forms'.[5] She concludes that this was done because it allowed drawings to present multiple structures and views ordinarily 'not visible at the same time'; it helped readers to understand and memorise the content of the image; and it supplied 'relational and spatial information' which could not be easily described in text.[6] As such, anatomical illustrations took a purposefully 'abstracting' approach to 'the interpretation of nature' in her view.[7]

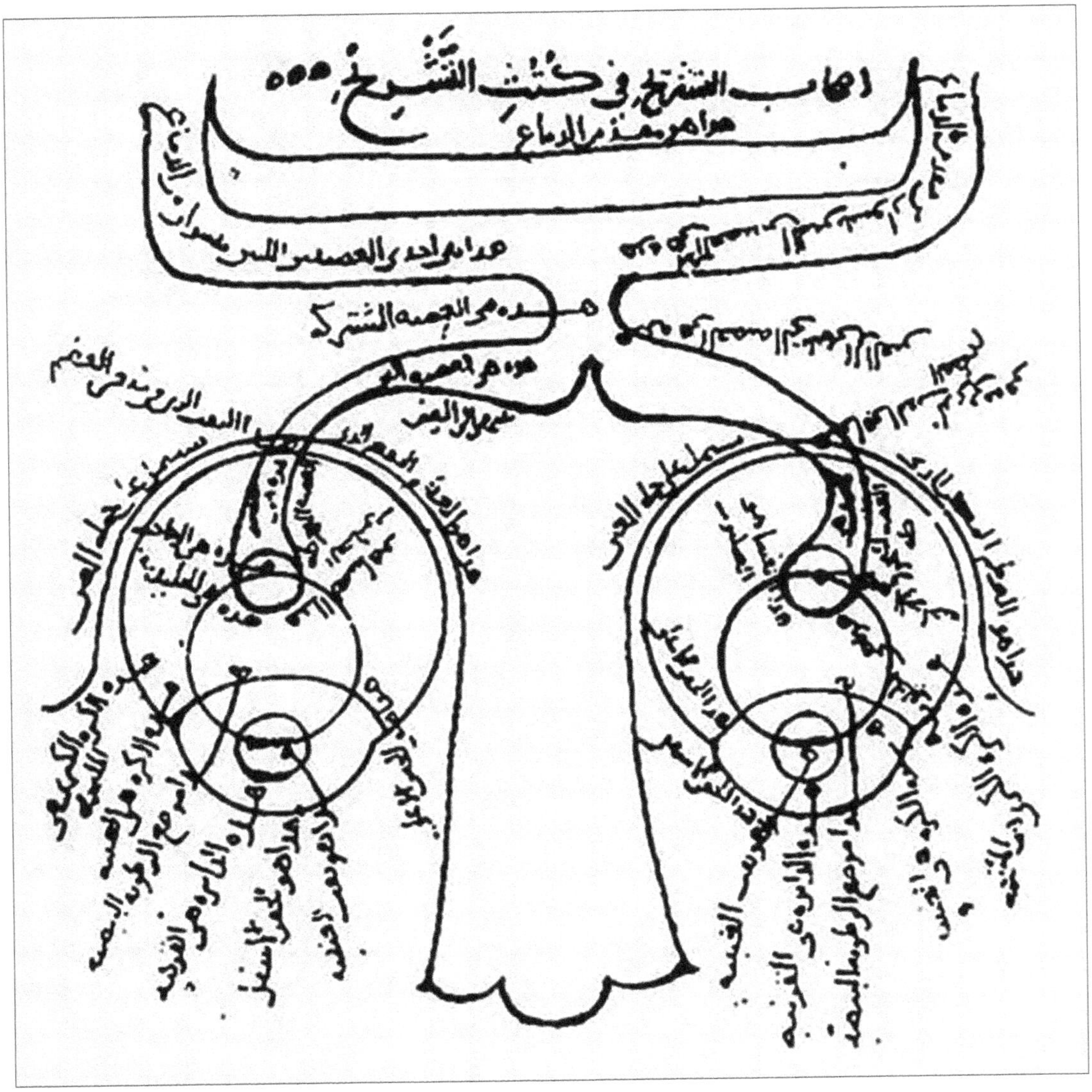

Figure 2.1 Illustration of the visual system in Ibn al-Haytham's *Kitāb al-manāẓir*. Süleymaniye Library, Istanbul, MS Fatih 3212, fol. 81b.

These conclusions, however, leave a number of questions concerning the development of anatomical illustrations unanswered. On the one hand, what were the key sources for the anatomical designs in early Arabic manuscript? Savage-Smith admits that there is 'little evidence' that original Greek anatomical texts (especially Galen's, d. c. 210, *On Anatomical Procedures* and *On the Uses of the Parts*) translated into Arabic in the 9th century 'were illustrated, or even that early copies of the Arabic translations were illustrated'.[8] On the other hand, if Muslim scholars never encountered anatomical illustrations in the Greek texts, then it is unclear how they developed their anatomical designs. Savage-Smith simply states that the drawings were 'executed by the use of compasses and straight edges', yet she never considers empirical methods like the dissection of human or animal subjects and the likelihood that such processes informed Muslim scholars' knowledge of anatomy.[9]

This chapter accordingly aims to consider the development and role of anatomical illustrations in early Islamic science. Concentrating on Islamic optical science (*ʿilm al-manāẓir*) and early Muslim opticians' attempts to define the structure of the visual system, the chapter's main aims are: first, to show the transmission and development of two key designs for representing the visual system in Islamic optics from the 11th to 16th centuries; second, to consider the likelihood that methods of dissection and the study of anatomy informed the development of these designs; and, third, to consider what anatomical illustrations can tell us about the relationship between science and art in the pre-modern period.[10] The study argues that, although key Muslim opticians like Ibn al-Haytham (d. 1040), Kamāl al-Dīn al-Fārisī (d. c. 1318), and Taqī al-Dīn ibn Maʿrūf (d. 1558) contributed to early Islamic science and achieved a high level of development in the field of optics, descriptive anatomical illustrations were never significant carriers of knowledge in optics and only ever occupied a marginal place in their writings. The study also argues that, while the lack of anatomical illustrations in optical treatises seems to indicate a disinterest in dissection and empirical knowledge, Ibn al-Haytham and al-Fārisī do in fact demonstrate extensive knowledge of anatomy in their chapters on the physical structure of the eye. These aspects have been overlooked by recent studies, which have set the lack of anatomical illustrations in the Islamic sciences against the new relationship between science and art that developed in early modern Europe.[11] This study seeks to critically engage with the studies' proposition that the prohibition on anatomical dissection in the Islamic context limited the development of descriptive anatomical illustrations, and thereby restricted the role of art in scientific advancement.

The chapter begins by examining three illustrations of the visual system in significant early Islamic optical treatises: Ibn al-Haytham's late-11th-century *Manāẓir*, al-Fārisī's early-14th-century *Tanqīḥ al-manāẓir*, and Taqī al-Dīn's 16th-century *Kitāb nūr ḥadaqat al-ibṣār*. The chapter next evaluates the reasons for the lack of scientific illustration in the Islamic context, with reference to recent studies in the history of Islamic science that have considered possible prohibitions against dissection of the human body as a key factor underlining the lack of Islamic anatomical illustrations. The chapter closes with an assessment of what this means for the relationship between science and art in pre-modern Islam.

THREE ILLUSTRATIONS OF THE VISUAL SYSTEM

Ibn al-Haytham's Kitāb al-manāẓir, *11th century*

The first design for the illustration of the visual system can be found in the *Manāẓir*, composed by Ibn al-Haytham in Cairo sometime between 1028 and his death in 1040 CE.[12] The text has been widely credited with providing the first truly systematic treatment of optics in the Islamic world, as its seven volumes cover a range of optical topics from the behaviour of light to the nature of vision.[13] In the first volume of the treatise on 'the manner of vision in general', Ibn al-Haytham devotes considerable attention to the anatomy of the eyes, with all of Chapter Five, entitled '*fī hay'at al-baṣar*' (literally, On the Configuration of Vision), concerning this topic.[14] Ibn al-Haytham provides nearly 10 pages of anatomical details here, which conclude with an illustration that graphically details with Arabic labels a number of the anatomical features of the eyes and brain discussed in the chapter.[15] Broadly, the image exposes an aerial view of the top of the human head that cuts through the eyes and moves towards the front of the brain at right angles to the nose, which is shown in frontal view.[16] The eyeballs are simply rendered as a series of nested and overlapping circles, consisting of 13 core parts. The emphasis on the iris and the pupil is likely due to Ibn al-Haytham's interest in the route of vision.

While the presentation of this illustration seems to make sense in the context of Ibn al-Haytham's discussion of the anatomy of the eye, Ibn al-Haytham himself never explicitly refers to the image in the body of his text. The last sentence before the illustration simply states: '[A]ll of what we have mentioned of the eye's coats and of its composition has been shown and expounded by anatomists [*aṣḥāb al-tashrīḥ*, literally the people of anatomy] in the books on anatomy'.[17] Yet, Ibn al-Haytham never mentions these anatomists by name and nor do any significant Islamic anatomy books (illustrated or otherwise) survive from his time.[18] It is accordingly not clear which anatomists and anatomical books Ibn al-Haytham is referring to, nor who wrote and illustrated these supposed texts, nor the reasons that they did not survive.

Al-Fārisī's Tanqīḥ al-Manāẓir, *13th to 14th century*

Ibn al-Haytham's *Manāẓir* was not widely circulated in the Muslim world until the late 13th century, around 250 years after its composition.[19] Under the instruction of the great Persian mathematician and astronomer Qṭub al-Dīn al-Shīrāzī (d. 1311), the noted Persian scholar al-Fārisī made a detailed study of Ibn al-Haytham's treatise entitled the *Tanqīḥ al-manāẓir li-dhawī -l-abṣār wa -l-baṣā'ir* (The Revision of *al-Manāẓir* for the Possessors of Sights and Insights).[20] Completed before 1309, the *Tanqīḥ* provided a detailed synopsis, commentary, and edit of Ibn al-Haytham's treatise and some of his shorter optical pieces.[21]

Al-Fārisī's *Tanqīḥ* follows the structure of Ibn al-Haytham's *Manāẓir*, being divided into seven core chapters, although the *Tanqīḥ* was published in two rather than seven volumes. Chapter Five of the first book of al-Fārisī's treatise has the same title as Ibn al-Haytham's fifth chapter, *fī hay'at al-baṣar*, to which al-Fārisī added *mabādi' ṭibiyya* (Medical Principles) and *aḥada 'ashar maqṣadan* (11 Sub-Topics), to further define the content of the chapter.[22] In the chapter, Al-Fārisī summarises Ibn al-Haytham's detailed description of the anatomy of the eye and includes an edited version of the *Manāẓir* illustration of the visual system (Figure 2.2).[23] The *Tanqīḥ* illustration closely follows the structure of the *Manāẓir* illustration by again presenting a horizontal cross-section of the eyes with their connections to the brain merged with a frontal view of the nose.[24] It also labels the key features of the eye-brain relationship in almost exactly the same manner as the *Manāẓir* illustration.

Like Ibn al-Haytham, al-Fārisī states that all of what he mentioned about the anatomy of the eye has been 'explained by the anatomists (*aṣḥāb al-tashrīḥ*) in their books'.[25] However, whereas Ibn al-Haytham followed this statement with the illustration, al-Fārisī follows it with the declaration

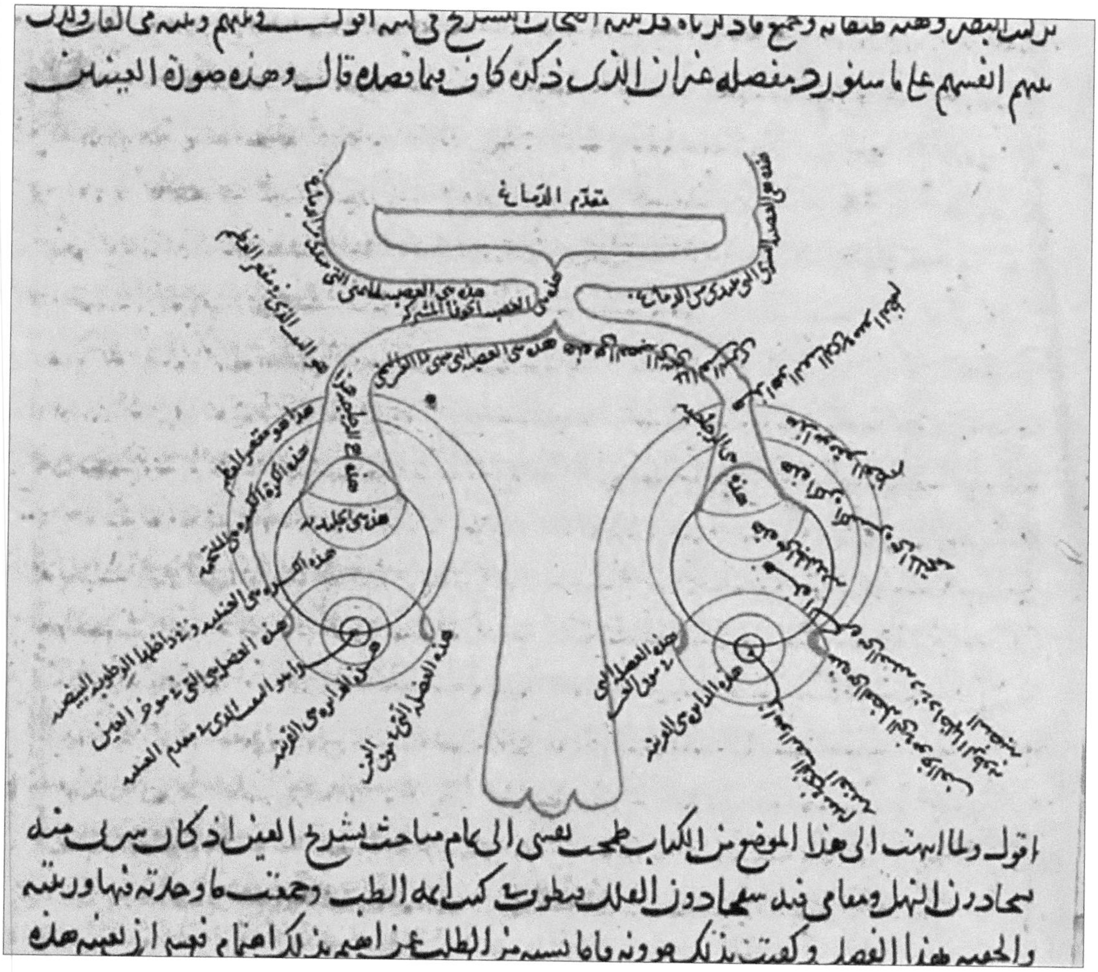

Figure 2.2 Illustration of the visual system in Kamāl al-Dīn al-Fārisī's *Tanqiḥ al-Manāẓir.* Topkapi Palace Museum, Istanbul, Ahmed III Library, MS 3340, folio 16a.

that 'there are many differences among Ibn al-Haytham and the anatomists and among the anatomists themselves'.[26] Yet, he adds that these differences do not undermine Ibn al-Haytham's study of optics. Al-Fārisī then reproduces the *Manāẓir* image (Figure 2.2), and states: 'When I arrived at this point in the book [that is, *Kitāb al-Manāẓir*], my soul aspired to complete the research into the anatomy of the eye (*itmām mabāḥith tashrīḥ al-ʿayn*)'.[27] In order to do this, al-Fārisī says he consulted 'the books of the leading physicians (*aʾimmatu -l-ṭibb*)'.[28] He mentions his sources by name, starting with 'the leading physician (*imām al-ṭibb*) Jālīnus (Galen, d. c. 210)' whose key anatomical treatise was *Fī manāfiʿ al-aʿḍāʾ* (On the Uses of the Parts); a commentary on this text titled *manāfiʿ al-aʿḍāʾ* (The Usefulness of Organs, c. 1068) by the Persian physician Ibn Abī Ṣādiq; the *al-Qānūn* (the Canon) and *al-Shifāʾ* (the Healing) of *al-Shaykh al-Raʾīs* (Ibn Sīnā, d. 1037); and the *al-Dhakhīra al-khwārazmshāhiyya*, a celebrated 12th century Arabic work on medicine by *ṣāḥib al-Dhakhīra* (Zayn al-Dīn Ismāʿīl Jurjānī, d. c. 1137/41).[29] Al-Fārisī then refers to *al-Muʿālajāt al-biqrāṭiyya* (The Treatments of Hippocrates) by the influential Persian scholar Abī al-Ḥasan Ahmad bin Muhammad al-Ṭabarī (d. 923); to *al-Ṭibb al-kabīr* (the Great Book on Medicine) by the celebrated Persian scholar imām Fakhr al-Dīn al-Rāzī (d. 1209); and to the *Sharḥ Tashrīḥ al-Qanūn* (Commentary on the Anatomy of the Canon) by the well-known Arab physician Ibn al-Nafīs al-Qurashī (d. 1288). He finally refers to a comprehensive medical reference known as *al-Malakī* (Complete Book on the Medical Art) by the 10th-century Persian physician Alī bin 'Abbās al-Majūsī (d. c. 982/94); and to several other concise references (*mukhtaṣarāt*).[30]

Al-Fārisī's list of sources confirms the existence of anatomical treatises in pre-modern Islam, some of which Ibn al-Haytham may have consulted. However, none of the surviving copies of these sources have, as far as we know, any anatomical drawings of the eyes or other organs. It is therefore surprising that al-Fārisī concludes his detailed elaboration of ocular anatomy, disease, and treatments based on his readings of these sources with *another* drawing (Figure 2.3).[31] This single eye illustration is again presented as a horizontal cross-section, with the eyeball facing down the page. However, more effort is taken to present the irregular shapes of anatomical parts in this image, while the use of red ink applied in hatching and thin strokes gives the impression of veins and blood vessels. The inclusion of this drawing may be what al-Fārisī meant by 'completing the research on the anatomy of the eye', as in the additional pages leading up to its presentation, al-Fārisī contests specific technical details concerning the structure of the eye as described by Ibn al-Haytham, and seems to aim to correct Ibn al-Haytham's errors with an accurate image.[32] Al-Fārisī's text accordingly offers further clues about the existence and use of illustrations in the early Islamic sciences.

Taqī al-Dīn's Nūr Ḥadaqat al-Ibṣār, *16th century*

A second design for the visual system is found in a manuscript entitled *Nūr ḥadaqat al-ibṣār wa-nawr hadīqat al-anẓār* (The Light of the Pupil of Seeing and the Blossom of the Garden of Sights), written by the renowned 16th-century Ottoman astronomer Taqī al-Dīn (d. 1558).[33] Taqī al-Dīn arranged his single-volume treatise on the science of optics and the problems of vision quite differently to Ibn al-Haytham's and al-Fārisī's preceding multivolumed optical treatises, and his fourth rather than fifth chapter was devoted to the topic of the anatomy of the eye. Taqī al-Dīn does not give his chapter on the anatomy of the eye the same title as Ibn al-Haytham. Instead, he simply announces Chapter Four (*al-faṣl al-rābiʿ*) and begins by writing *fīmā yuḥtāju ilayhī min tashrīḥi ālat al-ibaṣār fī -l-insān wa-hiya-l-ʿayn* (what is needed from the dissection of the human instrument of vision which is the eye).

Taqī al-Dīn gives only one page of anatomical descriptions before the drawing of the visual system is presented (Figure 2.4).[34] Although the overall structure of a horizontal cross-section of the human head is retained, the image makes a number of adjustments to the *Manāẓir* and *Tanqīh* illustrations. The eyes are not represented as a series of concentric or overlapping circles, and the frontal view of the nose is no longer included. Instead, the eyes assume a frontal view, being obviously set within the elliptical shape of eyelids. The overall structure of the optic chiasma is also elongated, and the brain is fully delineated rather than being shown as a partial frontal view. Legends again help the reader to learn the names of these anatomical structures. The eyes have approximately 10 labels each, whereas the optic chiasma and brain are described with only two labels each: *jirm al-dimāgh* (the body of the brain) and *multaqā al-ʿaṣabayn* (joint of the two [optical] nerves). Thus although the drawing offers a more explicitly panoramic view of the whole visual system, the interest seems to be focused on the eyes rather than on the optic chiasma.

Taqī al-Dīn's approach to the topic of the anatomy of the eye appears to differ in three key ways to his predecessors. Firstly, unlike al-Fārisī, who names the anatomical books he consulted

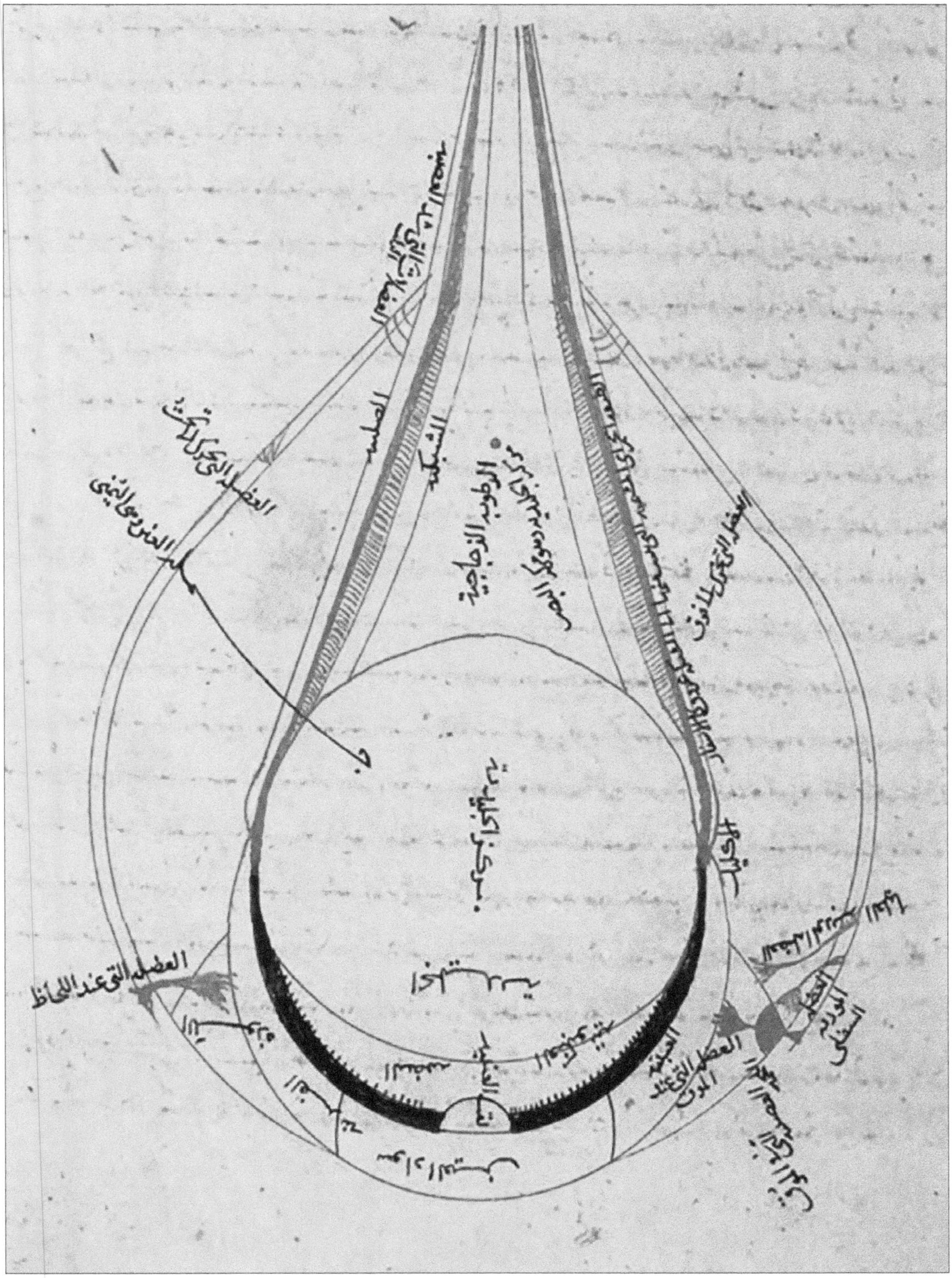

Figure 2.3 Diagram of the eye in Kamāl al-Dīn al-Fārisī's *Tanqīḥ al-Manāẓir*. Topkapi Palace Museum, Istanbul, Ahmed III Library, MS 3340, folio 25b.

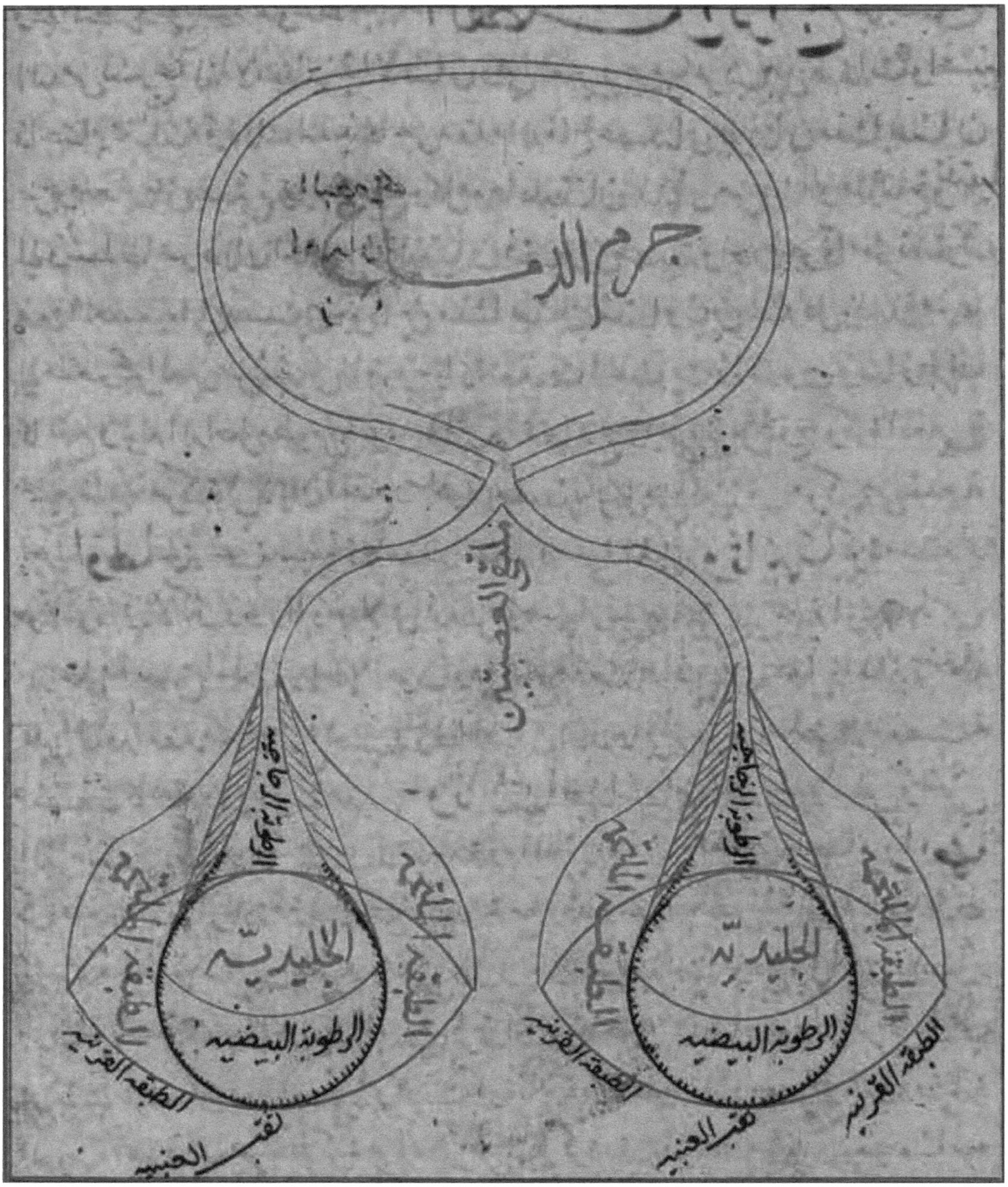

Figure 2.4 Illustration of the visual system in Taqī al-Dīn's *Nūr ḥadaqat al-ibṣār*. Dār al-Kutub al-Miṣriyya, Cairo, ʿUlūm Riyāḍiyya MS 893, folio 8a.

in his attempt to build upon Ibn al-Haytham's work, Taqī al-Dīn does not cite, or even seem to have consulted, anatomical sources. Further unlike al-Fārisī, who provides 24 extra pages of anatomical descriptions after the illustration of the visual system and adds the drawing of a single eye, Taqī al-Dīn simply progresses from the illustration of the visual system to the next chapter of his treatise entitled *fī kayfiyyat al-ibṣār* (On the Mechanics of Seeing, or How One Sees), which is the same as Chapter Six in Ibn al-Haytham's and al-Fārisī's texts.[35] Finally, whereas Ibn al-Haytham and al-Fārisī named their chapters on ocular anatomy *hay'at al-baṣar* (The Physiological Form and Constitution of Seeing), Taqī al-Dīn did not. One possible reason for this is Taqī al-Dīn's interest in astronomy, as, in addition to translating as 'form' or 'structure', *hay'a* was also used as a technical term to refer to the science of astronomy (*ʿilm al-hay'a*) in pre-modern Islam. Taqī al-Dīn may have simply been avoiding the confusing use of this term to refer to both astronomy and anatomy.[36]

Despite Taqī al-Dīn's reference to dissection in his introduction to the topic, he seems less interested in the anatomical details of the eyes than Ibn al-Haytham and al-Fārisī, and his brief presentation in Chapter Four seems superficial compared to the earlier opticians' chapters on the anatomy of the eye. Further, despite the title of his chapter foregrounding the practice of dissection, Taqī al-Dīn's presentation of ocular anatomy in his chapter gives the impression that he most likely did not bother with dissecting an eye, human or animal; or with examining a dissected one; or even with consulting physicians about such matters. His new design for the visual system is less descriptive than those in Ibn al-Haytham's and al-Fārisī's treatises, and though it contains the whole view of the brain, it has fewer labels overall and makes less effort to detail the key parts of the eye-brain relationship.

ANATOMICAL DISSECTION AND ILLUSTRATION IN EUROPE

The question of the development of anatomical illustration in the Islamic context has been discussed by the leading historian of science Toby E Huff, in his recent study (2011) on the Scientific Revolution. Huff proposed that, by the dawn of the Scientific Revolution in the 16th century, 'Europeans had considerable knowledge of human anatomy', as they 'had performed significant numbers of human dissections, especially post-mortem autopsies throughout the medieval and early modern era'.[37] These activities were concentrated in the pronounced growth of hospitals in Europe and newly established medical faculties in universities. Huff considers Andres Vesalius's (d. 1564) heavily illustrated anatomical treatise *De humani corporis fabrica* (On the Fabric of the Human Body, Figure 2.5), first published in 1543, as a key example of the Europeans' progress in medical training and knowledge, as Vesalius's collection of illustrations was based on medical research he completed as the chair of surgery and anatomy at the University of Padua from 1537 to 1543.[38]

Vesalius's treatise was divided into six books that presented a detailed examination of the organs and complete structures of the human body with over 250 accompanying illustrations showing bones, cartilage, ligaments, muscles, veins, arteries, nerves, digestive system, heart, and brain. The illustrations meticulously labelled each anatomical part with a letter that was keyed to a text providing the part's technical Greek or Latin name. Huff claims that Vesalius's richly illustrated books on human anatomy represent an extraordinary leap forward in the use of illustrations for scientific purposes. He considers the advances in both science and art that enabled the treatises' creation: on the one hand, extensive developments in dissection and medical research allowed physicians like Vesalius to refine Galen's anatomical descriptions, which had been the steadfast model of anatomical studies for over a millennium.[39] On the other, artistic developments in naturalistic visual representation and the technical development of printing with refined woodcut engravings allowed artists to produce illustrations superior to those in previous anatomical atlases.[40]

Yet, Huff claims that such a leap could never have taken place in Islam, as 'throughout Muslim history, there was a prohibition against post-mortem examinations' which prevented anatomical

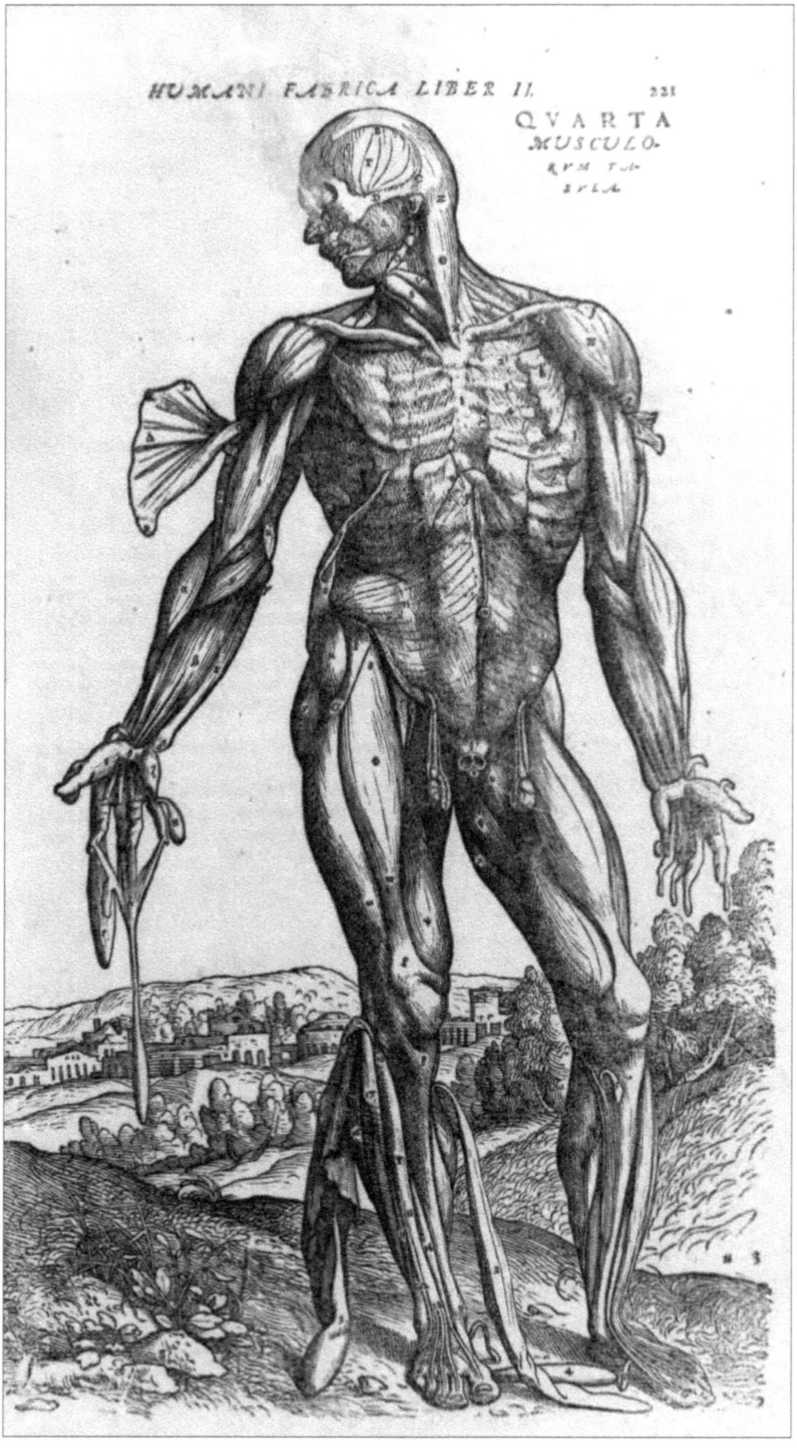

Figure 2.5 'De humani corporis fabrica (Of the Structure of the Human Body)' by Andreas Vesalius (Flemish, Brussels 1514-1564 Zakynthos, Greece), John of Calcar (John Stephen Calcar) (Netherlandish, Calcar, Cleves 1499-1546/50 Naples, Italy). Published by Johann Oporinus (publisher 1536-1567), Basel, 1555. Woodcut, 39.5 x 26.7 x 8.3 cm. The Metropolitan Museum of Art, New York, Acc. 53.682. (Licensed under CC0 1.0.)

exploration of the human body.[41] Huff argues that 'one source of this prohibition came from a saying (Hadith) attributed to the Prophet Muhammad and incorporated in the first rendition of Islamic law (called the *Muwaṭṭa'*), in which Muhammad prohibited the Muslims from mutilating (*tamthīl*) their opponents during the Battle of Uḥud (c. 625)'.[42] Huff argues that over time this Hadith 'was applied to the human body in general, and hence it prohibited postmortem examinations'.[43] In addition to this, Huff claims, the 'hands-on study of anatomy was impeded' through Islam's *madrasa* system of education. *Madrasas*, Huff claims, 'were not medical schools and, in some cases, founders of *madrasas* specifically forbade the teaching of medicine'.[44]

ANATOMICAL DISSECTION IN ISLAM

Despite the historical link between the development of anatomical dissection and illustration in Europe, Huff's core arguments and conclusions concerning the practices of anatomical dissection in Islam raise several issues. First, Huff never acknowledges some clear differences between the practices of 'dissection' (*tashrīḥ*) and 'mutilation' (*tamthīl*). The Arabic *tashrīḥ* (from the root *sh-r-ḥ*, 'to cut', also 'to clarify' and 'to explain') has been used since Islam's early modern period to denote both 'anatomy as a description of the human body and for the empirical science of dissection'.[45] In pre-modern Islam, *tashrīḥ* has a positive connotation, as it was used to refer to either the physical practice of cutting or theoretically examining a problem to 'expose an obscurity'.[46] *Tamthīl*, by contrast, is from the root *m-th-l* meaning 'likeness', 'similarity', 'example'. Hence, *tamthīl*, in the sense of mutilation, is to make a horrifying example of someone by mutilating his or her body, especial during warfare. This is the kind of violent activity that was prohibited by Muhammad in the Hadiths, not *tashrīḥ*.

Further, while evidence that dissection took place in pre-modern Islam is indeed scarce, evidence of a blanket prohibition against dissection in the Muslim world is likewise unavailable. If dissection was prohibited, then who were the *aṣḥāb al-tashrīḥ* (people of anatomy) Ibn al-Haytham and al-Fārisī referred to, and what was their disciplinary field and professional occupation? And how can there be so many differences in opinion among them, as al-Fārisī notes, if they did not have empirical knowledge of the anatomy of the visual system?

On the subject of the attitude towards dissection in pre-modern Islam, Savage-Smith shows how no explicit prohibition on the dissection of human or animal corpses can be found in the vast Islamic legal literature at all. She evaluates a range of legal sources to prove this point, including the numerous extant surviving books on jurisprudence and Hadiths; treatises on prophetic medicine (*al-ṭibb al-nabawī*); and manuals of the *muḥtasib* (inspectors of public services).[47] None of these sources explicitly mention the Hadith against the 'mutilating' of the body of enemies in the context of war being used to develop a legal prohibition against dissection and post-mortem examinations. Savage-Smith also highlights two periods of considerable Muslim interest in the subject of human anatomy and dissection in her article, the 9th century and the 12th to 13th centuries.[48] None of the early translators or readers of Galen, like the physician Ibn Masawayh (d. 857) and translator Ḥunayn ibn Isḥāq (d. 873), offered explicit criticisms of Galen's recommendation of the importance of dissection for avoiding incorrect anatomical speculations.[49] Later scholars like Ibn Sīnā (d. 1037) and Ibn Rushd (d. 1198) went on to repeat many of Galen's ideas and themes in their work, again, never explicitly criticising Galen's views on dissection.[50] As such, she concludes that human post-mortem examination was not impossible within the Islamic world and Muslim scholars may have pursued the dissection of corpses themselves.

Indeed, the extensive and precise details Ibn al-Haytham presents about the anatomy of the eye give the impression that he knows what he is talking about; that he had seen a dissected eye, even if he had not dissected one himself; and that he had consulted with physicians and was not just referring to what he had seen in their anatomy books. It seems clear that al-Fārisī had an even greater interest in the anatomy of the eye than Ibn al-Haytham, and that he had access to expertise and specialised knowledge about anatomy, either through books or personal contact with physicians. The many detailed descriptions he gives about the anatomy of the eye also make it seem highly likely that he had dissected an eye or seen a dissected one. The design of the visual system in Ibn al-Haytham's and al-Fārisī's texts also possibly indicates the view of the physician or anatomist when examining a patient or dissecting a body because the eyes are represented in face view.[51]

ILLUSTRATION IN ISLAM

Huff's criticism of the lack of anatomical illustration in the Islamic context also never acknowledges how the use of artistic conventions to convey scientific information varied between different disciplines. While the evidence of descriptive illustration in the field of Islamic optics is limited, it is very rich in the sciences of astronomy (*ʿilm al-hayʾa*) and astrology (*ʿilm al-aḥkām*), which even involved representations of the human body, despite the purported prohibition against both human representation and the astrological sciences.[52] The Persian astronomer ʿAbd al-Raḥmān al-Ṣūfī's (d. 986) *Kitāb ṣuwar al-kawākib al-thābita* (Book of the Images of the Fixed Stars), written around 964, is one notable example of this (Figure 2.6).[53] There are also great artistic illustrations of cosmological themes such as Zakariyya al-Qazwīnī's (d. 1283) famous cosmographical treatise ʿAjāʾib al-makhlūqāt wa gharāʾib al-mawjūdāt (literally, Marvels of Creatures and Strange Things Existing), despite the geometrical nature of theoretical astronomy.[54] However, as with the astronomical texts, these involved no anatomical drawings.

In optics, the situation was different again. Ibn al-Haytham's *Manāẓir*, al-Fārisī's *Tanqīḥ*, and Taqī al-Dīn's *Nūr ḥadaqat al-ibṣār* contain very few anatomical illustrations. Yet this lack of descriptive illustration in the optical sciences was not particular to the Islamic world alone. Very few anatomical illustrations occur in early European optical science, which began with the translation of Ibn al-Haytham's *Manāẓir* into Latin as the *De aspectibus* of Alhazen in the late 12th or early 13th century.[55] In broad outline, none of the surviving copies of the German mathematician Friedrich Risner's early collection *Opticae Thesaurus* (Dictionary of Optics), printed in 1572, includes the eye-brain illustration in the *Manāẓir*, though an aerial view of a single eye is shown in some copies (Figure 2.7).[56] Nor are anatomical illustrations featured in any of the key early European optical treatises of the 12th and 13th centuries, including Robert Grosseteste's (d. 1253) *Hexaëmeron* (c. 1230-35) and *On Light* (c. 1235-40); Witelo's (d. 1275) *Perspectiva;* Roger Bacon's (d. 1294) *De speculis comburentibus* (c. 1266) and *Perspectiva* (c. 1267); and John Peckham's (d. 1292) *Perspectiva communis*.[57]

Only scant evidence of anatomical illustration can be found in later treatises, of the 16th to 18th centuries (the period which Huff praises for their advancement of scientific illustration). Johannes Kepler's (d. 1630) *Astronomiae Pars Optica* (The Optical Part of Astronomy, published 1604) contains a single page with a number of drawings of the eye, rendered in semi-naturalistic detail (Figure 2.8), whereas René Descartes's (d. 1650) treatise on the formation of the foetus includes a number of anatomical illustrations, including a few diagrams of the eye (Figure 2.9) as well as profile views of the human body that demonstrate the passage of light to the eye.[58] By contrast,

Figure 2.6 *Kitāb ṣuwar al-kawākib al-thābita* (Book of the Images of the Fixed Stars) of al-Ṣūfī by ʿAbd al-Raḥmān al-Ṣūfī (Iranian, Rey 903-986 Shiraz). 18th century, Iran. Ink, opaque watercolour, and gold on paper 24.9 × 19.4 × 2.4 cm. The Metropolitan Museum of Art, Acc. 1975.192.2. (Licensed under CC0 1.0.)

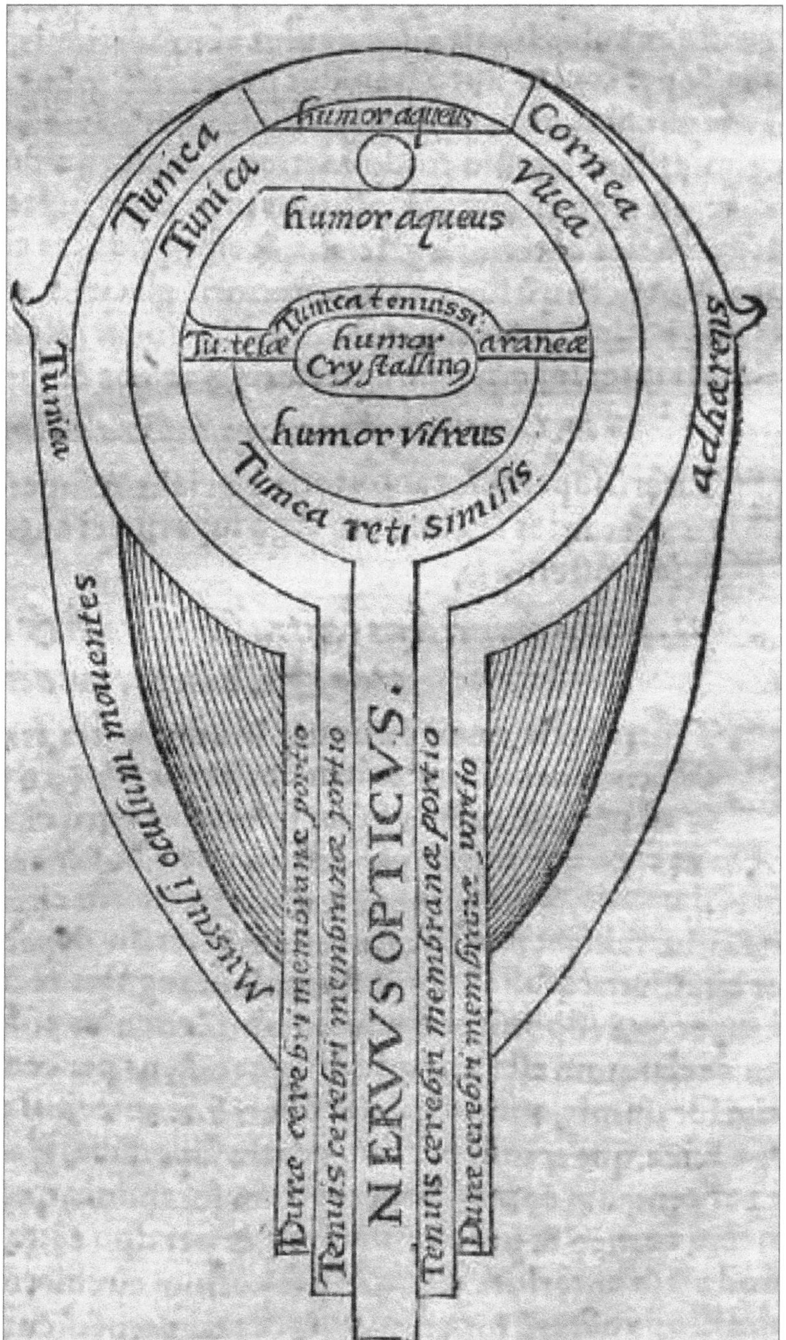

Figure 2.7 Illustration of the anatomy of the eye in Friedrich Risner's *Opticae Thesaurus*, 1572. ETH-Bibliothek Zürich, VD16 H 693, p. 6. (Licensed under Public Domain Mark 1.0.)

Christiaan Huygens's (d. 1695) *Opera reliqua* and *Traité de la lumiere*, and Isaac Newton's (d. 1727) *Opticks* (a treatise on the hypothesis of light and of colour), all appear to contain no anatomical illustrations.[59] Thus despite the flourishing of anatomical illustrations in early modern Europe, early European optical science seems to have had little use for anatomical illustration, either.

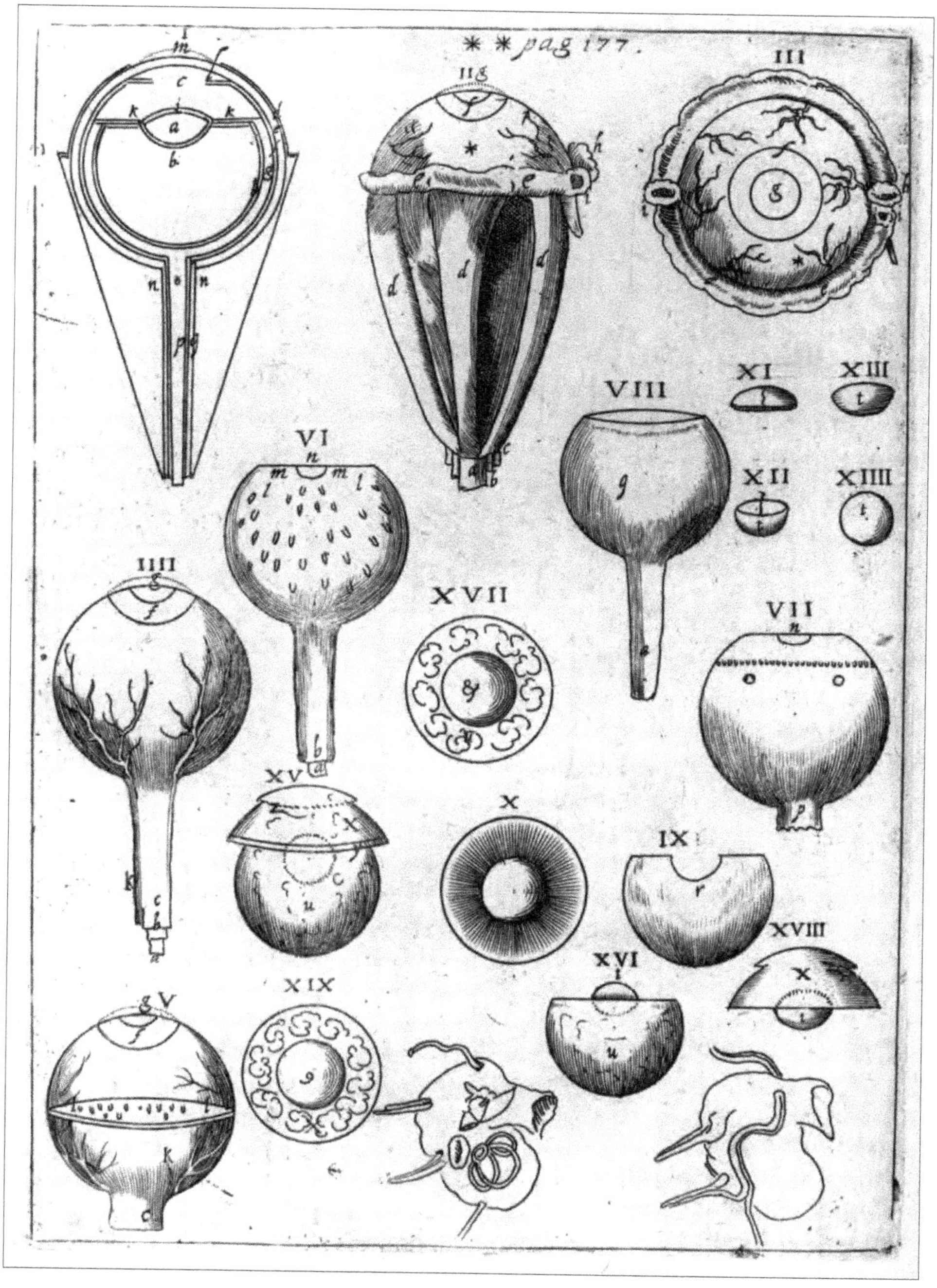

Figure 2.8 A plate from Johannes Kepler's *Ad Vitellionem Paralipomena, quibus Astronomiae Pars Optica*. Published by A Apud Claudium Marnium & Haeredes Ioannis Aubrii in 1604, page 177. Reproduced from http://www.hps.cam.ac.uk/starry/keplerbooks.html. (Licensed under Creative Commons via Wikimedia Commons.)

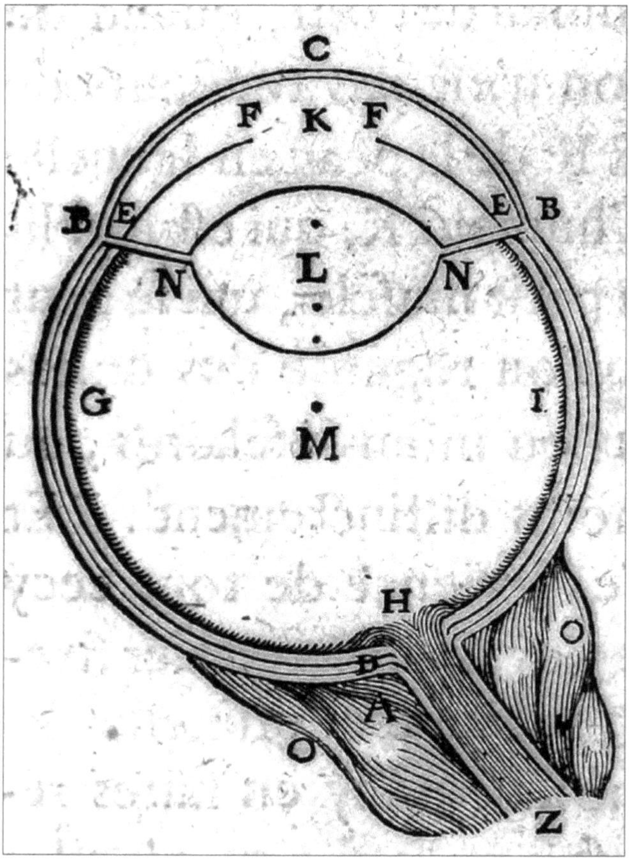

Figure 2.9 Illustration of the eye in René Descartes' *Optics: Discourse on Methods.* (Licensed under Creative Commons CC BY 4.0 via Wellcome Images.)

CONCLUSION: SCIENCE AND ART

The new relationship between science and art that emerged in Europe during the early modern period has often been discussed by historians. Declarative claims that 'art had gone scientific' are underlined by the belief that Europe alone 'saw the emergence in the realm of art of a new dogma of aesthetic theory which stated that a work of art is a direct and faithful representation of natural phenomena'.[60] This theory of naturalism is accordingly thought to have made visual representation relevant to the pursuit of scientific knowledge for the first time. However, the foregoing overview of illustrations in European optical treatises has shown how the relationship between science and art in early modern Europe was not so simple. Despite European scholars' interest in anatomy and dissection and their development of techniques for detailed visual representation and printing, pre-modern European opticians, like pre-modern Muslim opticians, rarely used descriptive illustrations in their treatises. The role of art in the advancement of scientific knowledge in this period should accordingly be understood as complex, variable, and discipline-dependent.[61]

At the same time, the shift to artistic naturalism that took place in early modern Europe should not be applied retrospectively to Islam. For, while the most important breakthrough in the use of illustrations for the communication of scientific knowledge appears to have taken place in early modern European anatomical compendia and atlases, illustrations were still used in the Islamic context for the effective communication of knowledge. Muslim opticians like Ibn al-Haytham in the 11th century and al-Fārisī in the late 13th century appear to have acquired extensive knowledge of the anatomy of the eye, and the design for the visual system developed by these scholars seems to have been informed not only through reading Greek sources on anatomy, but also though direct contact with patients as well as possibly through the dissection of corpses. Their illustrations also seem to have been understood to aid readers' comprehension of optical science, as the designs were reused and elaborated in later optical treatises. The geometrical designs of the visual system in early Islamic optical treatises should accordingly not be viewed as simplistic or lacking in naturalistic detail, but rather as rich in distinctive possibilities for the communication of *ʿilm*. For, although the development of various sciences in the pre- and early modern periods, including *ʿilm al-manāẓir*, *ʿilm al-tashrīḥ*, *ʿilm al-hayʾa*, and *ʿilm al-aḥkām*, was strongly encouraged by the important status of *ʿilm* in Islam, scientific illustrations contributed to this process by manifesting scholarly knowledge in visual form. Regardless of their background, viewers could comprehend illustrations, thereby enabling the acquisition, production, and dissemination of knowledge within and beyond the Muslim world.

NOTES

1 The copy was made by a relative of Ibn al-Haytham 'by marriage' (*ṣihr al-muṣannif*), named Ahmad b. Muhammad b. Jaʿfar al-ʿAskari, in 1083. For more information on the surviving manuscripts of Ibn al-Haytham's *Kitāb al-Manāẓir* see Abdelhamid I Sabra, 2007, 'The "Commentary" that Saved the Text: The Hazardous Journey of Ibn al-Haytham's Arabic Optics', *Early Science and Medicine* 12(2): 122-4. For the English translation of the *Manāẓir*, Books I-II-III, see Abdelhamid I Sabra, 1989, *The Optics of Ibn al-Haytham. Books I-II-III: On Direct Vision* (London: The Warburg Institute). For the Arabic edition of Books IV-V, see Abdelhamid I Sabra, 2002, *The Optics of Ibn al-Haytham. Edition of the Arabic Text of Books IV-V: On Reflection and Images Seen by Reflection* (Kuwait: The National Council for Culture, Arts and Letters). Books VI-VII are yet to be published in English and Arabic.

2 Sabra, 1989, Book I, 55-62 (Chapter 5), 63-100 (Chapter 6).

3 Sabra, 1989, Book, I, 63.

4 The full title of this work is *Kitāb al-manāẓir* (Book of Optics), hereafter referred to as *Manāẓir.*

5 Emilie Savage-Smith, 2007, 'Anatomical Illustration in Arabic manuscripts', in Anna Contadini, ed., *Arab Painting: Text and Image in Illustrated Arabic Manuscripts* (Leiden: Brill), 147.

6 Savage-Smith, 2007, 147. In broad outline, Savage-Smith notes the development of conventions for representing the brain as a triangle, in al-Rāzī's (d. 925) *al-Kitāb al-manṣūrī fī al-ṭibb* (The Book of Medicine for Mansur); the use of circles to represent the eyes, in an 11th/12th-century copy of Ḥunayn ibn Isḥāq's *Kitāb al-ʿashr maqālāt fī al-ʿayn* (Ten Treatises on the Eye); and the innovative combination of the two to illustrate the eye-brain relationship, in al-Haytham's 11th-century *Manāẓir*. She closes with an overview of anatomical illustrations of the entire human form, which appeared in the Islamic context in Persian manuscripts from the late 14th century.

7 Savage-Smith, 2007, 147.

8 Savage-Smith, 2007, 147, 151. Amongst the surviving Arabic translations and Greek copies of Galen's treatises, Savage-Smith cites only two illustrations: a modest triangular diagram of a shoulder muscle (deltoid) in a late copy (c. 1555) of the Arabic translation of Galen's *Anatomical Procedures* (UCLA, Biomedical Library, Los Angeles, col. 1062, MS 90, fol. 119r, dated Safar 962/Jan 1555); and the only preserved eye diagram in a Greek copy of Galen's *On the Uses of the Parts* (Vatican, Urbinas Rome, MS 69, fol. 118r, c. 10th-11th century).

9 Savage-Smith, 2007, 147.

10 For an overview of the *'ilm al-manāẓir* tradition, see Sabra, 2012.

11 See, for example, Toby E Huff, 2011, *Intellectual Curiosity and the Scientific Revolution: A Global Perspective* (Cambridge, NY: Cambridge University Press).

12 For an account of Ibn al-Haytham's biography and the key pre-modern Islamic sources that describe it, see Sabra, 1989, Book II, xix-xxxii.

13 Modern scholars including Sabra (1989) and Smith (2001) have divided the seven volumes of the *Manāẓir* into three core parts: Books I-II-III on the nature of visual perception; Books IV-V-VI on the visual effects of reflection (focusing on mirrors); and Book VII on the visual effects of refraction. See Mark A Smith, 2001, *Alhacen's Theory of Visual Perception: A Critical Edition, with English Translation and Commentary, of the First Three Books of Alhacen's* De aspectibus, *the Medieval Latin Version of Ibn al-Haytham's Manāẓir* (Philadelphia: American Philosophical Society). Systematic treatments of optics had been developed by the Greek intellectual tradition. These include Euclid's (c. 300 BCE) and Ptolemy's (c. 200 CE) dedicated studies, both entitled *Optika* (Optics). Aristotle (d. 322 BCE) considered optical topics in his *De sensu et sensato* (Sense and Sensibilia) and *De anima* (On the Soul), and Galen (d. 210 CE) in his *Deusu partium* (Uses of the Parts).

14 Sabra, 1989, Book I, 55-63. It is interesting to note that the technical term used to describe the anatomy of the eye, *hay'a*, literally means 'configuration' or 'form', and thus the title *Fī hay'at al-baṣar* refers to the physiological structure and constitution of seeing. For an assessment of the meaning of *hay'a*, see R. Arnaldez, 2012, 'Hay'a', in P Bearman et al., eds. *Encyclopaedia of Islam, Second Edition*, <http://dx.doi.org.proxy.library.adelaide.edu.au/10.1163/1573-3912_islam_SIM_2823>, accessed 6 March 2017.

15 See the illustration in Sabra, 1989, Book II, 52, for the translations of the Arabic labels. For the text, see Sabra, 1989, Book I, 55-63.

16 Savage-Smith (2007, 152) notes that the frontal view of the nose presented in the illustration 'plays little role [other] than to remind the viewer of where the eyes are situated'.

17 Sabra, 1989, Book I, 62.

18 The oldest images of the eye preserved in an Arabic text can be found in an 11th-12th-century copy of the 9th-century physician Ḥunayn ibn Isḥāq's (d. 873) *The Book of the Ten Treatises on the Eye* (see M Meyerhof, 1928, *The Book of the Ten Treatises on the Eye, Ascribed to Ḥunain ibn Isḥāq (809-877 AD). The Earliest Existing Systematic Text-book of Ophthalmology* (Cairo: Government Press). Savage-Smith (2007, 151) notes that these illustrations are very different from the only preserved eye diagram in a Greek copy of Galen's *On the Use of the Parts* (see endnote 8, above).

19 According to Sabra (2007, 127), there are 'no Arabic texts or reports concerning Arabic texts, in the Middle East, that represented or referred to substantial studies of [Ibn al-Haytham's *Manāẓir*] in the period between [Ibn al-Haytham's] death (in or after 432/1040-41) and the composition of [al-Fārisī's] *Tanqih*, probably not too long before the beginning of the year 708/1309'.

20 Sabra, 2007, 125-7. Sabra (2011, 11-16) notes that the *Tanqīḥ* is 'presently known to exist in at least 15 manuscript copies kept in libraries in Istanbul, Iran, India, Leiden, Jerusalem, Russia, and New York'.

21 Sabra, 2007, 128. For the published edition of this text see al-Fārisī, 2009, *Kitāb al-baṣā'ir fī 'ilm al-manāẓir*, ed. M Mawālidī (Kuwait: Mu'assasat al-Kuwait li-l-Taqaddum al-'Ilmī).

22 Kamāl al-Dīn al-Fārisī, 1929, 'Kitāb tinqīḥ al-manāẓir li-zawī al-abṣār wa al-baṣā'ir' (Ḥaydar Ābād al-Dakan: Dā'irat al-Ma'ārif al-'Uthmāniyya), 61.

23 The image can be found in a number of copies of the *Tanqīḥ*. The best preserved was transcribed in Nisabur in 1316 and is in the Topkapi Palace Museum, Istanbul, Ahmed III Library, MS 3340, folio 16a. See Sabra, 2007, 125.

24 The image appears to differ slightly between the 15 surviving manuscript copies of the *Tanqīḥ*. See, for example, al-Fārisī, 1929, illustration inserted between pp. 60-1. This version takes a more explicitly geometrical approach to representing the eyes, nerves, and nose.

25 Al-Fārisī, 1929, 1:61.

26 Al-Fārisī, 1929, 1:61.

27 Al-Fārisī, 1929, 1:61.

28 Al-Fārisī, 1929, 1:61.

29 According to al-Fārisī (1929, 1:61), this text was commonly cited by *al-kaḥḥālīn* (specialists in making and applying *kuḥl*, eyeliner, as we know it today), who then used the *kuḥl* as a protective medical treatment for the eyes against the sun.

30 Al-Fārisī, 1929, 1:61.

31 This elaboration equates to 50 pages in the published text.

32 Al-Fārisī, 1929, 1:61. The illustration (Figure 6) is inserted between 1:110-11; the page itself on which the illustration appears is unnumbered.

33 Taqī al-Dīn was born around 1521 in Damascus; he was an eminent astronomer, mathematician, and physician, and more than 50 works are attributed to his name. For Taqī al-Dīn's biography, see Samer Akkach, 2017, *Marṣad Istanbul: hadm al-rasd wa raṣd al-hadm. Taṭawwr thaqāfat al-ʿulūm fī al-Islām baʿd Copernicus* (Doha: Arab Centre for Research and Policy Studies). There are four main copies of the *Nūr hadaqat al-ibṣār*: Laleli Collections, Suleymaniye Library, Istanbul, MS 2558; Bodleian Library, Oxford, MS Marsh 119; Mehmet Nuri Efendi Collection, Suleymaniye Library, Istanbul, MS 163/3; Dār al-Kutub al-Miṣriyya, Cairo, ʿUlūm Riyāḍiyya MS 893.

34 Taqī al-Dīn, n.d., 'Nūr ḥadaqat al-ibṣār wa-nawr ḥadīqat al-anẓār' (Cairo: Dār al-Kutub al-Miṣriyya Ulūm Riyāḍiyya MS 893), f. 8a-b.

35 Taqī al-Dīn, n.d., f. 9a-b.

36 It is interesting to note that there was a treatise on theoretical astronomy by the Persian scholar al-ʿĀmilī (d. 1621) entitled *Tashrīḥ al-aflāk* (The Anatomy of the Spheres). For an overview of the *ʿilm al-hay'a* tradition, see David Pingree, 2012, '*ʿIlm al-Hay'a*', in P Bearman et al., eds., *Encyclopaedia of Islam, Second Edition*, <http://dx.doi.org/10.1163/1573-3912_islam_COM_0365>, accessed 31 March 2017.

37 Huff, 2011, 177.

38 For the *Opticae Thesaurus*, see Andre Vesalius, 1964, *De humani corporis fabrica, libri septem* (Bruxelles: Culture et civilisation); for an overview of Vesalius's text, including translations and annotations of the drawings, see Charles O'Malley and John Saunders, 1950, *The Illustrations from the Works of Andreas Vesalius of Brussels: With Annotations and Translations, a Discussion of the Plates and their Background, Authorship and Influence, and a Biographical Sketch of Vesalius* (Cleveland: World Publishing).

39 Vesalius himself claimed to have corrected more than 200 mistakes in the classic work of Galen (Huff, 2011, 184).

40 For an overview of the previously published anatomical illustrations, see O'Malley and Saunders, 1950, 16. For a discussion of the artisans responsible for the production of Vesalius's illustrations, see O'Malley and Saunders, 1950, 25-9.

41 Huff, 2011, 179.

42 Huff, 2011, 179.

43 Huff, 2011, 179.

44 Huff, 2011, 179.

45 See Emilie Savage-Smith, 1995, 'Attitudes Towards Dissection in Medieval Islam', *Journal for the History of Medicine and Allied Sciences* 50(1): 68-9 for an overview of the historical development of the meaning of the term *tashrīḥ*.

46 Savage-Smith, 1995, 68-9.

47 Savage-Smith (1995, 82) notes that some earlier jurists argued that the prohibition against mutilation should be applied to Muslim corpses only, thus possibly 'allowing dissection of non-Muslim corpses, had someone wished to undertake it'.

48 Savage-Smith, 1995, 83.

49 Savage-Smith (1995, 91) notes that in most cases animal dissection is intended (especially in the case of the dissection of apes), from which Galen then reasoned by analogy to human structures.

50 See, for example, Ibn Sīnā's famous encyclopaedia *Kitāb al-qānūn fī -l-ṭibb* (The Canon of Medicine) and Ibn Rushd's *Kitāb al-kulliyāt* (The Book of General Principles). Savage-Smith (1995, 96) notes that the importance of knowledge of anatomy and medicine was even upheld by the conservative scholar al-Ghazālī (d. 1111) in his *Iḥyā' ʿulūm al-dīn* (The Revival of the Religious Sciences).

51 Konstantinos Laios, Marilita M Moschos and Androutsos George, 2016, 'Ocular Anatomy in Medieval Arabic Medicine: A Review', *Italian Journal of Anatomy and Embryology* 121(1): 110.

52 For a brief discussion of the purported prohibition of the representation of the human form and how this might pertain to the development of Islamic anatomical illustrations, see Huff, 2011, 181-4.

53 Written in Arabic, the text was thoroughly illustrated and provided two drawings for each constellation, one from the outside of a celestial globe, and the other from the inside.

54 Over 300 paintings accompany al-Qazwīnī's descriptions of the physical description of the world in *The Wonders of Creation*; see Stefano Carboni, 2015, *The Wonders of Creation and the Singularities of Painting: A Study of the Ilkhanid London Qazvini* (Edinburgh: Edinburgh University Press). For an overview of Islamic cosmographical illustrations, see Ahmet T Karamustafa, 1992, 'Cosmographical Diagrams', in JB Harley and David Woodward, eds., *The History of Cartography*, vol. 2 (Chicago: The University of Chicago Press), 71-89.

55 The Christian exploration of Southern Europe in the 12th/13th centuries brought European scholars into contact with the Arabic scientific writings, and the Greek intellectual tradition preserved in Arabic texts. For an overview of the history of optics, particularly in the European context, see Olivier Darrigol, 2012, *A History of Optics from Greek Antiquity to the Nineteenth Century* (Oxford: Oxford University Press).

56 Full title: *Opticae Thesaurus: Alhazeni Arabis libri septem, nuncprimum editi; Eiusdem liber De Crepusculis et nubium ascensionibus* (Dictionary of Optics: Seven books by the Arab Alhazeni, edited for the first time, a book by Risner about twilights and the formation of clouds). This text included a book on twilight falsely attributed to Alhazen, as well as the 13th-century European scholar Witelo's (d. 1275) *Perspectiva*, which was greatly influenced by Alhazen's *De aspectibus*. See Friedrich Risner, 1572, *Opticae Thesaurus: Alhazeni Arabis Libri Septem Nunc Primum Editi, Eiusdem Liber De Crepusculis Et Nubium Asensionibus* (Item Vitellonis Thuringopoloni Libri X). As the translation activities from Arabic into Latin ended in the 13th century, the developments of the *Manāẓir* made by Kamāl al-Dīn al-Fārisī and Taqī al-Dīn were not transferred to Europe, and Islamic optics after Ibn al-Haytham was unknown to European scholars.

57 These treatises did, however, often include richly decorated frontispieces and simple line diagrams intended to illustrate mathematical concepts. See Robert Grosseteste, 1982, *Hexaëmeron*, ed. Richard C Dales and Servus Gieben (London: Published for the British Academy by Oxford University Press); and 1942, *On Light* (De Luce), trans. Clare C Riedl (Milwaukee: Marquette University Press); Witelo, 1977-83, *Perspectiva*, trans. and ed. Mark A Smith (Warsaw: Polish Academy of Sciences Press); Roger Bacon, 1983, *De Speculis Comburentibus* (Philosophy of Nature), trans. and ed. C David Lindberg (New York: Oxford University Press); and 1996, *Perspectiva*, trans. and ed. C David Lindberg (Oxford: Clarendon Press); and John Peckham, 1970, *Perspectiva communis*, trans. David C Lindberg (Madison: University of Wisconsin Press).

58 See Johannes Kepler, 1604, *Astronomiae Pars Optica* (Francofurti: Apud Claudium Marnium & Haeredes Joannis Aubrii); and René Descartes, 1664, *L'Homme, et un Traitté de la Formation du Foetus*, ed. Claude Clerselier (Paris: Charles Angot).

59 See Christiaan Huygens, 1782, *Opera Reliqua* (Amsterdam: Apud Janssonio-Waesbergios); and 1920, *Traité de la Lumiere* (Paris: Gauthier-Villars et cie); and Isaac Newton, 1721, *Opticks: or, a Treatise on the Reflections, Refractions, Inflection and Colours of Light*, 3rd ed. (London: printed for William and John Innys at the West End of St. Paul's).

60 O'Malley and Saunders, 1950, 22.

61 The transfer of these 'naturalistic' artistic conventions to the Muslim world did not commence until after the 17th century, and descriptive anatomical images of the human body like Vesalius's were not circulated in the Muslim world until the late 19th century.

CHAPTER 3

THE IMPERIAL MUGHAL HUNT: A PURSUIT OF KNOWLEDGE

SHAHA PARPIA

ABSTRACT

The Mughal emperors used the imperial hunt as an agency for knowledge acquisition. Investigation, experimentation, and analyses of natural phenomena encountered on the field were recorded by Mughal scholars with an emphasis on anatomy, taxonomy, and animal psychology. Detailed textual references were enhanced by naturalistic paintings that were of a technical nature and served as documents of scientific knowledge. Scientific inquiry also produced sound knowledge of animal behaviour and characteristics, thereby improving breeding programs and hunting techniques in the Mughal empire. This chapter examines the sophisticated culture of hunting as an integral part of the scientific enterprise. It reveals aspects of the nature of 'scientific' knowledge from a Mughal perspective, and shows its utility and functions in that cultural context. It discusses the agency of the influential *akhlāq* (ethics) texts, which postulate that acquiring scientific knowledge is a religious obligation necessary to achieve perfection, and analyses how conceptions of ethics and morality impacted the promotion, perception, and practice of natural science. This exposition contributes to the current rethinking of the relationship between science and religion by indirectly showing the lack of definitive boundaries between the two realms in the Mughal tradition. The line of discussion presented also contributes to undermining the claims made in mainstream scholarship on the history of science that South Asian scientific endeavour paled in comparison to rational Western systematic forms of knowledge. The chapter explores the complex nature of scientific activities that were motivated by the Mughal hunt and their links to art, while assessing the interrelated concepts of religion, ethics, government, and science within hunting contexts in early modern Mughal history.

INTRODUCTION

Abū'l Fazl, the emperor Akbar's historian and biographer, famously claims, 'Short-sighted and shallow observers think that His Majesty has no other object in view but hunting; but the wise and experienced know that he pursues higher aims', adding that Akbar 'always makes hunting a means of increasing his knowledge'.[1] He also notes that hunting was not an activity of senseless killing as 'ignorant' people believe, but one where Akbar could travel incognito and without notice to ascertain the battle-readiness of troops, conduct inspections over agricultural and charitable lands, assess the efficacy and fairness of taxations laws, and deliver justice. In this way the *shikār* (hunt) can be seen as a 'means of acquisition of knowledge', and the complex administration of the public realm was 'the real kind of hunting'.[2] Lahōri, Shāhjahān's biographer, notes that 'the emperors go on hunting and sight-seeing but intrinsically they aim at ascertaining the prosperity of the kingdom and state of peace as first-hand information'.[3] The dangers the emperor brought to himself during hunting and elephant fights were regarded as neither irresponsible behaviour nor neglect of kingly duties, but rather as being a test of the sincerity and 'business capabilities' of those who doubted him.[4] The hunt was moreover seen as an activity to lead such 'superficialists' into the 'path of true knowledge'.[5]

While Mughal primary sources frequently draw analogies between the imperial hunt and the pursuit of knowledge, references to such knowledge indicate that they were intended for the purposes of administration and good governance. However, the Mughals also seem to have used the cultural activity of the hunt to further 'scientific' knowledge and conduct investigations and analyses of 'science' as perceived by them. This chapter examines the ways in which the exercise of hunting can be seen as a medium of knowledge acquisition, and how the sophisticated culture of hunting actually promoted and enabled a kind of scientific development in the early modern Mughal tradition. Focusing on aspects of zoology, ornithology, and hunting techniques, the chapter aims to show the marriage between science, technology, and art, as seen through the lens of hunting during the reign of the Great Mughals (1525-1707). The study discusses how the Mughals — following the methodologies of observation, reasoning, comparison, and experimentation set by early Muslim scholars from the 10th century onwards — studied, tested, and often challenged established traditions in the exploration of South Asian flora and fauna they encountered during their hunts. Their scientific enterprise produced sound knowledge of animal psychology and characteristics, thereby improving breeding programs. It also helped develop hunting techniques, which were transferred to the battlefield as military tactics. Hunting also seems to have enabled technological innovations that ensured greater success in warfare and the hunt, whilst other inventions made imperial life more congenial during hunting expeditions. The visual records of these studies were systematically undertaken, and seem to have continued in the older Islamic tradition of illustrated natural history texts, such as the *Kitāb naʿt al-ḥayawān*, Arabic and Persian translations of Dioscorides's *De Materia Medica*, and Qazwīnī's *ʿAjāʾib al-makhlūqāt*. Hence, it could be argued that explorations of South Asian flora and fauna and their pictorial depictions were completed by Mughal emperors to further the causes of good governance, the moral values required of an upstanding ruler, and the legitimacy that was engendered by a continuity of older traditions.

By studying the agency of the hunt in knowledge acquisition in general, and scientific development in particular, the chapter sheds light on what 'science' meant to the Mughals. It offers an understanding of what might be called 'scientific' knowledge from an Indo-Persian perspective, and shows its utility and function in that cultural context. The chapter places an emphasis on the natural historical sciences, and particularly zoological and ornithological studies, as these were closely connected with hunting practices.[6]

The chapter also sheds light on the significance of natural sciences in the broader framework of science in Islam. In pre- and early modern Islam, the notion of 'science' in general, and 'natural science' in particular, had wide spectrums of meaning. Science (*ʿilm*) included all branches of human knowledge, while the natural sciences (*ʿulūm ṭabīʿiyya*) included medicine, geography, optics, astronomy, and other aspects of the physical world. Philosophy and mathematics were often aligned with the natural sciences, and so were occultism and astrology, which were considered as part of the scientific enterprise. Most importantly, however, the chapter aims to show how ethics and moral values were closely connected with scientific thinking. The text of *Akhlāq-i Naṣīrī* (The Nasirean Ethics) written by renowned philosopher-astronomer Naṣīr al-Dīn al-Ṭūsī (d. 1274), for example, shows how conceptions of morality impacted the ways in which science was conceptualised and practised in Mughal culture.[7] This text is discussed in some detail later in the chapter.

The chapter contributes to the current rethinking of the relationship between science and religion, by indirectly showing the lack of definitive boundaries between the two realms in the Mughal tradition. A similar situation is also found in the early modern Western intellectual tradition. As historian of science and religion Peter Harrison notes, 'So familiar are the concepts "science" and "religion", and so central to Western culture have been the activities and achievements that are usually labelled "religious" and "scientific", that it is natural to assume that they were enduring features of the cultural landscape of the West'.[8] This study of the hunt as an integral part of the scientific enterprise confirms recent findings that, until relatively recently, the boundaries of the two domains of science and religion were understood very differently, and that human meaning and moral values were rarely separated from the understandings of the nature of the universe and other activities we now consider as being firmly located within the realm of science.[9]

Furthermore, the lines of discussion presented in this study contribute to undermining the claims made in mainstream scholarship in general that South Asian science and scholarship was secondary to rational Western systematic forms of knowledge. The chapter reinforces Pollock's cautions against 'definitional consistency', as the English word 'science' is a 'pliable signifier' that points to no natural kind, and it is 'no straightforward matter to map onto it the congeries of terms and texts and medieval practices' of mediaeval India.[10] It is with these perspectives in mind that the current chapter explores Mughal scientific activity that was enabled and expanded by the hunt.

SCIENTIFIC INQUIRY

In Mughal India, Akbar's doctrine of *ṣulḥ-i kul* or 'absolute peace', as propounded by Abū'l Fazl, which sought to bring about a unity of religions and an acceptance of diversity, embraced a 'new outlook of sympathy and tolerance' towards philosophy, the sciences, and reason.[11] This is reflected in Akbar's reforms of prevailing *madrasa* education and his decision to include rational sciences in the syllabi, which 'cast a new light on schools, and cast a bright lustre over *madrasas*'.[12] Abū'l Fazl notes that students were taught in stages, and that the subjects included ethics, arithmetic, accountancy, agriculture/horticulture, surveying, geometry, astronomy, geomancy, architecture, government, medicine, logic — that is, the *ṭabī'ī* (physical) and *riyāzī* (quantitative) sciences, in addition to the *ilāhī* (divine) sciences. They were also taught Sanskrit, Vedantic philosophy, and the grammar of Patanjali.[13] These educational reforms, which indicate a regard for the classical sciences and the ancient Indian intellectual heritage, were planned and carried out by the Persian scholar Mīr Fath'ullāh Shirāzi, a polymath scientist who had 'no equal in Persia or India, or rather in the habitable world in all the sciences'.[14] Other writers of the age such as Chandrabhān Brahman and Bālkrishan also suggest that the introduction of rational subjects in the syllabi encouraged large numbers of Hindus to join the *madrasas*.[15] This implies that the sciences and rational education were systematic and institutionalised, and benefited from imperial patronage. However, the writings of François Bernier, a French physician in the Mughal court, suggest an absence of 'academies and colleges properly endowed'.[16] Perhaps Bernier, who was a student of the philosopher Gassendi and was familiar with the formal institutions of learning in Europe, was misjudging the intellectual extensiveness of *madrasas* and the informal nature of teaching circles held in mosques and bazaars, presided over by the *ahl-i ʿilm* (people of learning), who included physicians and astronomers.[17]

Nevertheless, even Abū'l Fazl acknowledges the role of inflexible tradition and ideology in hampering the growth of science and reason: 'From time immemorial, the exercise of inquiry has been restricted, and questioning and investigation have been regarded as precursors of infidelity', he wrote, adding that 'a few among the intelligent of their generation admit the imbecility of this procedure in others'.[18] Abū'l Fazl's reflections indicate that while scientific knowledge may not have been widespread, a courtly culture of learning existed, along with imperial patronage of scholars. Zoological and botanical writings compiled in India are diverse in origin and content. According to Rahman et al., over 10,000 scientific works were produced in Sanskrit, Arabic, and Persian between the 8th and 19th centuries, with over 200 volumes in zoology alone.[19] And as Pollock notes, 'with the coming of Pax Mughalana from the second half of the 16th century, a new and dynamic era of intellectual inquiry was inaugurated in many parts of the [Indian] subcontinent. Whole libraries of the manuscripts produced over the following three centuries exist today — and lie unedited, even unread'.[20] The flourishing intellectual tradition hence suggests that the emperors' scientific inquiry enabled by the hunt was not an isolated undertaking; there was a prevailing intercultural scientific milieu in the Mughal court.

The kinds of Mughal scientific activities that were enabled by the hunt need to be gleaned from a variety of sources, which are often unrelated. Official court writings such as memoirs, biographies, and gazetteers, for instance, contain detailed information on natural history in addition to ubiquitous historical and administrative matters. While this is not the pragmatic, analytical method of modern Western science, it follows the trend of Indo-Persian historiographies of the time, which used interconnected literary genres to encompass all aspects of India's culture: the richness of its lands, inhabitants, flora and fauna, as well as a commemoration of the society's scholarship, architectural achievements, and economic glories.[21] Hence, it could be argued that one of the reasons Mughal emperors included detailed natural historical information of species encountered during hunts was to propagate a view of India as a land of natural (zoological and botanical) wonders, which was an all-important consideration for the success of their imperial vision. Even Bābur, who often found the Indian lifestyle, topography, and lack of formal gardens disagreeable to his Central Asian sensibilities, found the Indian flora and fauna fascinating, and his memoirs, written in a text called the *Bāburnāma,* contain graphic descriptions of several species.[22] These natural historical studies were later extensively illustrated by artists in Akbar's atelier and comprise over 120 illustrated folios.[23]

Bābur was particularly taken with the mammals peculiar to India, such as the elephant, rhinoceros, and nilgai, and native species of birds, such as the peacock. His penetrating descriptions of these are reflective of his knowledge and 'born of careful and intelligent observation'.[24] They were often recorded from a hunting perspective. His studies of the rhinoceros, for instance, include detailed information about the length of its horn and its power as demonstrated in the number of men and horses it had gored during hunts. The thickness of the hide of the rhinoceros was measured in accordance with how far an arrow shot from a stiff bow drawn with full strength might penetrate it, namely four inches. Bābur further notes a similarity in the size of the animal's stomach and pastern to that of a horse.[25] He also gives information about the natural habitat of the rhinoceros, and its behavioural patterns, noting that it cannot be made submissive and obedient like the elephant. It is important to note here that hunting an animal like the rhinoceros armed with just bows and arrows required an intimate knowledge of animal anatomy in order to ascertain its most vulnerable spot, given its thick and relatively impenetrable hide. By Jahāngīr's reign (r. 1605-27), this knowledge was clearly commonplace, as Jahāngīr notes that while hunting in Nuh Ban, Aligarh, he killed a rhinoceros with a single shot aimed near the animal's earlobe.[26]

One of the consequences of the *shikār* was that it enabled a respect for the flora and fauna of the Indian subcontinent engendered by a keen and often sensitive observation of the diversity of wildlife encountered on the field. In Mughal India, zoological studies included animal anatomy, taxonomy, and psychology. They also included various diseases, diagnostics, treatments, and remedies. These were recorded employing all the empirical tools of research available, including observation, dissection, and experimentation, as well as comparison with other species and the challenging of longstanding traditions. Jahāngīr was an avid hunter and equally keen naturalist. His memoirs, the *Jahāngīrnāma* or *Tūzuk-i Jahāngīrī*, contain evocative but accurate and succinct descriptions of flora and fauna encountered during hunts. He is exacting in his methodology, as he notes that '[o]nly those that are really special can be recorded'.[27] Specimens were weighed and measured, and the details recorded included local names, geographical distribution, anatomical peculiarities, and food habits, as well as the specimens' habitats, climatic conditions, and behaviours. Foreign species were also often compared to indigenous counterparts. For instance, en route to Malwa province in 1617 and encamped in the halting place of Qasim-khera (Qasimgarh) with the imperial entourage, Jahāngīr records that he hunted an unfamiliar 'white' animal. It has been subsequently identified as the four-horned antelope, *Tetracerus quadrocornis,* and the naturalist Salim Ali opines that its colouring was probably pale brown.[28] Jahāngīr notes:

> [I]t resembled the *kūtāh pāya* (Hog Deer); it had four horns, two of which were opposite the extremities of its eyes and two finger-breadths in height, and the other two horns were towards the nape of the neck. These were four finger-breadths in height. The people of India call this animal *dūdhāriya.* The male has four horns and the female none. It was said that this kind of antelope has no gall-bladder, but when they looked at its intestines the gall-bladder was apparent, and it became clear that this report has no foundation.[29]

In another anecdote, while on a tour to Kabul in 1607, Jahāngīr and his court were encamped in the Safid Sang meadow, near Du'aba, where a great *qamarghā* ring hunt was organised for him. During the hunt, 116 deer, 24 *rang* (ibex), 50 red antelopes, and 16 markhor (wild goats) were taken. Jahāngīr notes that it was his first experience seeing a *rang,* which he describes as a fine-looking animal, even surpassing the Hindustan black antelope in appearance. He ordered that a mountain ram and a *rang* be weighed for comparison. The ram came to 1 maund and 33 seers, and the *rang* was 2 maunds and 10 seers. Jahāngīr also notes that in spite of its large size, the *rang* was a nimble animal, as 12 swift dogs were worn out in pursuit and seized it with 'a hundred thousand difficulties'.[30]

Regarding taxonomy, Jahāngīr reverts to the tradition of older Arabic texts, grouping them according to 'outward criterions [sic] and regardless of casual connections'.[31] He uses the word *'ālam* (world of) to indicate a specific family, grouping animals with comparable affinities, such as the coat or size and shape of bill.[32] For instance, Jahāngīr notes that the langur belongs to the world of the

Figure 3.1 Rhinoceros, *Vaki'at-i Baburi*. Or. 3714 vol. 4 fol. 379, British Library, London. © British Library Board (Or. 3714).

monkey (*'ālam maimūn*), and the dipper to the world of the bulbul.[33] The *Jahāngīrnāma* also contains explicit details regarding strange zoological phenomena and experiments that were carried out on the field during hunts in order to increase Jahāngīr's knowledge, and to verify established animal myths. Jahāngīr is known to have taken a rationalistic approach to experimentation, testing, and observation in order to reach a verified truth.[34] Some of his many experiments include dissecting a king cobra to observe its cannibalistic characteristics; dissecting the livers and gall bladders of wolves and lions to establish links to their proverbial courage; studying stress levels in antelopes hunted by cheetahs; and challenging the accepted belief that aggression in male mountain goats was caused by parasites in their horn.[35] However, as Koch observes, Jahāngīr 'fails to feed the results of his empirical research into a theoretical framework and his observations do not lead to a systematic body of knowledge'.[36]

Detailed textual descriptions of flora and fauna encountered during the Mughal hunts were developed by court artists into lavish paintings that were precise, well defined, and objective nature studies. By the end of Akbar's reign, a distinctive style had developed, focusing on artistic realism and the naturalistic treatment of independent studies of animals and birds.[37] Jahāngīr, who inherited a mature atelier, continued to champion artists such as the acclaimed *Ustād* Mansūr, who was seen as the master of the animal painting genre, given to portraying wildlife in an anatomically accurate manner with a degree of unparalleled naturalism. Verma claims that the imperial artists' long tradition of illustrating manuscripts of fables such as *Anwār-i suhaili, 'Iyar-i dānish,* and *'Ajā'ib-i makhlūqāt* properly acquainted them with animal characteristics and psychology.[38] The trend to document textual descriptions of animal species with corresponding visual studies was accordingly set in motion in the early stages of the Mughal painting tradition. Shāhjahān's albums continued this trend of realism, extending it to broad margin paintings of detailed animal, bird, and floral studies. It seems that Jahāngīr's rationale for the objective portrayal of wildlife, which enhanced the scientific nature of his textual descriptions, was his desire for historical documentation of the rarities of nature for posterity. He writes: 'I both wrote of them and ordered the artists to draw their likeness in the *Jahāngīrnāma* so that the astonishment one has at hearing of them would increase by seeing them'.[39] Koch notes that Jahāngīr also seems to imply the advantages of a dual method, written and visual, in representing natural phenomena.[40]

Paintings of particular hunts and independent studies that correspond to dated textual sources indicate that artists travelled to *shikārgāhs* and on extended tours with the emperor, as such paintings were meant to be visual records of the events. For instance, when encountering a new species of bird, which he identifies as a *sāj* or dipper, in the Sukh Nag stream in the Kashmiri hills during the 1620 trip, Jahāngīr observes its colouration, and compares it with the more common bulbul due to its appearance and its tendency to dive and stay underwater for a while before emerging elsewhere. He also examines its feet, to ascertain if they were like the feet of waterfowl or land birds, and records that they were not webbed like a duck.[41] Mansūr has depicted the *sāj* in a hilly Kashmiri landscape beside a flowing stream. Verma notes that 'the juxtapositioning of another bird, smaller in size and apparently viewed from a distance, and the receding contours of the hills painted in blurred colour, suggest perspective, besides giving relief to the central figure'.[42] While Mansūr may have used the smaller *sāj* and other artistic tools to convey perspective, by depicting another angle of the bird to show the colouration of its belly feathers his painting also fulfils the criteria of natural historical observations. According to Verma, Mughal painters portrayed the animal/bird as an 'individual'

Figure 3.2 Dipper/*Saj*, album leaf painted by Mansūr. Acc. 55.121.10.16, The Metropolitan Museum of Art, New York. (Licensed under CC0 1.0.)

with minimum movement, and an emphasis on realism and physiognomy, which best suited animal studies.[43] The finesse and accuracy with which the artists have portrayed the bodily contours, microscopic anatomical details, colouration and expression of the animals, as well as the treatment of space, liveliness of brushstrokes, and other techniques, have often been discussed at length for their artistic worth. Mughal animal illustrations have also been examined by naturalists, historians of science, and scientists who acknowledge their merit as valuable scientific studies.[44] Art thus remains a crucial medium in recording and disseminating the knowledge of nature in Mughal contexts.

SCIENCE AND MORALITY

As noted earlier, science, ethics, moral values, and religion were interrelated concepts in Mughal cultural contexts. Hence, ethical literature, such as Naṣīr al-Dīn al-Ṭūsī's *Akhlāq-i Naṣīrī* wielded considerable influence in religious, political, social, and cultural spheres.[45] To support his views al-Ṭūsī cites the teachings of classical Greek philosophers and pre-Islamic Persian sages; he also makes frequent references to the Quran and Hadiths, and anchors the *akhlāq* (Arabic for 'ethics') framework in the *sharī'a* (Arabic for 'law'), thus legitimising his work and making it politically compliant for imperial use. Alam opines that al-Ṭūsī uses the term *sharī'a* not in the 'narrow legalistic sense', but as 'a notion of laws as *norms'* by which the king was obligated to ensure the welfare of *all* his subjects.[46] Jahāngīr, like Abū'l Fazl, frequently invokes God's hand in the wonders of creation of unusual animals. Of the zebra, Jahāngīr notes: '[T]he painter of destiny had produced a tour de force on the canvas of time with his wonder-working brush'.[47] Religious perspectives, wherein animal studies enabled an appreciation of the wisdom of God, were often the rationale of Islamic scientific inquiry.[48]

Akhlāq ethical texts advocate the virtue of having the courage to 'retain firmness in situations of alarm and danger' and to act by the dictates of 'right reason' as one of the essential qualities of an ideal king.[49] Hunting was seen as a good and proper sport for a king if undertaken for the right reasons and in moderation.[50] Hence hunting became a pivotal agency through which the emperor's authority and public persona were projected.

Akbar's *Dastūru'l-'amal,* which was distributed to court officials, further counsels imperial officers to be 'not too fond of hunting; but to go out hunting occasionally, with the object of military exercise and for relaxation, which is an unavoidable adjunct of human existence'.[51] The moral dichotomy inherent in the act of killing animals during hunting was confronted by reference to *akhlāq* texts, which advocated the image of the emperor as a brave hunter who had a moral obligation to subdue wild nature in order to protect his people: 'Men, Animal and Conscience completed the circle of Akbar's authority'.[52] Sumptuous paintings by court artists who travelled with the court on hunts served to magnify this image.[53] Hence it could be argued that while hunting images served to endorse imperial authority over the zoological and botanical domain, independent images of natural historical studies affirmed the observance of equity required by the ruler towards God's creatures.[54]

Observing the mutual respect between man and beast can be seen as another reason for scientific inquiry. The *Akhlāq-i Naṣīrī* notes that elements, plants, and animals render aid to the human species whether as matter, as instrument, or by way of service, and that the human species needs the aid of the other species and the co-operation of its own kind to ensure survival.[55] This translated into the Mughal politico- and socio-cultural context in several different ways.

The superior breeding and selection of animals used during the hunt and on hunting expeditions, such as elephants, horses, and camels, not only ensured better hunting practices; they were also an integral element of the success of the Mughal military campaigns. Extensive anatomical knowledge was thus crucial for producing the optimal breed and ensuring the animals' welfare and comfort. The *Ā'īn-i Akbarī* devotes several reports to details such as the animals' physical characteristics, behavioural patterns, and breeding details; the maintenance of imperial stables; the classification of species; the ranks of the animals and the resulting food allocation, medical needs, riding methods, and harnesses allowed. It also includes a detailed compendium of officers and servants attached to these animals.[56] Abū'l Fazl attributes Akbar's patronage to the successful production of local horse breeds, such as *sanūjī, pachwariya gūt*, and *tānghan,* which were supposedly as fine as those from Iraq and Arabia, or even ranked higher.[57]

The universal nature of the *akhlāq* ethical models, with their emphasis on good values and high morals which could transcend religious faiths, led to the cultivation of a multicultural and socially inclusive imperial image. This extended to a flourishing Sanskrit literary culture alongside the use of the Persian language at court. Imperial patronage resulted in the development of detailed exegeses of Sanskrit texts in order to forge authority and benefit from different forms of knowledge.[58] Both pre-Mughal Sultanate and Mughal scientific writings hence benefited greatly from the existing rich intellectual repository of Sanskrit writings. Intellectual intercommunication between Sanskrit literati and Persian scholars resulted in several Sanskrit scientific treatises being translated and absorbed into Persian writings. The *Śālihotra somhita,* written probably around the 7th or 8th century, and the *Aśvavaidyaka* of Jayadatta, written between the 8th to 12th centuries, are possibly two of the most important Sanskrit zoological texts, which inspired several works throughout the ages in Sanskrit and Indian regional languages. Additionally, at least three Persian works, *Tarjuma-i Śālihotra* of Abdu'llāh Ṣafi (15th century), the *Farasnāma* of 'Abdu'llāh Khān Fīrūz Jung (17th century), and the *Farasnāma* of Zainu'l-'alamīn Abū'l-Hasan (16th century) are Persian adaptations of the *Śālihotra somhita,* which includes, among other concerns, classification, diseases, diagnostics, treatments, and surgical procedures for horses, as well as equine toxicology.[59] This is contrary to the observations of some scholars who note that the Muslim invaders of India stifled Hindu-Sanskrit learning, and that they were indifferent to any culture but that of Islam, and drew their knowledge and inspiration from Arabic and Persian sources alone.[60]

Falcons and birds of prey were cherished members of the imperial hunting establishment alongside elephants and cheetahs. These animals rendered invaluable service to the Mughal court and therefore needed to be respected as suggested by the *akhlāq* texts. Outcomes at the hunt depended on the taming and training programs, which required sound knowledge of anatomy and psychology. Treatises on birds of prey and falconry were a popular genre in the Mughal libraries. The *Bāznāma* of Bahādur Khān (17th century), the *Bāznamā* of Muḥibb 'Ali Khān (17th century), *Mir'ātu's-ṣa'īd* of Allāh Yār Jāmi (early 18th century), the *Shahbāznāma-i Firūz Shāh* of Firuz Shah (16th century), and *Dastūru'ṣ-ṣa'īd* of Riḍā Yūsuf include information on the capture, training, diet, diseases, and treatment of hunting birds. Interestingly, some of the authors of the treatises on falcons, such as Allāh Yār Jāmi and Riḍā Yūsuf, were *mīr-i shikārs* (masters of the hunt), which adds a further link between hunting and the pursuit of scientific knowledge.

The Mughal emperors' visceral connection with the natural world also enabled knowledge of the diseases afflicting animals. Jahāngīr, for instance, recorded the symptoms and effects of rabies in great detail when his personal elephant, Gajpati, was stricken by the disease.[61] The nature of animal illnesses and injuries was further studied at veterinary hospitals, called *pinjarapoles*. Pietro della Valle, an Italian traveller to the Mughal Empire in 1623-24, visited many specialised veterinary hospitals in Cambay, Gujerat.[62] Thevenot, a French traveller in Aurangzeb's court in 1666, also notes similar veterinary hospitals in Ahmedabad, where oxen, camels, horses, and other wounded beasts were cared for, and another dedicated to apes in Delhi.[63] Studies of poisons and venoms from snakes also formed part of the body of knowledge facilitated by the hunt. Manucci, an Italian traveller in India during the later reign of Shāhjahān and then Aurangzeb, notes that snakes were used as a punishment for and deterrent against official corruption. Under Shāhjahān's orders, an official supposedly kept several baskets of poisonous snakes at court. Snakes would be made to bite any official found guilty of miscarriage of justice, and Manucci was witness to the execution by cobra-bite of a magistrate found guilty of taking bribes.[64]

HUNTING TECHNIQUES

A sound knowledge of hunting techniques ensured not only that large quantities of game were brought down, but also that many of the methods used were transferred to the battlefield as military tactics. Bābur observes that the one of the merits of the Uzbeg armies was their use of a manoeuvre called the 'flank assault', which was a series of encircling, turning, and spinning movements called a *tūlghuma,* whereby the turning parties, officers, and ordinary soldiers, riding loose-rein, would wheel around to surround and discharge arrows towards the centre.[65] Hunting, especially in a *qamarghā*, provided many opportunities to perfect the movement.[66]

Bābur notes a battle formation used by the Uzbegs whereby officers were assigned particular positions, namely right wing, left wing, centre, and flank, with high-ranking officers taking the privileged positions towards the edge. This formation was also used during a *qamarghā*. If a dispute arose over these positions, it was usually settled by the agreement that one clan takes the honourable position in the *qamarghā* and the other in the battle array.[67] Bābur used the same Chinghisid battle formations and the *tūlghuma* technique to great effect during the decisive Battle of Panipat in 1525-26 against Ibrahim Lodi, throwing the greatly outnumbered Lodi army, comprising 100,000 soldiers and 1000 war elephants, into complete disarray and confusion.[68]

The *qamarghā* technique required game to be surrounded and encircled before being hunted. Mughal skirmishes were based on the same campaign plan, to surround the enemy and then close in towards the core. For instance, during the Battle of Khanua against Rāna Sangha in 1527, Bābur had the troops emerge from the right and left centre, leaving a space in the middle for the musketeers. The victorious Mughal army 'forced and drove the enfeebled left and right of the enemy into one mass with their centre'.[69] The 1567 *qamarghā* organised for Akbar in Lahore required over 15,000 animals to be driven in from the neighbouring hills for over a month by about 5000 beaters into a circle 16 kilometres in circumference. Akbar hunted in the steadily decreasing ring for five days.[70] The monumental double-page composition of this *qamarghā* in the Victoria and Albert Museum *Akbarnāma* is reflective of what has been billed the greatest hunt ever held.[71] O'Hanlon notes that hunting paintings exhibit a 'strong sense of place in a north Indian landscape, reflecting Akbar's role not only as divine king, moral exemplar, and dispenser of justice, but as a ruler profoundly attuned to the subtle ecological balance of the land and its people'.[72] While the painting serves to illustrate the necessary qualities of a warrior king, equally

Figure 3.3 Akbar hunts with cheetahs in a *qamarghā* ring in Lahore in 1567, painted by Miskīna with Mansūr and Sarwān, *Akbarnāma*. Reproduced from the Victoria and Albert Museum, London. Permission granted © Victoria and Albert Museum, London.

adept on the battlefield, court and *shikārgāh,* it is also a study of the natural history of the area around the Salt Range of the Lahore province, thus demonstrating a valid link between the hunt and zoological sciences. Divyabhanusinh has identified markhors (wild goats), Punjab urial (wild sheep), blackbucks, jackals, antelopes, civets, foxes, and hyenas. The three cheetahs on the loose and two more about to be released by their keepers have attacked nilgais (blue bulls), hares, and chital (spotted deer). He also notes that the accurate depiction of injured and dead animals implies that Miskīna and his colourists, Mansūr and Sarwān, would have witnessed the hunt.[73]

Hunting with cheetahs was another favoured hunting technique for the Mughal emperors, and cheetahs were held in high esteem at court. The anatomy, behavioural patterns, and skills naturally exhibited by the cheetah as it gave chase were studied at length, leading to regulations regarding training methods, food allocation, and proper transportation during tours. The cheetah's ability to go against the wind, along with its instinct to lie concealed before the ambush, as well as to kick up dust with its feet to confuse its prey, were all observed and used in training programs.[74] And as the following incident demonstrates, scientific data had to be constantly updated. Abū'l Fazl recalls a 'joyful occurrence' while Akbar was hunting with his cheetahs in Sanganir in 1527. While Akbar was pursuing a herd of blackbuck with a tame, favoured cheetah named Chitr Najan, which gave

Figure 3.4 Akbar hunting black buck with trained cheetahs in 1527, painted by La'l and Kēsav Khord, Akbarnama. Reproduced from the Victoria and Albert Museum, London. Permission granted © Victoria and Albert Museum, London.

chase, a large buck leapt into the air 'to a height of a spear and a half' to cross a ravine which was 25 yards (22.8 metres) wide. Chitr Najan cleared the ravine and hunted it down. Cheetahs are renowned for their speed, not their leaping abilities. This unusual characteristic of the cheetah, previously unknown, was hence recorded in the inimitable Mughal style — Chitr Najan was honoured as chief cheetah with a roll of drums.[75] The two artists from the imperial atelier, La'l and Kēsav, were at hand to visualise the incident, which also shows how the blindfolded cheetahs were transported in bullock carts to the *shikārgāh*. The hunting image hence reinforces the ever-present link between art and scientific knowledge.

TECHNOLOGICAL INNOVATIONS

Technological and mechanical arts were greatly appreciated at court. Mughal primary sources, although fragmentary with their descriptions, refer to a number of innovations unveiled at court. This study highlights only those pertaining to the hunt and used during hunting expeditions. Abū'l Fazl credits Akbar as being the author of several inventions, and the writings of Jesuit fathers visiting the Mughal court affirm Akbar's interest and hands-on approach to industrial crafts.[76] The Mughal court went on what it referred to as hunting expeditions over extended periods of time in order to consolidate its hold over distant provinces and deal with administrative matters, and these inventions would have made life at encampment sites more pleasurable for the royals. They include portable pavilion-palaces, which were capable of accommodating over 10,000 people, and which took over 1000 workmen to assemble. They were fitted with Akbar's innovative iron rings with 'male' and 'female' fasteners, posts, and wooden boards to increase structural stability.[77] Refrigeration techniques using saltpetre as a cooling agent, improvements to geared waterlifts, and luxury portable baths with several *ḥammāms* drawn by elephant or cattle were other considerable innovations.[78] Another mechanical device attributed to Mīr Fath'ullāh Shirāzi, the Persian scientist, who, as noted earlier, was responsible for the overhaul of *madrasa* education, is a cart-mill for grinding grain into flour.[79]

Abū'l Fazl notes that matchlocks were manufactured in Akbar's arsenal, and he credits Akbar himself with this invention. Abū'l Fazl's descriptions note that the matchlock did not require a match and needed only a slight movement of the trigger to fire the pellet.[80] Habib opines that the gun could have been a wheel-lock, and since the latter was only invented in Italy in the 1520s, and not yet widely used due to its delicate mechanism, it was a significant achievement of Mughal industrial technology.[81] The *(y)barghū*, a contraption for boring and smoothening gun barrels, is generally attributed to Fath'ullāh Shirāzi. Abu'l Fazl notes that this device, a wheel turned by an ox, smoothened the barrels of 16 handguns in a small amount of time.[82] Using Abū'l Fazl's drawing, Habib and Alvi and Rahman have reconstructed the mechanics underlying its workings, which use a pin-drum whose pins meshed with the pegs of eight vertical gear-wheels with projecting axles that could enter the gun barrel to smoothen them.[83] Akbar's other achievement was a procedure to strengthen the gun barrel.[84] While Abū'l Fazl's claims of Akbar's authorship for many of these devices may be debatable, there is no doubt that the prevailing milieu at the Mughal court, largely driven by Akbar's enquiring mind and patronage, spurred many technological advances. Mechanical innovations doubtless improved lifestyles during tours and boosted the prestige of the ruling family as patrons of technology. Others were directly responsible for greater success during wartime and during the hunt. Importantly, the inventions adhered to aspects of *akhlāq* literature

Figure 3.5 Shāhjahān hunting antelopes, perhaps Rupbas, after 1640, unknown artist. Reproduced from Folio 165A, Royal Collections Trust, Windsor Castle, Windsor. Permission granted Royal Collection Trust/© Her Majesty Queen Elizabeth II 2016.

whereby the emperor was committed to creating the best possible conditions of welfare for his subjects.[85]

Hunting images provide a further link between art and technology. O'Hanlon notes, 'It was also in hunting ... that the emperor appeared in closest communion with the north Indian landscape'.[86] This is certainly true of the painting of Shāhjahān and his son Dāra-Shikōh hunting antelopes around 1640, one of the most evocative images in the Royal Collections' *Pādshāhnāma*.[87] The hunting party, dressed in camouflage green, wait to take aim at the animals driven in by huntsmen using tame antelopes as decoys. The image is a metaphor for the prosperity and power of Shāhjahān's reign, and the artist has used it to draw analogies between the hunt and the emperor's legitimising role as promoting social welfare. However, it is also a study in firearm technology. Shāhjahān is about to pull the trigger of his royal matchlock named *Khassban*, which will fire the charge.[88] Although Shāhjahān's elbow is supported by his raised knee and the gun is steadied by the string attached to a ring on the barrel, the gun is mainly supported on the shoulder of the huntsman in front. This implies that matchlocks were still slow and unreliable at the time, and hence better suited for the less strenuous nature of the decoy hunt rather than the warlike *qamarghā*.[89]

CONCLUSION

The reluctance of the *madrasa* — the principal institution of higher learning in Arab-Islamic civilisation — to include systematic instructions on rational or natural sciences in its curriculum has often been cited as one of the primary causes of the failure of Islamic science to grow and develop beyond the 14th century.[90] However, judging from the level of scientific and intellectual activity in Mughal India, the situation seems to have been extraordinary. In spite of ample evidence to the contrary, Mughal scientific inquiry has come under frequent criticism by Orientalists and their claims that natural history and experimental philosophy were not cultivated in India.[91] Western travellers to the Mughal court such as Bernier attribute the 'profound and universal ignorance' of the Indian society to the lack of formal educational institutions.[92] Ironically, Dānishmand Khān — Bernier's patron, the Mughal courtier and scholar, who requested the translations into Persian of the works of several European scholars (such as Descartes, Gassendi, Harvey, and Pecquet) — was also responsible for Bernier being immersed in the dynamic intellectual community and Sanskrit literati in India. Dānishmand also introduced him to several Persian translations of Sanskrit texts, which he subsequently carried back to Europe.[93] Perhaps Bernier's lament regarding the dearth of systematic and institutionalised knowledge in Mughal India arose as a result of his training in science marked by 'the pragmatic and critical method of modern Western science which has guided Western thinking into the right course'.[94] Indeed, Abū'l Fazl's ruminations regarding the predominance of ideological tradition summarise the state of affairs in the Mughal court — 'the blowing of the chill blast of inflexible custom (*taqlid*) and the low flicker from the lamp of wisdom'[95] — and the fact that, despite the introduction of scientific and rational syllabi in schools, the 'socio-economic and ideological stimulants that this was producing were not apparently provocative enough to bring about a paradigm change in the structure of Indian science'.[96] Education remained firmly in the domain of the privileged.[97] And the languages of science — Sanskrit in ancient India, Persian in Mughal India — were not the languages of the masses, and were seen as aristocratic and elitist.[98] Scientific knowledge acquisition was hence a courtly undertaking. However, this study has shown the extensive level and range of scientific and technological activities furthered by the hunt, which was cultivated and fostered by imperial patronage. Abū'l Fazl and other court historians frequently note the complex knowledge-based noble reasons that vindicated the imperial *shikār*. These include dispensation of justice, articulation of good governance, and implementation of administrative affairs. The line of discussions presented in this chapter seeks to recalibrate the received wisdom of these 'higher aims' with the implication that the acquisition of scientific knowledge was likely perceived as an added dimension to the superior motives of the hunt.

NOTES

1 Abū'l Fazl, 2010, *Ā'īn-i Akbarī*, vol. I, trans. H Blochmann, ed. DC Phillott (Calcutta: The Asiatic Society, First published 1866-94, edited 1927), 292.

2 Abū'l Fazl, 2010, vol. I, 292. Abū'l Fazl, 2000, *Akbarnāma*, vol. II, trans. H Beveridge (Calcutta: The Asiatic Society, First published 1897-1921), 343. Abu'l Fazl is making a reference to Akbar engaged in hunting/ trapping wild elephants in the jungles of Narwar in 1564, while putting down a rebellion caused by 'Abdu'llāh Khān Uzbeg. II, 345-53.

3 Abdul Hamid Lahōri, 2010, *Lahōri's Pādshāhnāmah (1592-1638)*, trans. Hamid Afaq Siddiqi (Delhi: Idarah-i Idarah-i Adabiyat-i Delli), 57.

4 Abū'l Fazl, 2000, vol. II, 232. Abū'l Fazl is referring to Akbar mounting a *mast* elephant Hawai and engaging it in a fight in 1561.

5 Abū'l Fazl, 2000, vol. II, 232.

6 Mughal contributions to botanical studies have not been covered due to this chapter's emphasis on hunting.

7 Naṣīr al-Dīn al-Ṭūsī, 1964, *Akhlāq-i Naṣīrī* (The Nasirean Ethics), trans. GM Wickens (London: George Allen & Unwin); see especially 26-7, 30-1.

8 Peter Harrison, 2015, *The Territories of Science and Religion* (Chicago: Chicago University Press), 3.

9 Harrison, 2015, 3, 5, 90.

10 Sheldon Pollock, 2011, 'The Languages of Science in Early Modern India', in Sheldon Pollock, ed., *Forms of Knowledge in Early Modern Asia, Explorations in the Intellectual History of India and Tibet 1500-1800* (Durham: Duke University Press), 4, 21.

11 Irfan Habib, 1996, 'Reason and Science in Medieval India', in JN Jha, ed., *Society and Ideology in India, Essays in Honour of Professor RS Sharma* (New Delhi: Munshiram Manoharlal Publishers), 168.

12 Abū'l Fazl, 2010, vol. I, 289.

13 Abū'l Fazl, 2010, vol. I, 289.

14 Shah-Nawaz Khan, Nawab Samsam al-Dawla and Abdul Hayy, 1979, *Ma'athir-ul-Umara*, vol. I, trans. H Beveridge and Baini Prashad (Patna: Janaki Prakashan, first published 1911-52), 545.

15 Cited in Momin Mohiuddin, 1971, *The Chancellery and Persian Epistolography under the Mughals: From Babur to Shahjahan, 1526-1658: A Study on Inshá, Dar al-Insha, and Munshis Based on Original Documents* (Calcutta: Iran Society), 41, 228-34.

16 François Bernier, 1983, *Travels in the Mogul Empire AD 1656-1668*, trans. Archibald Constable (Oxford: Oxford University Press, first published 1934), 229.

17 Zuhuri, *Saqinamah-yi Zuhuri*, cited in Sunil Sharma, 2011, '"If there is a Paradise on Earth, it is Here": Urban Ethnography in Indo-Persian Poetic and Historic Texts', in Sheldon Pollock, ed., *Forms of Knowledge in Early Modern Asia, Explorations in the Intellectual History of India and Tibet 1500-1800* (Durham: Duke University Press), 245.

18 Abū'l Fazl, 2010, vol. III, 4-5.

19 A Rahman et al., 1982, *Science and Technology in Medieval India — A Bibliography of Source Materials in Sanskrit, Arabic and Persian* (New Delhi: Indian National Science Academy), xiv-xv. See also CA Storey, 1977, *Persian Literature, A Bio-Bibliographical Survey*, vol. II (Leiden: The Royal Asiatic Society of Great Britain and Ireland), 3, 442-5.

20 Pollock, 2011, 5.
21 Sharma, 2011, 240-1.
22 Zahiru'd-din Muhammad Pādshah Ghāzī Bābur, 1990, *Bābur-Nāma, The Memoirs of Babur*, trans. Annette Susannah Beveridge (New Delhi: Munshiram Manoharlal, first published 1921), 488-515.
23 Som Prakash Verma, 1999a, *Mughal Painter of Flora and Fauna, Ustad Mansur* (New Delhi: Abhinav Publications), 37.
24 Salim Ali, 1927, 'The Moghul Emperors of India as Naturalists and Sportsmen', *Journal of the Bombay Natural History Society*, Part I 31(4): 836.
25 Bābur, 1990, 489-90, 450-1.
26 Jahāngīr, 1999, *Jahāngīrnāma, Memoirs of Jahangir, Emperor of India*, trans. Wheeler Thackston (New York: Oxford University Press), 402-3; Jahangir, 2003, *Tūzuk-i Jahāngīrī, The Memoirs of Jahāngīr*, vol. II, trans. Alexander Rogers, ed. Henry Beveridge (New Delhi: Munshiram Manoharlal, first published 1909), 270.
27 The unusual characteristics of animals in the imperial menagerie and of the exotic species that were brought to court and described extensively by Jahāngīr are beyond the scope of this chapter, which mentions only those encountered during hunts. However, note that Jahāngīr's study of the breeding habits of sarus crane, and his observations on the gestation period of the elephant are considered pioneering work for the age. See Jahāngīr, 1999, 266, 269-70, 274, 277, 160. See also MA Alvi and A Rahman, 1968, *Jahangir — The Naturalist* (New Delhi: Indian National Science Academy), 5.
28 Ali, 1927, Part II, 32(1): 38.
29 Jahangir, 2003, vol. I, 352.
30 Jahangir, 2003, vol. I, 121-2. Note that 1 maund = 40 seers = ~37 kilograms.
31 Joseph Somogyi, 1950, 'Ad-Damiri's Hayat al-hayawan: An Arabic Zoological Lexicon', *Osiris* 9: 34.
32 Alvi and Rahman, 1968, 5.
33 Jahāngīr, 1999, 255, 339.
34 MA Alvi, 1999, 'Jahangir's Passion for Exotic Animals', in Som Prakash Verma, ed., *Flora and Fauna in Mughal Art* (Mumbai: Marg Publications), 91.
35 See Jahāngīr, 1999, 418, 207, 213, 316, 65. Jahāngīr carried out many other experiments including cross-breeding various species. However, only those performed during hunting have been highlighted.
36 Ebba Koch, 2009, 'Jahangir as Francis Bacon's Ideal of the King as an Observer and Investigator of Nature', *Journal of the Royal Asiatic Society of Great Britain and Ireland* 19(3): 328.
37 Verma, 1999a, 37.
38 Verma, 1999a, 22.
39 Jahāngīr, 1999, 133.
40 Koch, 2009, 298. See Jahāngīr, 1999, 133.
41 Jahāngīr, 1999, 339.
42 Som Prakash Verma, 1999b, 'Portraits of Birds and Animals under Jahangir', in Som Prakesh Verma, ed., *Flora and Fauna in Mughal Art* (Mumbai: Marg Publications), 13.
43 Verma, 1999b, 20.
44 See for instance Salim Ali, 1968, 'Dodo', in MA Alvi and A Rahman, *Jahangir — the Naturalist* (New Delhi: Indian National Science Academy), 15-17. A significant ornithological study of the Mauritian dodo is attributed to Mansūr, and is now in the St. Petersburg Album, St. Petersburg. It created much excitement at the XII International Ornithological Congress in Helsinki in 1958 when first unveiled as it is one of the earliest depictions of the bird, and it is now generally believed that it was painted from a living specimen. See also Alvi and Rahman, 1968, 4-9.
45 For discussions on Ikhtiyar al-Husaini's *Akhlāq-i Humāyuni* which is modelled on al-Ṭūsī's *Akhlāq-i Naṣīrī* and other *akhlāq* texts such as Jalal al-Din Muhammad Asad Dawani's *Akhlāq-i-Jalāli* (1427-1521), see Iqtidar Alam Khan, 2009, 'Tracing Sources of Principles of Mughal Governance: A Critique of Recent Historiography', *Social Scientist* 37(5-6): 45-54; Muzaffar Alam, 2004, *The Languages of Political Islam, India 1200-1800* (Chicago: University of Chicago Press), 71-5; Muzaffar Alam, 2000, 'Akhlaqi Norms and Mughal Governance', in Muzzafar Alam et al., eds., *The Making of Indo-Persian Culture — Indian and French Studies* (New Delhi: Manohar Publishers), 67-95.

46 Alam, 2004, 5, 77 (emphasis in original).

47 Jahāngīr, 1999, 360.

48 Seyyed Hossein Nasr, 1976, *Islamic Science: An Illustrated Study* (England: World of Islam Festival Publishing Company Limited), 66.

49 Jalal al-Din Muhammad Asad Dawani, 1895 (*Akhlāq-i-Jalālī*), *The Akhlak-i-Jalaly, Practical Philosophy of the Muhammadan People*, trans. WF Thompson (Lahore: Caxton Printing Works), 27.

50 Al-Ghazālī, 1964, *Naṣīḥat al-Muluk of al-Ghazālī* (Counsel for Kings), trans. FRC Bagley, ed. Huma'i Jalal (London: Oxford University Press), 80.

51 Abū'l Fazl, 1998, Akbar's '*Dasturu'l-'amal* (A Circular Enumerating the Duties of Officers) Addressed to the 'Ummāl and Mutasaddīs of the Empire (21 March 1594)', in Mansura Haidar, trans., *Mukātabāt-i-'Allāmī (Inshā'i Abu'l Fazl)* (New Delhi: Munshiram Manoharlal), 83.

52 Khaliq Ahmad Nizami, 1989, *Akbar and Religion* (New Delhi: Idarah-i-Adabiyat-i-Delli), 185.

53 Rosalind O'Hanlon, 2007, 'Kingdom, Household and Body History: Gender and Imperial Service under Akbar', *Modern Asian Studies* 41(5): 898.

54 See Dawani, 1895, 153. Jalali notes that a king's 'proper return for this magnificent appointment [sovereignty] is the observance of equity towards God's creatures and his own subjects'.

55 Al-Ṭūsī, 1964, 188-9.

56 Abū'l Fazl, 2010, vol. I. Elephants 123-39, horses 140-50, camels 151-6.

57 Abū'l Fazl, 2010, vol. I, 140.

58 Audrey Truschke, 2016, *Culture of Encounters: Sanskrit at the Mughal Court* (New York: Colombia University Press), 4-5, 142.

59 Rahman et al., 1982, 531-48.

60 See for instance George Sarton, 1947, *Introduction to the History of Science: Science and Learning in the Fourteenth Century*, vol. III (Baltimore: Williams and Wilkins) 1, 107.

61 Jahāngīr, 1999, 145-6.

62 Pietro della Valle, 1892, *The Travels of Pietro della Valle in India*, vol. I, trans. G Havers, ed. Edward Grey (London: Hakluyt Society), 67-8.

63 Jean de Thevenot, 1687, *The Travels of Monsieur de Thevenot into the Levant in Three Parts, viz. into I. Turkey, II. Persia, III. The East-Indies, Newly Done out of French*, vol. III, trans. Archibald Lovell (London: H Clark), 11-13, 41.

64 Niccolao Manucci, 1907, *Storia do Mogor or Mogul India 1653-1708*, vol. I, trans. William Irvine (London: John Murray), 197.

65 Bābur, 1990, 140, 473.

66 See for instance Bābur, 1990, 325. Bābur's descriptions regarding getting into position and turning movements before delivering the final blow to the wild ass during the 1507 *qamarghā* in Kattavaz plain are indicative of a *tūlghuma* movement.

67 Bābur, 1990, 155.

68 Bābur, 1990, 465-74.

69 Abū'l Fazl, 2000, vol. I, 264-5. See also Bābur, 1990, 563-73.

70 Abū'l Fazl, 2000, vol. II, 416-17.

71 Abū'l Fazl, 2000, vol. II, 416, fn. 2.

72 O'Hanlon, 2007, 898.

73 Divyabhanusinh, 1999, 'Hunting in Mughal Painting', in Som Prakash Verma, ed., *Flora and Fauna in Mughal Art* (Mumbai: Marg Publications), 103-4.

74 Abū'l Fazl, 2010, vol. I, 296-7, 299. See also Fr. Monserrate, 1922, *The Commentary of Father Monserrate on the Journey to the Court of Akbar*, trans. JH Hoyland, annotated SN Banerjee (London: Oxford University Press), 77-8.

75 See Abū'l Fazl, 2000, vol. II, 539. See also Divyabhanusinh, 1999, 98.

76 John Correia-Afonso, 1980, *Letters from the Mughal Court, The First Jesuit Mission to Akbar (1580-1583)* (Anand: Gujarat Sahitya Prakash), 56. (See Fr. Acquaviva's letter to Fr. Mercurian in 1580.)

77 Abū'l Fazl, 2010, vol. I, 47-9, 55-7. See also Muhammad Ārif Qandahāri, 1993, *Tārikh-i Akbarī*, trans. Tasneem Ahmad (New Delhi: Pragati Publications), 61-2. For reconstructions of these devices, see Irfan Habib, 1997, 'Akbar and Technology', in Irfan Habib, ed., *Akbar and his India* (New Delhi: Oxford University Press), 129-48. See also MA Alvi and A Rahman, 1940, *Fathulllah Shirazi, a Sixteenth Century Indian Scientist* (Delhi: National Institute of Sciences of India), 4-8.

78 Abū'l Fazl, 2010, vol. I, 58. Water was poured into a sealed metallic bottle and moved around a pan containing a mixture of water and saltpetre cooling it in about 12 minutes. Saltpetre is potassium nitrate. When added to water, there is an endothermic reaction which has the effect of cooling the surrounding water. See also Abū'l Fazl, 2010, vol. I, 285.

79 Abū'l Fazl, 2010, vol. I, 285.

80 Abū'l Fazl, 2010, vol. I, 120.

81 Irfan Habib, 1980, 'The Technology and Economy of Mughal India', *Indian Economic and Social History Review* 17(1): 17.

82 Abū'l Fazl, 2010, vol. I, 122. Abu'l Fazl's drawing of the *barghū* is in the *Ā'īn-i Akbarī* MS Add. 7652, British Library.

83 Habib, 1997, 140-1; Alvi and Rahman, 1940, 5-7.

84 Abū'l Fazl, 2010, vol. I, 120. The gun-barrel was flattened and twisted obliquely in a roll with overlapping edges, and then joined over an iron rod to form a barrel. Akbar supposedly supervised every step of the prototypes's manufacture, suggesting improvements and making trials at every stage.

85 Dawani, 1895, 156, 161.

86 O'Hanlon, 2007, 902.

87 *Pādshāhnāma*, meaning 'Chronicle of the King of the World', is a biography and history of the Emperor Shahjahan's reign (1628-58) by the court historian Abdul-Hamid Lahori. The Royal Collections' manuscript is extensively illustrated.

88 Koch, 1997, in Milo Cleveland Beach and Ebba Koch, *King of the World: The Padshahnama, An Imperial Mughal Manuscript from the Royal Library, Windsor Castle* (London: Azimuth Editions), 193.

89 Koch, 1997, 193.

90 See for instance Toby E. Huff, 2003, *The Rise of Early Modern Science: Islam, China and the West*, 2nd ed. (Cambridge, UK: Cambridge University Press), 84.

91 See for instance the Translator's Preface to *Dabistan* by its Orientalist translators, Shea and Troyner, and their critical viewpoint, 9-11. *Dabistan-i Mazahib* is a Mughal text of comparative religions of Mughal India; it explores the complexities of religious tolerance of the age. Its attribution to Mohsan Fání by the translators is questionable.

92 Bernier, 1983, 229.

93 Bernier, 1983, 324-5, 352-3. See also Mohamad Tavakoli-Targhi, 2011, 'Early Persian Modernity', in Sheldon Pollock, ed., *Forms of Knowledge in Early Modern Asia, Explorations in the Intellectual History of India and Tibet 1500-1800* (Durham: Duke University Press), 264-5.

94 Somogyi, 1950, 33.

95 Abū'l Fazl, 2010, vol. III, 4-5.

96 Iqbal Ghani Khan, 1997, 'Scientific Concepts in Abu'l Fazl's *Ain-i Akbari*', in Irfan Habib, ed., *Akbar and his India* (New Delhi: Oxford University Press), 128.

97 Habib, 1996, 163.

98 Habib, 1996, 163.

Chapter 4

The House of Stars: Astronomy and the Architecture of New Science in Early Modern Lucknow (1831-49)

Katharine Bartsch and Peter Scriver

ABSTRACT

This chapter examines the cross-cultural pursuit of new science during the brief history of the *Tarewali Kothi,* popularly known as the House of Stars, a modern astronomical observatory built in the 1830s in Lucknow, capital of the former Shīʿa kingdom of Awadh in northern India. Established during the reign of Nawab Naṣīruddīn Ḥaidar (r. 1827-37) under the direction of British experts, the observatory had been operational for less than a decade before it was decisively shut down by the last monarch of Awadh, shortly before the kingdom itself was absorbed by the expanding British-Indian Empire. Cross-examining the political circumstances of the observatory's brief life and premature closure in the light of the extraordinary history of Indo-Islamic endeavours in astronomy, this chapter offers a more nuanced reading than previous accounts have afforded of the symbolic capital and diplomacy vested in this shared Indo-British pursuit of scientific knowledge. In the microcosm of this early modern Islamic state, the Lucknow Observatory was, arguably, the apex of *ʿilm* in terms of scientific knowledge production and exchange. The chapter describes a state-of-the-art facility that was distinguished equally by its architecture, not least the hybrid architectural science of its design, and its 'high-tech' instrumentation dedicated to practical astronomy. Acknowledging parallel experimentation ongoing in the cosmopolitan culture of pre-colonial Lucknow with the modern styles of European architecture, the observatory building and institution is also interpreted as a site of cultural intersection and diplomatic exchange, where the higher ideal of pure science was, at least briefly, shared. While the decommissioned observatory building was ultimately re-purposed for other more worldly uses, the original joint venture in scientific discovery (for which the observatory had been built) was deemed to be a failure. In the geopolitical context in which the Indo-Islamic world had been enveloped by European imperialism, the focus of astronomy and allied sciences of observation had shifted from the heavens to the more terrestrial purposes of territorial mapping and control.

INTRODUCTION

On 20 January 1849, Wajīd ʿAlī Shāh, the last Nawab of Awadh (r. 1847-56), ordered the closure of the Lucknow Observatory.[1] Known locally as the *Tarewali Kothi* (House of Stars), this modern astronomical observatory had been founded in Lucknow at the behest of Nawabi patrons to advance scientific knowledge, presented in this chapter as the pursuit of *ʿilm* as science.[2] The observatory was founded at a time when Lucknow, according to the notable historian of astronomy in India SM Razaullah Ansari, 'was then bustling with the confrontation of traditional and modern scientific culture'.[3] Established in 1831 but not completed before the 1840s, the costly, cutting-edge facility had only been fully operational for less than a decade before its seemingly capricious yet decisive closure. This suspension of the observatory's advanced scientific activities was all the more surprising given the rich legacy of astronomical observation and scholarship in India over the preceding six centuries of political and cultural integration with the Islamic world.[4] The actual royal decree to close the observatory, as multiple previous accounts have corroborated, resulted rather circumstantially, it would appear, from Wajīd ʿAlī Shāh's displeasure with an unflattering account of himself in a popular contemporary history of the lives of the Nawabs, which had been published locally in the Urdu language.[5] As prominent Lucknow historian Rosie Llewellyn-Jones recounted the colourful anecdote, Wajīd ʿAlī Shāh vented his anger at the author of the 'scurrilous' text by closing both the observatory, where the writer was employed, as well as the local government printer and lithographic press where it had been published and circulated.[6] However, as Llewellyn-Jones herself remarked subsequently, the closure of the observatory was more than a petty act of retaliation.[7]

It was probable, for instance, that the observatory was already circumstantially inoperative at the time, following the death of its British chief astronomer in the previous year (to whom we will return presently). Moreover, Wajīd ʿAlī Shāh, who has been greatly maligned on some accounts as 'a profligate and dissolute man, indolent and easy-going, unfit to govern', has also been celebrated for his personal accomplishments in music, poetry, dance, choreography, and theatre as well as his patronage of these arts.[8] This Nawab's passion for the artistic development of his cosmopolitan early modern Islamic state distinguishes him from the observatory's founder, Naṣīruddīn Ḥaidar (r. 1827-37) — an anglophile, like his predecessor Ghāzīuddīn Ḥaidar (r. 1814-27), who sought to establish institutions based on English models and who specifically championed the pursuit of scientific knowledge during his reign.[9]

What, then, can we learn from the actual design and operations of the Lucknow Observatory and the cultural diplomacy implied in the joint pursuit of science at its inception? This chapter discerns potential rhetorical subtleties and implications that have been overlooked in previous accounts of the seemingly epiphenomenal incident that provoked the closure of the *Tarewali Kothi*, while taking equally into account the more likely political and economic grounds that have been emphasised in the most recent reassessment of this Nawabi legacy.[10] It locates the foundation of the observatory within both the historical trajectory of astronomical science in the region and the joint Nawabi-British patronage of what appears to have been a conscious enterprise in 'new science' in terms of early modern thinking within the greater Islamic world in the early 19th century.

To do this, it is necessary to begin with an outline of the immediate political and cultural history of Awadh. Awadh's kings had originally been appointed as vice-regal governors, under the title of Nawab (literally 'assistant'), to assist in extending the rule of the Mughal Emperor over the Indian subcontinent.[11] By the late 18th century, however, the former Mughal province had effectively become an autonomous and independently wealthy kingdom, graced by the revenue of India's richest agricultural region, the Indo-Gangetic Plain (Figure 4.1).[12] According to historian of religion Justin Jones, Awadh in this epoch was also 'one of the world's most significant post-Safavid [Imami] Shīʿa kingdoms', regarded in this sense as a 'universal kingdom' whose aegis

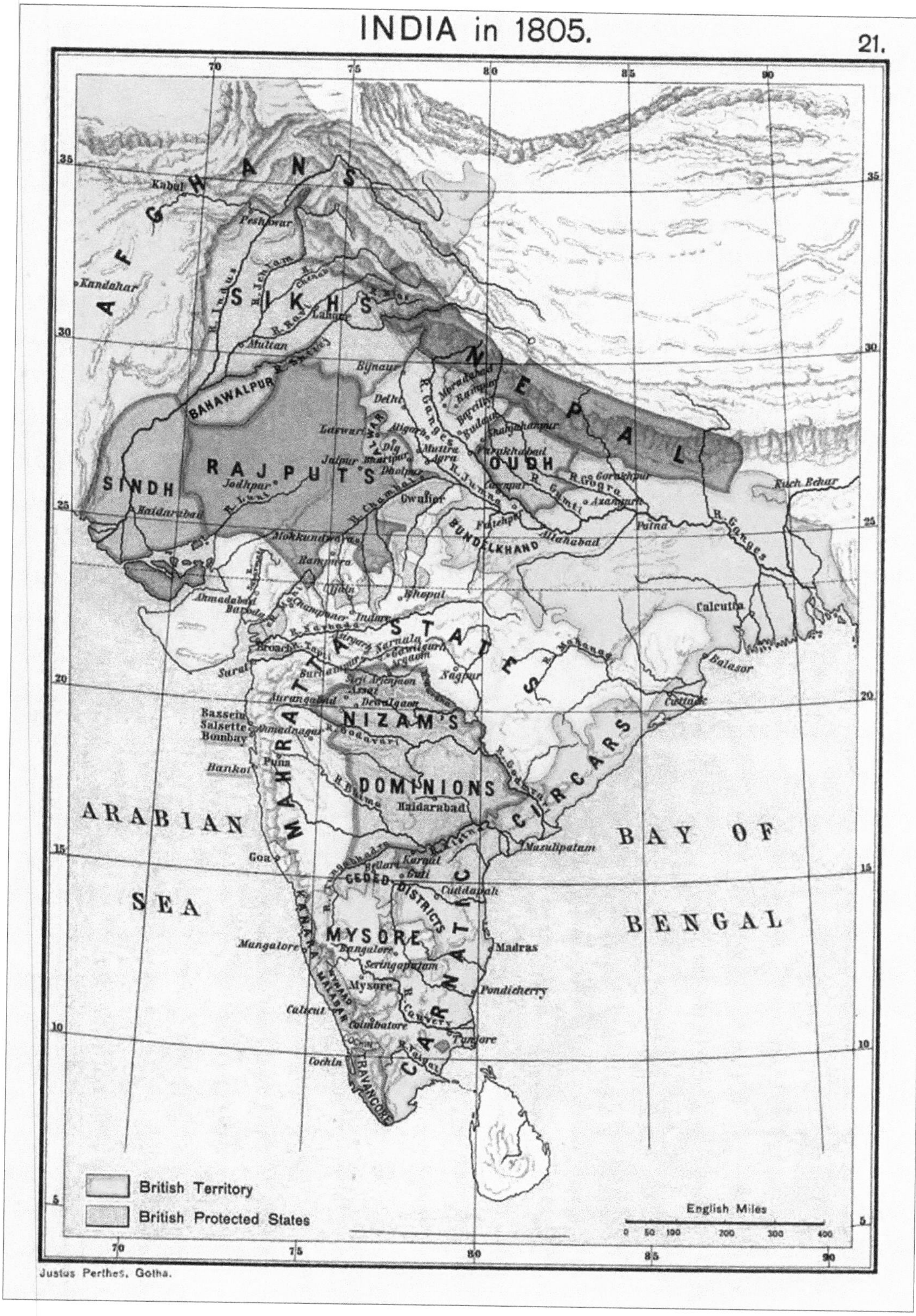

Figure 4.1 Map of India, 1805. Joppen, Charles SJ. 1907. *A Historical Atlas of India for the use of High-Schools, Colleges, and Private Students*, London: Longman Green and Co.

extended across the subcontinent as the Shīʿa coequal to the Sunni Empire of the Mughals centred in Delhi.[13] Lucknow itself, which had become Awadh's new capital in 1775, was to grow under the Nawabs to be even greater than Delhi in size and splendour.[14] Lucknow became India's fourth most populous city by the early 19th century, exceeded only by the key colonial port-cities of Calcutta, Madras, and Bombay.[15]

Flushed with seemingly boundless wealth, and therefore largely disinterested in territorial expansion or dispute, Lucknow's founder, Nawab Āṣaf-ud-Daulah (r. 1775-97), and his successors had turned their resources to other purposes, becoming energetic patrons of the arts, not least architecture, along with science and new technologies.[16] As we have explored elsewhere, these interests were fed and developed through the opulent and well-connected Nawabi court culture.[17] Open and receptive to ideas from afar, the Nawabs frequently hosted merchants, artists, scholars, poets, translators, clerics, dignitaries, artists, and scientists from Bengal and Mughal Shahjahanabad through to the Shīʿa shrine cities in southern Iraq and beyond, to western Europe.

But Awadh's rapid rise to wealth and worldliness also reflected a complex and often contradictory political relationship with imperial Britain due to the steady advance of British commercial and political interests in northern India following the conquest of Bengal by the East India Company in 1765. This increasingly strained and inequitable entente was ultimately to

Figure 4.2 The 'Tara Kothee' (Star House). *Tarewali Kothi* Observatory, Lucknow. Photograph by Felice Beato (English, born Italy, 1832-1909), 1858. Albumen silver print 23 x 30 cm (9 1/16 x 11 13/16 in.). Partial gift from the Wilson Centre for Photography. Digital image courtesy of the Getty's Open Content Program.

come to an abrupt end with the annexation of Awadh and the exile of the Nawab and his court in 1856.[18] Before that fateful juncture, however, and in the broader context of the general divisiveness that characterised the political and cultural patchwork of the Indian subcontinent in the early 19th century, the commissioning of the Lucknow Observatory, with its strikingly 'modern' architecture — a neoclassical temple dedicated to the pursuit of modern science — stands out as a particularly salient example of the precocious culture of intellectual exchange and experimentation that was briefly sustained in the cosmopolitan enclave of pre-colonial Lucknow (Figure 4.2).

This chapter pinpoints the Lucknow Observatory as an apex of both cultural and scientific knowledge exchange in this early modern Islamic state. Architecture as a discipline straddles the fields of science, technology, and art. Moreover, a work of architecture, in addition to fulfilling specified functions, is a material expression of the cultural values and aspirations of its patron. Accordingly, several domains of knowledge intersect in this intriguing building. Drawing on the substantial, yet largely discrete, scholarship which deals with these domains of knowledge — science (and especially astronomy), Nawabi court culture, and architecture (most especially stylistic concerns) — we seek to make an intentional cross-reading to interpret the Lucknow Observatory as a manifestation of best practice in science and architecture, so as to reveal a thicker dialogue about cultural diplomacy exercised through the dedicated pursuit of *ʿilm* as science.

PRACTICAL ASTRONOMY IN INDIA

The pursuit of practical astronomy by Muslim scholars can be traced to the emergence and diffusion of Islam. Early Umayyad and Abbasid Caliphs championed this disciplinary knowledge as a necessary enterprise, as the historian David King observes, in order to accurately determine prayer times (*ʿilm al-mīqāt*), the direction of the Kaʿba (*qibla*), and the sighting of the lunar crescent (*hilāl*) at sunset, which marks the beginning of the first day of every month of the Islamic calendar.[19] Accordingly, Muslim scholars, in keeping with Prophetic and Quranic injunctions to seek knowledge, translated extant scientific works in the Ptolemaic tradition (with the earth occupying a central and static position amid eight spheres). Knowledge of astronomy escalated during the reigns of the Abbasid Caliphs such that 'Sasanian, Indian, and finally Greek astronomy and mathematics were assimilated and led to the writings of great scholars'.[20] In *A History of Islamic Astronomy*, George Saliba identifies the development of astronomy as a 'homogeneously Islamic' discipline after the 9th century with the emergence of 'works devoted to observational astronomy, instruments, timekeeping for religious purposes, and uranography'.[21] This concept of astronomy — which must be distinguished from astrology or the determination of ritual activities — is referred to as *ʿilm al-falak* (science of the spheres) or as *ʿilm al-hayʾa* (science of the [heavenly] configurations).[22]

Patronage of astronomy continued in mediaeval India during the Sultanate and Mughal periods and later in Nawabi Lucknow. Acknowledging the legacy of Fīrūz Shāh Tughlaq (r. 1351-88) — who possessed five astrolabes, and who promoted knowledge of these important instruments, along with rigorous knowledge exchange amongst scholars of diverse ethnic and religious backgrounds, the active circulation of scientific texts, and ongoing cordial relations between Mughal and Safavid rulers — Ansari argues that scholars from Central Asia 'flocked to the courts of medieval Indian sultans and emperors who patronized them liberally'.[23] Moreover, Yukio Ôhashi, a Japanese scholar who has examined astronomy across cultures, both within and beyond the Indian subcontinent, argues that the 'time of Fīrūz Shāh Tughluk was the beginning of the exchange of Islamic astronomy (expressed in Arabic and Persian) and Hindu astronomy (expressed in Sanskrit) in both directions'.[24] Moreover, from the reign of Akbar (1556-1605), the rational sciences were taught in Indian *madrasas* where 'Muslim and Hindus together acquired their higher education without any prejudice'.[25] In this context, practical astronomy flourished. This comprised the foundation of observatories, the compilation of *zīj* (plural *zījāt*) or tables to calculate the position of the sun, moon, and planets, and the use of astrolabes (and an increasingly complex array of instruments including telescopes), which intersected with increasing knowledge of modern European astronomy, not least in Lucknow.[26]

Naṣīruddīn Ḥaidar was a keen proponent of this climate of scholarly exchange, and the observatory was instituted under his official patronage in 1831. The initial capital outlay for the building and the instruments, as well as the significant continuing operational expenses including the employees' salaries, were funded entirely by the Nawab and his successors. This independence from the *madrasas* is noteworthy in the Indian subcontinent. While conflict between modern astronomy and faith was perceived in Turkey, Iran, and elsewhere in the Islamic world, Ansari argues that it did not lead to conflict between Muslim intellectuals and the *'ulamā'*:

> The *'ulamā'* were teaching in Arabic *madrasas*, without any hinderance [sic], obsolete Ptolemaic astronomy and mathematics through Arabic medium, and the modern Muslim intellectuals were promoting their new learning by establishing modern Western colleges or by founding scientific societies.[27]

In the spirit of this nominally 'joint' enterprise, however, the prerogative to appoint the chief astronomer was reserved, officially, for the governor general of British India.[28] Accordingly, this post was initially filled by Major James Dowling Herbert (1791-1833 or 1835), a highly accomplished British officer who had previously served as deputy surveyor general in Calcutta.[29] Upon arrival in Lucknow in December 1831, Herbert put the Nawab's plans in motion and promptly ordered instruments from England. Shortly afterwards, *The Journal of the Asiatic Society of Bengal* reported: 'From the magnificence conspicuous in all oriental undertakings, we may safely prognosticate, that the Lucknow observatory will become a richly endowed establishment, if the life of the founder be spared to complete it'.[30]

After his premature death, Herbert was succeeded by Lieutenant Colonel Richard Wilcox (1802-48), another highly credentialled officer in the scientific branches of the East India Company's military establishment who was then serving as an assistant in the Great Trigonometrical Survey of India (GTS). Herbert himself held Wilcox in high esteem but it was evidently the praise of the presiding surveyor general, George Everest (d. 1866), and the attraction of a high salary (1000 rupees per month, compared to his prior salary of 618 rupees per month), paid by the Nawab, that secured Wilcox's appointment in 1835.[31] Over the next six years Wilcox completed the observatory that would later be described as the '[b]est equipped in India ... on par with Greenwich and Cambridge'.[32] World-class equipment from Troughton and Simms was set out to emulate the current benchmark facility at Madras, with which Wilcox would have been familiar through his work on the GTS, with the aim of producing and recording observations comparable but superior to the Madras Catalogue.[33] Wilcox confidently stated: 'I believe that our transit observations — in which I take no part myself (being left to the "Hindoo lads") — will compete with those of any observatory'.[34] Specifically, two of Wilcox's assistants were Kalee Charan and Ganga Pershad, who were led by a Greek called Kallanus.[35]

Some earlier commentators have interpreted such boasts as evidence that whilst the observatory belonged to the King, 'scientific control was in the hands of the British'.[36] Architectural historian Banmali Tandan also links the foundation of the observatory to British interests and the goal to further William Lambton's ambitious scientific survey of India under the auspices of the East India Company.[37] To complicate matters, Llewellyn-Jones attributes the pursuit of modern science in Awadh, not to Naṣīruddīn Ḥaidar, but to his chief minister, Ḥakim Mehndi, who, quietly but insistently, encouraged certain initiatives (the observatory, a hospital, a canal, the erection of the Iron Bridge) for his personal gain as he sided with the company.[38]

In this sense, then, the observatory might be dismissed as a foreign enterprise. While such a case might be made for the aforementioned observatory in Madras — where astronomy was primarily exploited not to expand knowledge of the cosmos but to calibrate cartographic knowledge and command of terrestrial territory, ultimately underpinning the GTS of the South Indian peninsula (supplanting astronomy in the service of British commerce and concomitant maritime knowledge) — Naṣīruddīn Ḥaidar actively sought the opportunity to advance scientific knowledge in Lucknow.[39] In addition to the pursuit of empirical science, the observatory was intended as a didactic institution, 'more particularly as a school for young courtiers in which some knowledge of astronomy and general physics might be taught'.[40] Ansari provides a detailed account of Ḥaidar's goals:

> To establish an observatory upon a liberal scale worthy of the wealth and importance of the government as well for the advancement of the noble sincerely new discoveries as for the defusion [sic] of its principles amongst the inhabitants of India, for the establishment is intended to embrace translation into the native language and to instruct the inhabitants here. It is contemplated to deliver lectures upon astronomy to the students of the College and select talented youth for instructions in every branch of the science.[41]

One individual who more than benefited from this knowledge was Maulvi Mohammed Ismā'īl Khān, who had made 'considerable progress in the sciences of mathematics and astronomy' under Herbert.[42] The Maulvi was sent to England by Ḥaidar with a dual mission, to escort diplomatic gifts to William IV and to find a suitable principal for a new college the Nawab intended to establish. Based on the Maulvi's demonstrated knowledge of astronomy during his regular visits to the Royal Observatory, he was presented with a certificate of proficiency by George Biddell Airy, the Astronomer Royal, and he returned to India with an orrery, a portable mechanical model of the solar system.[43] The advantages of such a larger, less narrowly strategic and immediate, application of scientific knowledge was also recognised by the Nawab's British overseers, who argued that the institution would serve to advance new discoveries and circulate knowledge in the kingdom through the provision of lectures and the preparation of translations of important texts into Urdu.[44]

In addition to funding the facilities and operation of the observatory, the Nawabs also sponsored their own research programs, akin to the program and publications that were prepared a century earlier in the court of another Nawab of the Mughal Empire, Sawā'i Jai Singh (1688-1743) of Jaipur. Sawā'i Jai Singh was an erudite scholar of Sanskrit literature and astronomy who sought to improve ancient and mediaeval Indian astronomy through an array of monumental observatories that he had built across northern India, the most spectacular of which were in Delhi (1724) and Jaipur (1734), but which also included several smaller assemblies at Mathura, Ujjain, and Varanasi as well. Some previous commentators, notably Kochhar, have dismissed these as a mere royal pastime, more impressive for their sculptural beauty than for their capacity to generate accurate and useful scientific observations.[45] However, more recent scholarship identifies a veritable renaissance in observational astronomy benefiting from the open patronage of scholars irrespective of their cultural, ethnic, or religious leanings. Regardless of the questionable utility of the monumental observatories, Sawā'i Jai Singh also established a school of translators at Jaipur with the purpose of transferring the knowledge embedded in Islamic astronomical treatises into Sanskrit, and, later, European scientific texts as well.[46] Key among these were Philippe de La Hire's astronomical tables and Johann Baptist Homann's *Grosser Atlas über die Ganze Welt*.[47]

In this context, the Mughal emperor, Muhammad Shāh (r. 1719-48), directed Jai Singh to get a modern (*jadīd*) Zīj compiled (*Zīj-i Jadīd Muhammad Shāhī*) which is largely based on the earlier tables of Ulegh Beg (Samarqand). However, the manuscript also provides clues about de La Hire's theory of heliocentrism, about which Jai Singh sought further clarification from French Jesuits who arrived in Jaipur from Bengal, in 1734, at Jai Singh's request, to whom he posed several queries in relation to de la Hire's tables. In his examination of Philippe de La Hire's influence on the court of Jayashimha, David Pingree identifies a diagram of de La Hire's heliocentric model of a superior planet and the illustration of de La Hire's third lunar equation that is annotated in Sanskrit as follows: '[I]n this figure it is assumed that the earth moves, and the sun is assumed to be fixed'.[48]

Through the translation of scientific texts and their transmission in northern India in the 19th century, knowledge of the heliocentric theory of the solar system was propagated as a further focus of Nawabi patronage coinciding with the construction of the Lucknow Observatory. In a study of Hindu culture's scientific contributions to Indo-Persian culture, Ansari brings to light a substantial and revealing text. Entitled *Hadā'iq al-Nujūm* (Gardens of Astronomy), this accurate treatise on modern European astronomy comprises 1158 pages, with several editions printed lithographically in 1837, 1841 (in Lucknow), and 1843, respectively.[49] Prepared at the behest of Muhammad 'Alī Shāh alias Naṣīr-ud-Daulah (r. 1837-42), the *Hadā'iq al-Nujūm* was compiled and written by Raja Ratan Singh (1782-1851) — also known by his *nom de plume*, 'Zakhmī' — a notable scholar, historian, and linguist conversant in Arabic, Persian, Turkish, and Sanskrit as well as English, who had served the Nawabi court since the reign of Ghāzīuddīn Ḥaidar (r. 1814-27).[50]

Ratan Singh's 'excellent and systematic treatise', in Ansari's view, addressed the work of many of the key astronomers associated with the era of European scientific revolution, including Copernicus, Tycho Brahe, Kepler, Galileo, and Newton, as well as the more recent work of the author's European contemporaries such as Hevelius, Flamsteed, John Herschel, and Cassini, of which he was well aware.[51] Telescopes (*durbin, sitrahbin*), and even micrometers (*raizah-i paima*) with cross-wires, are among the instruments mentioned, along with details about the establishment of the Greenwich (1676) and Paris (1664) Observatories.[52] Ansari remarks on the fact that 'Ratan Singh clearly states that "the orbits of all planets and of their satellites, together with those of the comets [he observed Halley's Comet on 15 October 1835], are elliptical', *baidi* in Persian (p. 135), and he gives a *heliocentric* diagram of the solar system (p.179) [Diagram 85 in the treatise]"'.[53] Moreover, he identifies the modern order of the planets and their satellites, and his knowledge of the planetary system is current. Notably, in one of his sections, which he entitles 'Proof that the Sun is stationary', he discusses the transits of Venus in particular, as transit observations were made at the Lucknow Observatory.[54] Moreover, such proofs of a heliocentric system correspond to Ratan Singh's acknowledgement of observations of Venus on the face of the sun by Muslim scholars including Ibn Sīnā, Abū 'Imrān, and Muhammad abī Bakr and to comparable observations of *Venus* and *Mercury* by Ibn al-Māja and Ibn al-Haytham.[55]

This comparative but collaborative pursuit of science — as Ansari and Sen, among others, maintain — which was conducted in parallel and in consort with the British-directed operations of the observatory, should be considered alongside a 'sketch of the solar system for use in schools' produced by the Lucknow Observatory, most likely under the supervision of Herbert, and printed at Lucknow's lithographic press in 1835. An English commentary pasted over the original text echoed the quasi-biblical rhetoric of contemporary champions of science and technological development elsewhere in the nascent British Indian colonial technocracy, who argued that astronomical knowledge was a sure path to 'pure and reasonable knowledge'.[56]

> Astronomy give[s knowledge] of the works of the Great Invisible Being who created and now sustaineth all things ...The Heavens declare the Glory of God! And the Firmament sheweth the works of His hand! He hangeth the earth upon nothing! By His spirit He hath garnished the Heavens; Lo these are parts of His ways but how small a portion is heard of Him! The fear of God is the beginning of Wisdom ... [57]

As the historian CA Bayly interpreted this intriguing document, '[T]his exhortation to faith does not actually specify any particular religion. As might be expected from a joint Islamic and Christian venture, the Creator to be contemplated might as easily have been Allah as Jehovah'.[58]

This is a particularly revealing illustration, not only of the instrumental paedagogical objectives of the observatory in the practical realm of knowledge dissemination through education, but of a higher symbolic function as well. Both parties in the collaboration evidently imagined that the institution could also perform as the medium for a diplomatic exchange in the realm of comparative scientific and religious epistemologies. In the context of Awadh's complex political and economic relationships with the expanding British Indian Empire, the 'Science' of astronomical observation, in which both the Indian and the greater Islamic civilisations that elided in Lucknow had such a long and independent cultural investment, was also clearly a form of cultural capital. Temporarily, at least, astronomy was one seemingly 'safe' medium in which a mutual investment could be made in the procurement and production of higher knowledge, purely for its own sake. From the British perspective it was also a mode of cultural diplomacy in which a delicate balance of deference and respect for the 'Kingdom' of Awadh and its 'universal' religious and cultural aegis among the Shīʿa sect in India could be counterpoised to the waning religious and civil authority of the (Sunni) Mughal Empire centred in Delhi.

During this same period, historian John Pemble argues that Lucknow had an established 'reputation as a seat of Muslim scholarship' which could be traced back to the end of the 17th century, when the *farhangi mahal* (or 'Scientific Academy', literally a Palace for 'foreign' knowledge) was founded.[59] Scholars were held in high esteem and the academy was known for advances in Arabic, philosophy, mathematics (including astronomy), rhetoric, jurisprudence, the exegesis of the Koran, Islamic tradition, Islamic mysticism, and medicine.[60] In this context, the establishment of the Lucknow Observatory in the first half of the 19th century had a firm foundation of prior investment in knowledge and its institutional infrastructure, continuing and extending the astronomical renaissance in India which, according to Ansari, had already occurred the century before — a renaissance that was 'smothered' as a result of the process of European colonisation.[61]

It seems hasty, therefore, to dismiss Naṣīruddīn Ḥaidar's interest in the observatory as just a royal pastime or the mere emulation of European institutions. Considering the broader cultural aspirations and experiments of Naṣīruddīn Ḥaidar, and his evident intention to seek knowledge and

18—Tara Khothe or Star house.

Figure 4.3 Side elevation of former *Tara Kothe* or Star House, Lucknow. c. 1870. Photograph by Darogha Abbas Ali. Published in The Lucknow Album. Plate 18. Reproduced from https://archive.org/details/gri_000033125008608313. Digital image courtesy of the Getty Research Institute. Note the damaged weather-vane and other evidence of relative disrepair following the decommissioning of the observatory over two decades earlier, and the subsequent siege of Lucknow during the Rebellion of 1857-58.

disseminate it through an institution devoted to astronomy, along with the subsequent patronage of Muhammad ʿAlī Shāh, the Lucknow Observatory cannot simply be regarded as a tool that furthered British scientific interests in India unilaterally.

While Ḥaidar was undoubtedly attracted personally to European fashions and tastes, evident in images of the Nawab depicted in European dress, or the coin struck in his name which featured a coat of arms in the European style, this Nawab was also regarded as an 'open-minded' patron who sought to benefit his diverse subjects with progressive institutions and amenities.[62] He was connected with the foundation of a modern hospital in addition to the modern observatory, which he ensured was equipped with state-of-the art instruments. The procurement of such scientific equipment was a testament to the network of trade and communication that linked pre-colonial Lucknow to Europe. A few years after the establishment of the observatory, a modern prefabricated Iron Bridge, which had been ordered and delivered in kit form from England, was erected across the Gomti River nearby (Figure 4.4).[63] Such technologically advanced infrastructure was an additional form of symbolic capital in which the substantial sums invested had not necessarily been expected to reap immediate practical returns.

Figure 4.4 The Iron Bridge. c. 1870. Photograph by Darogha Abbas Ali. Published in The Lucknow Album. Plate 36. Reproduced from https://archive.org/details/gri_000033125008608313. Digital image courtesy of the Getty Research Institute. The bridge was built in 1848-50 and founded by Wajīd 'Alī Shāh.

THE ARCHITECTURE OF THE OBSERVATORY: A TEMPLE TO NEW SCIENCE

A closer look at the architecture of the observatory building and its immediate context provides further insight into the complexity of Nawabi cultural politics and aspirations in this epoch. Flamboyant, hybrid, and 'debased' are the words by which the architecture of Nawabi Lucknow has typically been characterised.[64] Tandan maintains that 'apart from an overpowering bias against it, [there] has remained a readiness to treat it, in its initial phase, as an evolution from the Mughal style in its period of decline, and, in its later stage, as a disagreeable Indo-European mixture, which took birth chiefly under the influence of La Martinière', a flamboyantly mannered private palace built in the 1790s to the designs of a resident French mercenary, colonial agent, and amateur architect, General Claude Martin (Figure 4.5).[65]

The vast and luxurious palace known as the Kaiser Bagh (Figure 4.6), built during the reign of Wajīd 'Ali Shāh, typifies the eclecticism of the late Nawabi architectural style. While there are elements of classical architecture in the symmetrical composition of the façade and the use of classical columns mounted on pedestals and topped with a triangular pediment, the flourishes

Figure 4.5 La Martiniere, Lucknow, India. Albumen print. Photographer unidentified. From a series of photographs of India commissioned by Francis Frith and Co. between 1865 and 1875. Courtesy of Special Collections, Fine Arts Library, Harvard University.

reveal a taste that can be compared with the decorative invention and indulgence of the later Rococo style in Europe of the 17th and 18th centuries, influenced as that was by its contact with the adjacent Ottoman Empire. At the same time, the scale and orthogonal organisation of the site recalls the vast maidans of Safavid Iran.

Other contemporary structures within the Kaisar Bagh reveal a simultaneous and continuing connection with the building crafts and elements of Mughal architecture (which can also be observed in the earlier commissions of Āṣaf-ud-Daulah). This is evident in the case of the delicate white marble Summer House built after the closure of the observatory, in 1848-50. Considered as a whole, however, this eclectic palace complex cannot be categorised as either Classical or Mughal. It demonstrates the distinctive, openly hybrid Nawabi style that had evolved with the experiments of successive rulers.

For James Fergusson, one of the earliest and most influential European historians to study Indian architecture, '[t]he unintelligent vulgarity with which the "Orders" are there used, by a people who were capable of such noble things in their own styles, is one of the most startling phenomena in the history of architecture'.[66] Similarly, Tandan identifies Führer's criticism of copies from 'debased European models', and 'the mongrel vulgarities', particularly of the later Nawabi period.[67] Moreover, he declares, 'Nowhere can we more markedly see the influence of a depraved

Figure 4.6 Kaiser Pasand Palace [or Kaiser Pasand Kothi at Kaiser Bagh — King's Palace], Lucknow. 1874. Photograph Darogha Abbas Ali. Published in The Lucknow Album. Plate 27. Reproduced from https://archive.org/details/gri_000033125008608313. Digital image courtesy of the Getty Research Institute.

Oriental court and its politics upon art and architecture than in Lakhnau'.[68] Tandan identifies similarly contemptuous assessments in later accounts well into the 20th century, attributing these to a number of factors: 'a genuine disgust for its loose and careless handling of classical detail, or simply from an inherent contempt of the Nawabi, or even a jaundiced view of Indian art'.[69]

By contrast, in the case of the observatory — a mid-Nawabi-era architectural work of a markedly different character not accounted for in Tandan's critical spectrum of excess and hybridity — we behold a strikingly chaste and sober neoclassical composition that clearly and confidently emulates the contemporary Greek-revival style that was fashionable in Georgian Britain and continental Europe and, increasingly, in the colonies. With its unadulterated volumetric purism and the ostensible universalism of its early Doric order, this had become the favoured style for the design of modern institutions of learning since the scientific and political revolutions of the previous century. The parallels between the Lucknow Observatory and an observatory built at Cambridge (Figure 4.7) less than a decade earlier (1823) are unmistakable. Tandan also identifies a 'faint likeness' with the South African Observatory in Cape Town (constructed based on drawings sent from London in 1821).[70] All three observatories are built in the Greek-revival style and they were all, ultimately, subject to the management of England's Astronomer Royal. In Tandan's more recent study, he states that Herbert sent the plans for an observatory to the Prime Minister of Oudh in April 1832;

Figure 4.7 'The Observatory'. Coloured print of Cambridge Observatory. Possibly by J and HS Storer of Cambridge, c. 1829. Courtesy of the University of Cambridge, Institute of Astronomy.

Raja Bakhtawar Singh is identified as the building supervisor.[71] Given the similarities between all three structures, it is plausible that they were all based on similar plans sent from England.

In addition to the obvious similarities in the façade, most notably the ceremonial tetrastyle portico (compare Figures 4.2 and 4.7), the Lucknow Observatory included a circular masonry podium on the axis of this main portico which is compared to the extant podium in Cambridge. This critical feature of the observatory, located under a moveable cupola, was designed to isolate the platform from vibrations elsewhere in the building to achieve the most accurate readings possible, thus constituting 'the most advanced form of building technology then available in England for the erection of its "balancing column"'.[72] Certainly, there is evidence for such outright emulation of European architectural precedents in the design of other Lucknowi buildings, such as the *Dilkusha Kothi*, together with homes commissioned by Europeans in Lucknow and a later Greek-revival church.[73] But, arguably, the Lucknow Observatory was among the finest of all of Lucknow's modern buildings, far exceeding the amateurish architectural standards of most European forays in classicism elsewhere in colonial India, and even improving on the original rather pedestrian model at Cambridge.

But, yet again, all is not as it seems. The observatory building is another, more stealthy, kind of hybrid, a modern hybrid. The staid exterior with its Doric order and simple details is a façade that masks surprising cross-cultural innovations within. These included, in particular, an innovative functional plan, careful siting, retractable screens between the basement and the ground floor which could control the entry of light into the interior, and the elevation of the structure to achieve a dry basement suitable to house and preserve the highly sensitive and expensive astronomical instruments.[74] While the structure was ostensibly European with its neoclassical purism, the design had been adapted and improved by incorporating local building principles and techniques. These, in turn, had enabled the innovation of further operational devices optimising the lighting and climate-control of the building. The allied function of the observatory and Lucknow's modern lithographic printing press in propagating and disseminating scientific knowledge was evidently of equal if not even greater importance in the texture of this brief history. Considered as conjoined institutions, the observatory press, as it were, served to translate into local languages the great astronomical texts that had been preserved through the Indo-Persian transmission of knowledge and the circulation of European knowledge of the stars.

In a more refined and monumental manner than was the general case, the intrinsically hybrid nature of the observatory building reflected the empirical experimentation and innovation in the evolving colonial-modern typology of domestic and minor institutional architecture that was emerging across India in the first half of the 19th century, in this still open-ended moment of cultural contact and intercourse with the encroaching European world. The typical Anglo-Indian bungalow, for instance, was a radically peculiar fusion of the cultural and the scientific ideals of both worlds, mitigated by local practice and contingencies. The aspirations, failures, and achievements of fabulous Nawabi Lucknow in high architecture, as in the high science of astronomy, only made larger, more visible, and perhaps more critically acute the fundamental dilemmas and contradictions that were inherent in colonial modernity, for colonisers and colonised alike.[75]

CONCLUDING REMARKS: THE ENTERPRISE OF KNOWING

When Wajīd ʿAlī Shāh, the Nawab who was fated to be Awadh's last reigning monarch, first came to power in 1847, he had continued to lavish money on the function and fabric of the observatory.[76] But his later disenchantment with this noble enterprise of knowing was symptomatic, it would appear, of larger changes that were now in motion. After the seemingly trivial but demeaning diplomatic debacle that, indirectly, had precipitated the decision to decommission the observatory, the King wrote to the British Resident at Lucknow explaining, in defence of his decision, that 'the great outlay incurred in maintaining the observatory has produced no advantage whatever either to the state or to the people and learned of Oudh [sic]'.[77] Moreover, the observatory had ceased to attract young courtiers, and greater numbers of students were now being taught at the Shīʿa college, a more traditional form of *madrasa* based in Lucknow's Great Imambara. In a possible tit-for-tat response to the King's ostensible withdrawal from science, the latter was also to be closed down by decree of the British authorities, shortly after the annexation of Awadh, to avoid supporting 'an educational establishment which teaches and fosters an exclusive creed, and religious tenets to which the Government cannot subscribe'.[78]

Such bitter reassessments on both sides of Lucknow's astronomical joint venture reflected an equally cynical awakening to inexorable changes in the broader socio-political landscape by the late 1840s, in which Awadh's future now hung in the balance. This included a perceivable shift in the agency of science, no longer a continuum which could be traced to the legacy of Arab-Islamic science and the Indo-Persian transmission of knowledge. Science, now an applied tool of state craft and empire building, was ever more firmly in the control of the nascent British Indian Empire, which now enveloped the landlocked kingdom in its strategic push towards the vulnerable northwest frontier. This perceived loss of agency in the pursuit of pure science foreshadowed the moment when Awadh would be swallowed whole, and Lucknow, one of India's largest and most splendid cities at the dawn of its modern age, would be decimated in the ensuing military struggle and further technocratic retributions that were to follow. While the observatory building survived to serve other purposes, the scientific equipment was plundered, and the precious records of the knowledge that the observatory had produced were either lost or destroyed.

The authors wish to acknowledge Dr Elise Kamleh for bringing the case of the Lucknow Observatory to our attention and for her assistance in sourcing additional material toward the preliminary draft of this chapter.

NOTES

1 The successive reigns of the Nawabs of Awadh were: Saadat Khān (1722-39), Safdar Jung (1739-54), Shujā-ud-Daula (1754-75), Āṣaf-ud-Daula (1775-97), Wazīr 'Alī (1797-98), Saadat 'Alī Khān (1798-1814), Ghāzi-uddīn Ḥaidar (1814-27), Naṣīr-ud-dīn Ḥaidar (1827-37), Muhammad 'Alī Shāh (1837-42), Amjad 'Alī Shāh (1842-47), and Wajīd 'Alī Shāh (1847-56). Rosie Llewellyn-Jones, ed., 2006, *Lucknow, City of Illusion* (Munich: Prestel), 259-61.

2 Alternative spellings include *Tarunvali Kothi*, and *Taronwali Kothi*, both of which translate as 'Star House'.

3 SM Razaullah Ansari, 2016b, 'Raja Ratan Singh', in Helaine Selin, ed., *Encyclopaedia of the History of Science, Technology, and Medicine in Non-Western Cultures* (Dordrecht: Springer), 3693.

4 Namely the Sultanate Period (1191-1526; Mamluk, Khilji, Tughlaq, Sayyid, Lodi) and the later Mughal Period (1526-1857).

5 Rosie Llewellyn-Jones, 1985, *A Fatal Friendship: The Nawabs, The British, and the City of Lucknow* (Delhi: Oxford University Press), 72-3, fn 33; Rosie Llewellyn-Jones, 2014, *The Last King in India: Wajid Ali Shah* (London: Hurst), 103. The incident is also recorded by SM Razaullah Ansari, 1978, 'The Establishment of Observatories and the Socio-Economic Conditions of Scientific Work in Nineteenth Century India', *Indian Journal of History of Science* 13(1): 66, fn 19; and SM Razaullah Ansari, 1985, 'The Observatories Movement in India during the 17th to 18th Centuries', *Vistas in Astronomy* 28. See also Saiyed Anwer Abbas, 2010, *Incredible Lucknow: A Selection of 51 Published Articles on Lucknow's Monuments, History and Culture* (Lucknow: Saiyed Anwer Abbas), 83.

6 Llewellyn-Jones, 1985, 72-3.

7 Llewellyn-Jones, 2014, 213.

8 KC Kanda, 2005, *Masterpieces of Patriotic Urdu Poetry: Text, Translation, and Transliteration* (New Delhi: Sterling), 61. A thorough and objective biography of Wajīd 'Alī Shāh was written by Llewellyn-Jones, 2014. Madhu Trivedi also asserts the accomplishments that Kanda lists: Madhu Trivedi, 2010, *The Making of Awadh Culture* (Chennai: Primus Books), 16.

9 Insight into Naṣīruddīn Ḥaidar's emulation of English customs and dress, his use of the English language, his collection of European artefacts and his patronage and hospitality shown to Europeans, and especially Englishmen, is provided by William Knighton, whose book is based on earlier accounts by visitors to Awadh, including Mrs Meer Hassan Ali's *Obervations on the Mussulmans of India*. William Knighton, 1921, *The Private Life of an Eastern King* (London: Humphrey Milford Oxford University Press), x.

10 Joydeep Sen, 2016, *Astronomy in India, 1784-1876* (Abingdon: Routledge), 75.

11 See Ravi Bhatt, 2006, *The Life and Times of the Nawabs of Lucknow* (New Delhi: Rupa and Co), 11. Saadat Khan (r. 1722-39) was appointed as the first Nawab of Awadh by the Mughal Sultan Muhammad Shah (r. 1719-48), and Awadh flourished due to this Nawab's fiscal and military acumen. Saadat Khan founded the new city of Faizabad, near the ancient Hindu capital of Ayodhya — from which the name Awadh

derives — before Asaf-ud-Daula (1775-97) relocated the capital to Lucknow in 1775. For a full discussion of the origins of the Nawabs see Juan Cole, 1989, *Roots of North Indian Shi'ism in Iran and Iraq: Religion and State in Awadh, 1722-1859* (Berkeley: University of California Press).

12 Saiyid Zaheer Husain Jafri presents an original and erudite study of this wealth particularly in relation to the agrarian economy based on a fascinating range of archival sources in Jafri, 2016. See Surya Narain Singh, 2003, *The Kingdom of Awadh: Its History, Polity and Administration* (New Delhi: Mittal), 53-72.

13 Justin Jones, 2012, *Shi'a Islam in Colonial India: Religion, Community and Sectarianism* (Cambridge, UK: Cambridge University Press), 2. Jones's book focuses on the 'Ithna-'Ashari branch of Shi'ism (also known as Twelvers or Imamis, for their belief in the Twelve Imams as successors to the Prophet)': Jones, 2012, 6.

14 This splendour was captured in an exhibition showcasing the arts of Lucknow held at the Los Angeles County Museum of Art. Stephen Markel and Tushara Bindu Gude, eds., 2010, *India's Fabled City: The Art of Courtly Lucknow* (Los Angeles: Los Angeles County Museum of Art). This distinction between Lucknow and Delhi is examined by Michael Fisher, 1987, *A Clash of Cultures: Awadh, the British and the Mughals* (Riverdale, Md: Riverdale Company).

15 VT Oldenburg, 1989, *The Making of Colonial Lucknow, 1856-1877* (Delhi: Oxford University Press), 19.

16 Maya Jasanoff, 2005, *Edge of Empire: Lives, Culture and Conquest in the East, 1750-1850* (New York: Knopf) 52-114.

17 Katharine Bartsch and Elise Kamleh, 2014, 'Karbala in Lucknow: An Itinerary of Architectural Mobility', *International Journal of Islamic Architecture* 3(2): 267-302.

18 This was vigorously challenged just a year later by the Sepoy Rebellion of 1857-58, which came to a climax in Lucknow with the 90-day siege of the British Residency.

19 David King, 1993, cited in SM Razaullah Ansari, 2016a, 'Astronomy in Medieval India', in Helaine Selin, ed., 2000, *Encyclopaedia of the History of Science, Technology, and Medicine in Non-Western Cultures* (Dordrecht: Springer), 717. King is a historian of note who has examined mediaeval astronomy in the Islamic context. For his most recent scholarship, see King, 2012a.

20 Ansari, 2016a, 717.

21 George Saliba, 1995, *A History of Islamic Astronomy: Planetary Theories During the Golden Age of Islam* (New York: NYU Press), 73.

22 Saliba, 1995, 66. An overview of *'Ilm al-Hay'a* is presented in David Pingree, 2012, *"Ilm al-Hay'a'*, in P Bearman et al., eds., *Encyclopaedia of Islam, Second Edition*, <http://dx.doi.org/10.1163/1573-3912_islam_COM_0365>, accessed 31 March 2017.

23 Ansari, 2016a, 717. For a discussion of the first ever treatise by Mahendra Surī titled *Yantarāja* (the King of Instruments), which was written about 1370 and of which there are more than 100 extant manuscript copies, see Yukio Ôhashi, 1997, 'Early History of the Astrolabe in India', *Indian Journal of History of Science* 32(3): 211. Such texts included the writings of Abu'l Rayhan al-Biruni (d. 1048), Nasirudin Tusi (d. 1274) of Maragha, Sultan Ulugh Beg (d. 1449) of Samarqand, and Baharddin al-Amili (d. 1622).

24 Yukio Ôhashi, 2008, 'Introduction of Persian Astronomy into India', *Tarikh-e 'Elm: Iranian Journal for the History of Science* 6: 62. For a broader investigation of astronomy in the region see Selin, ed., 2000.

25 Ansari, 2016b, 3690.

26 Ansari (2016a, 724) provides a survey of Zijes compiled in India.

27 SM Razaullah Ansari, 2014, 'Transmission of the Modern Exact Science to the Muslim World', in Ibrahim Kalin, ed., *The Oxford Encyclopedia of Philosophy, Science, and Technology in Islam*, vol. 1 (Oxford: Oxford University Press), 383.

28 According to a recent reappraisal of this joint-venture, the East India Company had reservations about the utility of an observatory in Lucknow: Sen, 2016 (see Chapter 3 'Constructing Knowledge, c. 1830-c. 1860', 75-110).

29 Matthew Edney, 1997, *Mapping an Empire: The Geographical Construction of British India, 1765-1843* (Chicago: University of Chicago Press), records that Herbert lived until 1835, holding the post of Astronomer from 1831 to 1835.

30 James Princep, ed., 1833, 'VIII. Progress of European Science. Practical Astronomy', *The Journal of the Asiatic Society of Bengal* 2: 49.

31 RK Kochhar, 1991, 'The Growth of Modern Astronomy in India, 1651-1960', *Vistas in Astronomy* 34: 91.
32 Kochhar, 1991, 91.
33 Kochhar, 1991. See also SM Razaullah Ansari, 1978, 'The Establishment of Observatories and the Socio-Economic Conditions of Scientific Work in Nineteenth Century India', *Indian Journal of History of Science* 13(1): 65.
34 Kochhar, 1991, 91.
35 SM Razaullah Ansari, 2011, 'Early Modern Observatories in India, 1792-1900', in Debi Prasad Chattopadhyaya, ed., *History of Science, Philosophy and Culture in Indian Civilization* (New Delhi: Pearson Education), 361. Referring to original correspondence by Wilcox and Sleeman, Sen identifies Wilcox's high regard for the education and talent of these two assistants in particular; see Sen, 2016, 79.
36 Kochhar, 1991, 91.
37 Banmali Tandan, 2001, *The Architecture of Lucknow and its Dependencies, 1722-1856: A Descriptive Inventory and an Analysis of Nawabi Types* (New Delhi: Vikas), 110.
38 Llewellyn-Jones, 1985, 68.
39 For the role of observatories in the GTS, see Edney, 1997. See also Ansari, 1978, 65.
40 Abbas, 2010, 83. See also DB Diskalker, 1937, 'Foundation of an Observatory at Lucknow', *Journal of the United Provinces Historical Society* 10(1): 10-11.
41 Ḥaidar's goals were communicated to the current Governor-General of India, Lord William Bentinck, via the Resident of Lucknow: quoted in Ansari, 2011, 360.
42 This role is documented in a letter from the EIC Resident at Lucknow, Colonel Low, to William Macnaghten, the EIC Political Secretary at Calcutta, on 15 December 1833, concerning the dispatch of gifts to the King of England as well as the appointment of Captain James Herbert's successor at the observatory, cited in Malcolm Brown, 2001, 'A "Complimentary Mission" from Nawab Nasir-Ud-Din Ḥaidar to King William IV', *Asian Affairs* 32(3): 280.
43 This recognition is documented in the diary of Hobhouse, President of the EIC Board of Control, cited in Brown, 2001, 284.
44 Ansari, 1978, 65.
45 Kochhar, 1991, 71.
46 SR Sarma, 1998, cited in Ansari, 2016a, 723.
47 Johann Baptist Homann's *Grosser Atlas über die Ganze Welt* (1725), published in Nürenberg, is discussed in detail in David Pingree, 2002, 'Philippe de La Hire at the Court of Jayashimha', in SM Razaullah Ansari, ed., *History of Oriental Astronomy* (Netherlands: Springer), 123.
48 Pingree's translation from Sanskrit in Pingree, 2002, 130.
49 SM Razaullah Ansari, 2005, 'Hindu's Scientific Contributions in Indo Persian', *Indian Journal of History of Science* 40(2): 205-21. Ansari, 2016b, 3692.
50 Raja Ratan Singh also authored an earlier study, *Ma'yar al-Zamun*, a treatise on calendar and chronology. Also printed at Lucknow, in 1819, its two chapters discuss times, month, year, and eras, including Christian, Hindu, Greek, and Egyptian. See Ansari, 2005, 212-13.
51 Ansari, 2005, 213.
52 Ansari, 2005, 213.
53 Ansari, 2005, 214. Ansari provides italics for *baidi* and *heliocentric* and identifies the specific page numbers in the original treatise. Halley's comet, identified by the authors in square brackets, is mentioned in a later section of the treatise, pp. 805-10.
54 Ansari, 2005, 214; Kochhar, 1991, 91.
55 Ansari, 2016b, 3692.
56 The document itself is discussed by CA Bayly, 1994, 'Colonial Star Wars: The politics of the Heavens in India c. 1780-1880', unpublished manuscript, May 1994, cited in Edney, 1997, 316-17. Edney attributes the quoted words to the Bombay Chief Engineer.
57 Quoted in Edney, 1997, 316.
58 The text quoted here is Edney's paraphrasing of Bayly's reading: Edney, 1997, 316.

59 John Pemble, 1977, *The Raj, the Indian Mutiny and the Kingdom of Oudh, 1801-1859* (Hassocks: The Harvester Press), 16.

60 Pemble, 1977, 16-17. Physicians of Yunani medicine, or the Yunani School, flourished in Lucknow: David Arnold, 2000, *Science, Technology and Medicine in Colonial India* (Cambridge, Mass.: Cambridge University Press), 6. See also Abdul Halim Sharar, 1975, *Lucknow: The Last Phase of an Oriental Culture*, trans. and ed. ES Harcourt and Fakhir Hussain (London: Paul Elek), 97.

61 Ansari, 1985, 380-3; Ansari, 2016a, 725.

62 Trivedi, 2010, 15.

63 Saadat 'Ali Khan (r. 1798-1814) had ordered the bridge from a foundry in England, but it was not erected until the 1840s during the reign of Amjad 'Ali Shah (r. 1842-47). The English East India Company employed British and French military engineers throughout northern India, some of whom were evidently engaged to assemble this substantial structure: Tandan, 2001, 274.

64 Scholars have long debated the merits of this late 'debased' style of Indian architecture. Giles Tillotson, 1989, for instance, argues in *The Tradition of Indian Architecture: Continuity, Controversy and Change since 1850* (New Haven and London: Yale University Press), 6-17, that the tradition of Mughal architecture, in the sense of a grammatically rigorous and poetic language, had long since died.

65 Tandan, 2001,192.

66 James Fergusson, 1899, *History of Indian and Eastern Architecture*, Book VII, chapter X, 'Indian Saracenic Architecture' (London: John Murray), 604.

67 Tandan, 2001, 189.

68 Tandan, 2001, 189.

69 Tandan, 2001, 189.

70 Tandan, 2001, 110.

71 Banmali Tandan, 2008, *The Architecture of Lucknow and Oudh, 1722-1856: Its Evolution in an Aesthetic and Social Context* (Cambridge: Zophorus), 200; see also Tandan, 2008, 434, fn. 174. Moreover, Herbert's diary entries document the construction progress: fn. 172.

72 Tandan, 2008, 201.

73 Bartsch and Kamleh, 2014, 282-4.

74 Tandan, 2008, 201, fn. 181.

75 For 'colonial modernity' and its implications for the interpretation of the architectural history of India in the modern era, see Peter Scriver and Vikram Prakash, eds., 2007, *Colonial Modernities: Building Dwelling and Architecture in British India and Ceylon* (London: Routledge).

76 Wajīd 'Alī Shāh spent a fortune on both the annual upkeep of the observatory as well as improvements and repairs to the Building: Abbas, 2010, 83.

77 'Reply of the King to the Resident's Letter of Aug. 18 1849, dated Sept 1849', *Foreign (Political) Consultations* No. 130-136, Oct. 6, 1849, quoted in Ansari, 1978, 66, fn 18.

78 Llewellyn-Jones, 2014, 229, citing India Political Consultations, 31 October 1856, No. 109, India Office Records.

Part II

ʻ*Ilm* as Religion

Chapter 5

'By the Pen!': Spreading 'ilm in Indonesia through Quranic calligraphy

Virginia Hooker

ABSTRACT

In the world's largest Muslim majority nation, mainstream Indonesian Muslims are seeking to deepen their knowledge of Islam. This was initially stimulated by the transnational Islamic revival of the 1970s and strengthened by a concurrent policy of Indonesia's governing New Order regime. That policy restricted public expressions of Islam to culture and education and forbade any political expression of the religion. In that milieu, activities to spread knowledge of the Quran (*ʿilm*) proliferated through Quranic study groups, Quranic recitation competitions, and exhibitions of Islam-inspired calligraphic art. Responding to this thirst for *ʿilm*, Didin Sirojuddin, an internationally recognised Indonesian calligrapher, established the Institute of Quranic Calligraphy (LEMKA) in 1985. The institute is committed to spreading *ʿilm* through study of the Quran and the practice of Quranic calligraphy or *dakwah bi'l-Qalam* (teaching Islam through the pen). Its statement of purpose emphasises that when transmitting *ʿilm* through the process of calligraphy, the calligrapher receives guidance, ethics, aesthetics, and creative inspiration directly from the Quran. Sirojuddin teaches that once students have acquired *ʿilm,* they must put it into practice in the form of good deeds (*ʿamal*) for the benefit of the individual and society. In 1998, LEMKA established the only *pesantren* in Indonesia devoted wholly to teaching Quranic calligraphy. The deliberate siting of the *pesantren* in the mountains of West Java inspires students to remember the Quranic teaching that Allah created the beauty of the universe as a source of pleasure and enjoyment. To ignore that beauty, Sirojuddin teaches, is to ignore an aspect of Allah's greatness. To give expression to that beauty through calligraphic art bears witness to His greatness. Sirojuddin believes that beautifully presented Quranic calligraphy makes the themes and meaning of *ʿilm* even more beautiful and appealing than they already are, so that when Muslims see the calligraphy they will be motivated to apply *ʿilm* through good deeds in their everyday lives.

INTRODUCTION

It is 2016. In an Islamic residential school (*pesantren*) near the picturesque hill resort of Sukabumi, West Java, students practise the beautiful, flowing, classical styles of Islamic calligraphy to copy verses of the Quran (Figure 5.1).[1] Guided by the principles associated with 10th-century master calligrapher Ibn Muqla (d. 940), young men and women write with traditional reed styluses, felt pens, various inks, and acrylic paints, to create a diverse range of work.[2] When they need to

Figure 5.1 Students of *Pesantren Kaligrafi LEMKA* near Sukabumi in West Java prepare work for a competition. Photograph by V Hooker.

double-check the wording or spelling of a Quranic verse they use smartphones to consult a Quran website. At one end of their studio are rows of trophies that staff and students have won at national and international calligraphy competitions. The students come from across Indonesia, as well as Malaysia and Brunei Darussalam, to study at this *pesantren,* which focuses on Quranic calligraphy and is the only one of its kind in Indonesia. Enrolment is limited to 120 students annually and, after a two-semester program, the students gain a diploma accredited by the Ministry of Religion.

The *pesantren,* called Pesantren Kaligrafi LEMKA, was established in 1998 by an internationally recognised Indonesian calligrapher, Didin Sirojuddin AR (b. 1957).[3] Since the early 1980s Sirojuddin has dedicated his life to spreading religious knowledge through Quranic calligraphy. In the handbook for new students enrolling at the *pesantren,* he writes that their education will be a synthesis of *ʿilm* (knowledge, in this context 'Quranic knowledge') and *akhlāq* (ethics and moral values). They will study how to be pious Muslim human beings who have *ʿilm*, a sense of ethics and self-reliance, the ability to reason, high motivation, entrepreneurship, and creativity. The aim of the *pesantren,* the handbook continues, is to produce graduates who will promote and develop the art of calligraphy throughout the homeland, as their contribution to implementing *ʿilm* in accordance with the moral values of the Quran.[4]

Sirojuddin is one of many Indonesian religious scholars who take seriously the Quranic injunction to spread knowledge — knowledge that enables an individual both to understand their obligations to God and to lead an ethical and moral life in their community. For such scholars, Al-Bukhārī's Hadith 'The best of you are those who study the Quran and teach it' has a personal significance. This chapter explores the meaning of *'ilm* through the writings and practice of Sirojuddin and other Indonesian calligraphers and calligraphic artists. It situates them in their socio-political context in order to show how they identify and use opportunities provided by that context to facilitate the spread of Quranic knowledge.

The chapter considers first the *'ilm* repertoire — that is, the knowledge considered essential to teaching Quranic knowledge. Second, it describes the aesthetic and ethical foundations of Quranic calligraphy and calligraphic art; third, it shows how Quranic knowledge is disseminated. The fourth section looks at how the Institute for Quranic Calligraphy (LEMKA) and its offshoot, the Pesantren Kaligrafi LEMKA, both founded by Sirojuddin, put *'ilm* to work. The fifth section briefly describes one of Sirojuddin's own calligraphic paintings, so as to show how he embeds images that will enhance the affective aspect of *'ilm* in visual Islam.

THE *'ILM* REPERTOIRE

The picture of the 'arrival' of Islam in island Southeast Asia is incomplete and regularly updated with the results of new research. One recent, authoritative source places the 'institutionalisation' of Islam in Southeast Asia as beginning around the 13th century in north Sumatra with the conversion of a local ruler. Further epigraphic evidence indicates that there were Muslim rulers in Brunei Darussalam in the 14th century, with textual evidence for the conversion of the Malay ruler of Malacca in the 15th century, followed by active coastal communities in Java in the 16th century.[5] With Islam came manuscripts of the Quran, commentaries, and reference works, all in Arabic and requiring translations into local languages. An industry of religious teaching (basic doctrine, Quranic recitation in Arabic, and reading and writing Arabic script), mosque building, translating, manuscript copying, and regular contact with Mecca and Madina began.[6]

In the late 1830s, Raja Ali Haji (d. c. 1870), Malay language expert, methodical historian, and religious scholar, designed a study course in Quranic knowledge for one of his royal relatives. Raja Ali Haji had made the pilgrimage to Mecca and Madina in 1827 and became an adviser and confidant for the 19th-century rulers of the Sultanate of Riau-Lingga, a prestigious Malay sultanate commanding much of the international trade in the southern Straits of Malacca and forerunner to Singapore. His own teachers were Middle Eastern scholars who were employed on salaries to settle and teach for several years in the Sultanate. Raja Ali Haji read and wrote Arabic fluently and in his major history of the Malayo-Indonesian archipelago, covering the 17th to the late 19th centuries, he lists the manuscripts he used to teach his relatives about Islam.[7] He started with the classical works on Arabic language and grammar: Zawzanī's works for the system of inflections; for Arabic grammar, *'Awāmil al-mi'a* (al-Jurjānī, d. 1073) and *al-Muqaddima al-ajurrūmiyya* (Ibn Ajurrūm, d. 1323) and their commentaries, followed by the *Alfiyya* (Ibn Mālik, d. 1274). Theology was from *Umm al-barāhīn* (al-Sanūsī, d. 1490), and also from extracts from the *Jawharat al-tawḥīd* (Ibrahim al-Laqqānī, d. 1631), both with commentaries. The basic texts for the study of *taṣawwuf* (Islamic mysticism) were *Bidāyat al-hidāya* and *Minhāj al-'ābidīn*, both by al-Ghazālī (d. 1111).[8]

The list is of interest not only for identification of the teaching texts used in the Malayo-Indonesian world in the mid-19th century, but also for comparison with texts used in Indonesian *pesantren* in the late 20th century. During the 1980s, the Dutch scholar Van Bruinessen compiled lists of the texts used for teaching Islam in *pesantren*, mostly in Java. His survey shows that the works used by Raja Ali Haji in the 1830s are still the mainstay of foundation courses for teaching Quranic knowledge to non-Arabic speakers. But there are also changes. Texts are now printed, rather than being manuscript copies, and further branches of knowledge have been added.[9] As Van Bruinessen explains, up to the late 19th century, Quranic exegesis (*tafsīr*) was not considered an important element in *'ilm*, but when the reformers in Egypt, like Muhammad 'Abduh (d. 1905) and Rashīd Riḍā (d. 1935), argued for a return to basic sources of Islam, their calls were taken up by Indonesian *'ulamā'* who added the study of *tafsīr* (exegesis) and Hadiths to the basic *pesantren* curriculum.[10]

The *pesantren* teaching materials described above fall squarely within mainstream Sunni traditions of Islam. When Sirojuddin started his secondary education in 1969, he enrolled in the highly regarded Pondok Moderen Gontor *pesantren* in East Java.[11] He studied the same basic curriculum of Arabic, the classical texts of the Islamic sciences, as well as Quranic calligraphy. The Gontor *pesantren* is known across Indonesia for its use of modern educational principles, for its support of rational analysis, and for encouraging students to seek knowledge from a wide range of sources. One of these was a book published in 1948, *The History of the Quran* (*Sedjarah al-Qoeran*) compiled by famous Acehnese scholar Haji Aboebakar (c. 1900-70). It was widely used in *pesantren* and ran to at least six editions.[12] Sirojuddin says his understanding of the Quran comes from that book.

Haji Aboebakar's vision

Aboebakar began compiling his history after Sukarno declared Indonesian Independence from colonial Dutch rule in August 1945. He completed it about one year before the United Nations officially recognised Indonesia's sovereignty in December 1949. In his preface and conclusion he presents the Quran as the handbook for a new nation entering a new era and writes that if the holy scripture could create an *'umma* in the deserts (where it was revealed), it can also give spirit to the Indonesian peoples as they struggle for independence and God's justice.[13]

Throughout the *History*, Aboebakar both reiterates the message that the Quran is a guide for every aspect of life and emphasises that to understand their religion Muslims must go to its original sources, the Quran and the life of the Prophet. The tone of the history is motivational, the content 'modernist' in the style of al-Afghānī (d. 1897), 'Abduh, and Riḍā, and the target readership is the young women and men of a newly independent Indonesia. The book is lavishly illustrated with photographs every few pages of sites which have significance in the life of the Prophet, of Islamic architecture, of manuscripts of the Quran, and of influential individuals, both Muslims and non-Muslims. Readers can see with their own eyes that Islam is a world religion practised by modern men and women.

Through its 33 chapters, the book traces the formation of the Quran from revelation to the establishment of the written text. It describes its exegesis; its attitude to science, philosophy, and women; and how Islam is taught in countries ranging from the Ḥejāz to China, Japan, and Indonesia itself. Aboebakar's *History* concludes with his reminder that the Quran was the life-guide for the Prophet Muhammad in his campaign to combat tyranny and wrongdoing; it provided the law for Muslim sultanates as they arose; and the Quran connected the Prophet with Allah.[14] Indonesian Muslims are alert to allusions and subtle references and they would understand these last words in the *History* as a reference to the well-known horizontal and vertical connections between Allah and humankind and humans with each other.[15]

Aboebakar's motivation for writing his history was to connect Indonesians with the Quran so they could turn to it as the source of advice for all their needs. He describes the Quran as 'an infinite lake of knowledge' which has powerful messages to help people live in this world and prepare for the next.[16] Attempting to understand and comprehend the limitless extent of the *'ilm* within the Quran is perhaps a way to begin to understand the true nature of Allah's transcendence and omniscience.[17]

It is that spirit of engagement and awe that Sirojuddin shows in his many writings and in his discussions about the Quran. When responding to questions about Islam, his sources of first reference are the Quran and *sunna*. For example, when I emailed him with a question about the nature of *'ilm*, Sirojuddin responded with a quotation from the words of the Prophet Muhammad, supported by further information from the Prophet's wife, Aisha.

> If someone has knowledge, then at the same time they are raising their level (because humans of the highest level are those with knowledge). Furthermore, the Prophet on whom be blessings and peace, himself taught, 'Truly I have been sent to be a teacher'. The Prophet as the greatest teacher is 'The walking Quran', who made the Quran a way of life. The Quran is the source of knowledge.[18]

To summarise: in contemporary Indonesia, the repertoire for teaching the *'ilm* enshrined in the Quran draws first on the Quran itself, and then on the classical texts and commentaries of the traditional Islamic sciences. The repertoire includes the teachings of eminent 19th-century Egyptian reformer Muhammad 'Abduh, mediated by Rashīd Riḍā, to establish an Islam-based modernity. Sirojuddin draws on all of these and presents them in the spirit of Aboebakar's *History of the Quran* — the Quran as the living embodiment of Allah's presence in this world, symbolising the immediacy of the links between humankind and Allah as well as between humans themselves. Like Aboebakar, Sirojuddin's position is modernist, his style motivational, and his target group young Indonesian women and men. Like Aboebakar he presents his 'work' of spreading Quranic knowledge as a contribution to the whole of Indonesian society. Indonesia will become a just and prosperous nation, he believes, if the teachings of the Quran are implemented in daily life.

QURANIC CALLIGRAPHY: ETHICS AND AESTHETICS

Sirojuddin is often invited to give public lectures and talks. In 2003 during Ramaḍān, the season of religious study and reflection, he was invited to speak on the role of Islamic art in social life, focusing on the relationship between beauty, goodness, and Islamic art.[19] The talk he gave then begins by explaining that creating good art is an act of worship (*'ibāda*). Art created in this way expresses beauty, and the realisation that Allah is the source of all beauty inspires believers to do good deeds in this world and the next. Quoting two verses from the Quran (*Qāf* 50:6, and *al-Naḥl* 16:6), he explains that Allah created the beauty of the universe to be a source of pleasure and enjoyment for humankind. To ignore the beauty of Allah's creation is to ignore an aspect of Allah's greatness; to give expression to that beauty is to bear witness to His greatness. Sirojuddin refers also to al-Ghazālī's *Iḥyā' 'ulūm al-dīn* (Reviving the Sciences of Religion), where it is written that the beauty of nature stimulates reflection and contemplation. In a similar way, Sirojuddin argues, a beautiful work of Islam-inspired art can also inspire reflection, or *dhikr* (remembrance, being mindful of Allah).

Sirojuddin next describes the beauty of God's decrees and the beauty of His attributes.[20] Drawing on two Hadiths, that Allah is the most beautiful and loves beauty, and that Allah is the most good and loves goodness, he presents a step-by-step explanation to argue that beauty and goodness are inseparable.[21] Both, he says, are divine attributes, which, because they come from the essence that is the One (Allah), are fused. Their inseparability means that beauty (art) is never expressed purely for its own sake but always so that it inspires goodness and morality. Enjoying beauty for its own sake can lead to immorality. Thus in Islam, he concludes, aesthetics are linked with ethics and form the basis for the conception of Islamic art.

Sirojuddin's talk uses his knowledge of the Quran, Hadiths, and al-Ghazālī's *Iḥyā'* to teach his audience and to motivate them to emulate the attributes of Allah. His reasoning is that if, even in our limited human way, we try to develop and express Allah's attributes, we might approach Allah through ethical behaviours (*akhlāq*) which are sanctioned by Him.[22] Sirojuddin's argument is premised on the contrast between the transcendent nature of Allah's being and the limited nature of humans. As described above, the awareness of that contrast and the attempt to close the gap by the effort to emulate Allah's attributes are the beginnings of true understanding of the nature of Quranic knowledge.

It follows that *'ilm* — an understanding of the knowledge enshrined in the Quran — is insufficient to lead a pious life. It is a first and necessary step but must be followed by the effort to put that guidance into practice (*'amal*). This was a concern of al-Ghazālī and, as Rosenthal notes, al-Ghazālī 'is concerned about the relationship between knowledge and action as the principal theme of Muslim theological ethics'.[23] Rosenthal's incisive summary is particularly appropriate to the Indonesian context: 'Of singular significance for the fate of the term *'ilm* in societal organization and in education was its pairing with *'amal* "action"'.[24] In fact, continues Rosenthal, they became 'a standard combination'.[25] Since the 1970s, when contemporary Indonesian Islam-inspired art was first exhibited, Sirojuddin and his senior colleagues have hoped that viewers might be moved by the beauty (aesthetics) of their works to reflect on the *'ilm* that inspired the art — in other words, that art is both an act of worship (*'ibāda*) and a beneficial act (*'amal*) for artist and for viewer.

The best known of this group of artists is Abdul Djalil Pirous (b. 1932), who describes his aims in this way: 'I am trying through the language of beauty to give people something that will stir them to appreciate ethical values. By this I mean those ethical values that have a close connection with the values found in Quranic verses'.[26] Sirojuddin wrote, 'When the [Quranic] verses are placed in a beautiful painting, their themes and meaning will be even more beautiful and appealing'.[27] Agoes Nugroho (b. 1957), another acclaimed calligraphic artist, believes the most important response to his works is what he terms 'a psychological one' which stimulates viewers to become better people.[28]

During the month of Ramaḍān in 1995, an international exhibition of Islam-inspired art was held in the precincts of Indonesia's national Independence Mosque (*Mesjid Istiqlāl*). Named 'Exhibition of Istiqlal Contemporary Art, Festival Istiqlal II', the event attracted over 11 million visitors and featured the works of 165 Muslim artists from all over the world. In their catalogue essay for the exhibition, the curatorial team included a statement about the nature of Islam-inspired art.

> As the one God is the most beautiful, His beauty is evident in all kinds of beautiful forms and objects that are His works and are manifestations of His attributes and names. The beauty of His names and attributes is condensed in the quality of *al-Raḥmān* and *al-Raḥīm* and can be condensed

> further into the term 'love' *(Cinta)*. A Muslim artist's heart which overflows with love of beauty and truth will reflect the names of the creator. All forms of beauty have their origin in the One.[29]

Sirojuddin was not a member of the curatorial team who wrote this statement, but the speech he delivered in 2003, outlined above, is a more detailed explication of the same aesthetic philosophy. Because it is obvious to Sirojuddin and his fellow artists and alluded to in the curatorial team's words, '[a] Muslim artist's heart which overflows with love of beauty and truth', they feel no need to state that the 'love of truth and beauty' has its roots in Quranic knowledge. There is a circularity in the thinking underlying Islam-inspired artistic practice. Knowledge of the Quran, through reading and reflection, inspires calligraphic art that expresses what the Quran has inspired. As with human life, the spirit returns to its point of origin.[30]

PIETY AND POLITICS: ISLAM IN NEW ORDER INDONESIA

President Suharto sponsored the Festival Istiqlal II exhibition, as well as an earlier exhibition in 1991, which had an attendance of 6.5 million.[31] It seems ironic that President Suharto's New Order regime (1966-98), which came to power through a military take-over in 1965 followed by the widespread killing of civilians, should also foster the cultural expression of Islam. This was not inspired by a love of Islamic civilisation. Rather, it was the method the New Order used to restrict and control the political expression of Islam.

Muslim intellectuals, religious teachers, and activists, both students and established figures, realised the danger of direct confrontation with the New Order. Historian Merle Calvin Ricklefs provides an overview of the strategies that they developed to advance Islam without attracting retaliation.[32] The approach of forward-looking and respected intellectual Nurcholish Madjid (d. 2005) was gradually accepted and adopted by mainstream Indonesian Muslims. In an interview with Ricklefs in 1977, Madjid said, '[T]he older generation emphasise too much politicising Islam, making Islam a political weapon to gain power ... The younger generation, especially represented by my friends and I, emphasise the ethics and not the political ideology of Islam'.[33]

Between the 1970s and 1990s in Indonesia, a confluence of socio-economic and political factors produced the conditions for a marked increase in expressions of Islamic piety. President Suharto's 'New Order' introduced policies of economic development and social engineering (mass literacy campaigns, population control, forced internal migration), and technological innovation and industrialisation that delivered spectacular economic growth. Servicing this growth was an expanding bureaucracy, an uncontrolled financial system, and an aggressive military that was beyond the reach of the law and ruthless in crushing dissent.

From the economic expansion grew an educated and well-off middle class, with money to spend on education and travel, and with an appetite for consumption. At the other end of the scale, although the number of Indonesians living below the poverty line decreased under the New Order, millions still suffered extreme deprivation and lived in dire conditions. Inequality was, and remains, a major social issue in Indonesia. Across the social spectrum, growing numbers began to feel uncomfortable with the pace of change and the obvious increase in corruption, collusion, and nepotism (as it was popularly known). They realised they knew little about their own religion and began to attend discussion groups, Quranic study classes, and Sufi groups.[34] Those with the means dressed in Muslim fashions, made the pilgrimage to Mecca in increasing numbers, followed Arab styles of music, and heeded calls to deepen their piety through learning to read and write the Quran.

These calls took many forms but are all referred to by the Indonesian term *dakwah* (Arabic *daʿwa*). To quote a recent description: 'Islam's normative sources make *dakwah* a compulsory activity for all Muslims, and the particular form to be practised should be one that is suitable to the talents, capacities and circumstances of individual Muslims'.[35] Although in theory *dakwah* takes the form that best suits individual talent, most Muslims think of *dakwah* as *bi'l-lisān* (by the tongue) — that is, verbally.[36] There should be no coercion. As one contemporary Javanese religious teacher explains it, 'The goal of *dakwah* is to transmit the rules [of Islam], but in a subtle and polite way that will please the heart, that will not be offensive'.[37] Another definition states simply that *dakwah* can mean 'to make Muslims better Muslims'.[38]

In the context of a rapidly modernising New Order Indonesia, the growth of a Muslim middle class seeking greater knowledge of their religion, and the restriction of Islam to the cultural sphere, the conditions were perfect for *dakwah* activities.[39] Supporting this were the advances in communication technology, which the New Order implemented to spread their propaganda and development programs. Ironically, these advances also facilitated the spread of religious teachings by radio, television, mass media, and publications.[40]

Dakwah, Quranic recitation, and calligraphy

The popularisation of Quranic calligraphy was fostered by its association with the Indonesian national Quran recitation contests (*Musābaqat Tilāwati-l-Qur'ān* (MTQ)), which are highlights of 'performed Islam' and attract mass audiences of all ages. The first national MTQ was held in 1968 and the contests have been held annually ever since, alternating between national and regional levels.[41] In 1979, MTQ organisers agreed to hold an exhibition of Quranic calligraphy in conjunction with the competition finals. For the first time, calligraphic art by leading artists, such as Ahmad Sadali and Abdul Djalil Pirous, was shown in a religious rather than a secular context. This provided a structure and status for 'visual Islam' and an appreciative audience. Pirous continued to be closely involved with later MTQ exhibitions and, from 1981, the MTQ officially included calligraphy competitions as part of its regular events.

Quranic recitation competitions at the local level have been popular in Indonesia from at least the 1930s, but their organisation into a structured national event required a single institution to oversee the process. In 1977, the Ministry of Religious Affairs and the Department of Home Affairs supported the establishment of a non-government body called the Institute for the Development of the Recitation of the Quran or LPTQ (*Lembaga Pengembangan Tilawatil Quran*).[42] Its functions include running programs to develop the recitation, memorisation, calligraphy, and exhibition of the Quran; improving understanding of the Quran by sponsoring translations; providing commentaries on the Quran; and encouraging 'the practical application of Quranic teachings in Muslims' daily lives'.[43] The aims and activities of the LPTQ paved the way for Sirojuddin when he set up an Institute for Quranic Calligraphy, as will be described in the next section.

'ILM AT WORK: *LEMBAGA KALIGRAFI AL-QURAN*

Sirojuddin's talent for Quranic calligraphy was recognised and nurtured during his years at the *pesantren* Pondok Moderen Gontor. When he enrolled at the progressive State Islamic Institute (now university) Syarif Hidayatullah in 1976, he studied Islamic theology and history as well as calligraphy.[44] After his graduation in 1982, he worked as a journalist for the very popular Muslim magazine *Panji Masyarakat*.[45] This gave him the opportunity to travel throughout Indonesia and to visit the Middle East, writing feature articles on Islamic culture and Quranic calligraphy. He interviewed many of Indonesia's leading Muslim scholars and intellectuals and made networks he would later use when he developed his plans for a centre where young Indonesians could learn Quranic calligraphy. *Panji Masyarakat*, and other Indonesian journals and newspapers, maintain an interest in Sirojuddin's work. They publish articles on his projects and commission him to write articles and cultural reviews.[46]

In 1983, still working as a journalist and earning a reputation as a calligraphic artist, Sirojuddin was appointed lecturer in his former Faculty of Islamic Civilisation, to teach calligraphy and Islamic culture and history. There was no basic course outline, nor were there many textbooks, so Sirojuddin set about composing both. The first print-run of his text *Seni Kaligrafi* (The Art of Calligraphy) was 5000 and sold out in seven months. There have been many reprints and its structured and intensive approach remains the basis of the 'LEMKA method'.[47] Sirojuddin began receiving scores of letters (nowadays he receives messages by social media, tweets, and smartphone apps) from people across Indonesia asking where they could learn calligraphy. He realised that there was a real demand for knowledge of Quranic calligraphy and sufficient support to establish an institute to teach it.

On 20 April 1985, Sirojuddin, his colleague Ece Abidin, and some supporters met the dean of the faculty with a plan for such an institute. The dean gave it his full support. When discussing its proposed name, the founding members agreed that *Lembaga Kaligrafi al-Quran* (LEMKA, the Institute of Quranic Calligraphy) best described their aim to '[f]acilitate the popularisation of calligraphy through all layers of society, especially among young people, throughout the homeland'.[48] To some extent, LEMKA's aims echo those of the LPTQ, the institute established to oversee Quranic knowledge including calligraphy. In practice, however, the LPTQ focuses mainly on Quranic recitation. Sirojuddin wanted LEMKA to meet the specific needs of those wanting to learn calligraphy. It was important that 'al-Quran' be an essential part of the name of the institute because in his words

> [t]he Quran is the source of ethics for a calligrapher when inscribing Arabic calligraphy. So, the result of the process is Arabic calligraphy; the ethics of the actual process originate from the moral values [*akhlāq*] of the Quran. Thus, a calligrapher will always be controlled and under the protection of the concepts, creative inspiration, aesthetics, and teachings which are reflected from the rays of the will of the Quran. In simpler terms: a calligrapher should have high moral standards and impeccable behaviour, should be pious, and should work for the glory of religion in accordance with the teachings embodied in the holy Quran.[49]

This statement, LEMKA's manifesto, recognises al-Ghazālī's concern with the 'the necessary moral qualifications of scholars'.[50] It also reflects the Quran's own promises that 'a change in moral state occurs through direct and affective engagement with the Quran'.[51] Further, when the calligrapher works 'under the protection' of the aesthetics and teachings of the Quran, readers of that calligraphy will benefit also from those Quranic teachings.[52]

When Sirojuddin designed the LEMKA courses he was inspired by what he saw as his religious obligation to invite and encourage young Indonesians to learn calligraphy.[53] He and his fellow teachers at LEMKA believe that through the beauty of calligraphy, students will love Islam and the Quran.[54] Calligraphy is beautiful on two levels, they explain. The first is the physical beauty of the calligraphed letters; the second is the metaphysical beauty of the messages in the verses which the calligraphy records.[55]

LEMKA thrived from its inception, attracting students who became teachers, who in turn attracted more students. Practical lessons included intensive courses in learning to write the five styles of classical Quranic calligraphy and, for more advanced students, contemporary styles.[56] Each lesson is designed to awaken the aesthetic sense of the beautiful. Students are also taught sufficient Quranic exegesis to understand the significance and meaning of the verses they are copying. This enables them to design their works in a way that enhances the meaning of the text and makes them more effective mediums for spreading knowledge of the Quran.

LEMKA alumni are always successful in calligraphy competitions and in 1987 Sirojuddin himself was awarded first prize in the ASEAN calligraphy competition sponsored by Brunei Darussalam.[57] He continues to be in demand as a judge in national and international competitions, and each year he co-ordinates major calligraphy events across Indonesia and coaches the judges as well as the participants.[58] Between 1995 and 1998, LEMKA helped set up 52 studios to teach calligraphy in various towns and cities across Indonesia and, in Jakarta, LEMKA has 36 staff to assist Sirojuddin in his work. He also advises Indonesian provincial governments on ways to improve the standard of Quranic calligraphy for their own staff and in their local mosques.

In 1998, LEMKA and Sirojuddin realised their ambition to establish *Pesantren Kaligrafi LEMKA* in the mountains of West Java to teach a two-semester-long calligraphy program (Figure 5.2).[59] The teaching philosophy draws on Sirojuddin's appreciation of his Gontor education, with its synthesis of traditional and contemporary methods. He says he uses the Socratic method of teaching through posing questions, and he encourages students to read relevant works by non-Muslim scholars. Like Haji Aboebakar, he urges students to study day and night and to see the library as an essential resource for their education.[60]

Pesantren Kaligrafi was deliberately sited in beautiful surroundings, and its buildings were constructed as open pavilions or with windows to take advantage of the mountain views. Thus, students can recognise Allah's 'signs in the universe' (*'ālam*)[61], experience the sense of awe at His greatness, and reflect these feelings in their works. The curriculum includes several art excursions to beautiful locations where students respond to their surroundings and follow the guidance of the Quran: 'Travel throughout the earth and see how He brings life into being' (*al-'Ankabūt* 29:20).

The reputation of both LEMKA and its 'out-station' *Pesantren Kaligrafi* is now well established in Islamic art and calligraphy circles. Outside those circles, LEMKA's activities are publicised at special times in the Muslim calendar such as Ramaḍān, when calligraphy competitions and Islamic art exhibitions are popular. The LEMKA calligraphy method has been featured on TV and receives regular coverage in the print media as well as on the internet.[62]

Sirojuddin estimates the number of LEMKA's Jakarta alumni since 1985 at around 6000, with an extra 1500 graduates from *Pesantren Kaligrafi* since 1998. These are Indonesians who are familiar with LEMKA's teachings about Quranic calligraphy and Quranic values. They have also been exposed to inclusive interpretations of the Quran and have been encouraged to think, question, and work for the good of their communities as *Pondok Moderen Gontor* taught Sirojuddin to do.

Figure 5.2 Sirojuddin shows *Pesantren Kaligrafi* students how to write calligraphy on glass, 2016. Photograph by Nasiqin.

INTERPRETING *'ILM* THROUGH CALLIGRAPHIC ART

This final section focuses on the artistic practice of Sirojuddin and the second aspect of *'ilm* — the use of intellect and perception to come to grips with information and give it meaning. In the context of 'visual Islam' — that is, Quran-inspired art and the critical importance of beauty in its expression — two further human faculties are important to the reception of those works. They are memory and emotions. Engaging with calligraphic art involves reading as well as looking, so I use the term 'reader-viewer' to emphasise the double engagement.

Sirojuddin painted the work *Kuasa Sang Maharaja* (The Power of the Mighty Ruler) (Figure 5.3) in 2001, just three years after political and financial turmoil in Indonesia forced President Suharto to step down. The New Order regime was followed by a period of instability and inter-religious violence between Christians and Muslims, as various groups in Indonesia struggled for ascendancy and reforms. Sirojuddin's choice of verse reminds reader-viewers that temporal power is Allah's gift: 'You give control to whoever You will and remove it from whoever You will; You elevate whoever You will and humble whoever You will. All that is good lies in Your hand: You have power over everything'.[63]

The Quranic verses are linked to visual images of the *hajj* (the three black pillars resemble the Kaba) and textual fragments refer to *hajj* rituals (such as the *wuqūf* at 'Arafa). Many interpretations

Figure 5.3 Didin Sirojuddin AR, *Kuasa Sang Maharaja* (The Power of the Mighty Ruler), 2001. 30 x 30 cm, mixed media. Courtesy of Darren Boyd.

are possible. The *hajj*, one of the five 'pillars' of Islam, is a ritual which brings together all Muslims, whatever their status, as equals and as servants of Allah. The Kaba is the central pivot of the *hajj*, as well as marking the direction that all Muslims face when they perform their daily prayers. These visual elements remind believers of their ritual obligations in Islam, of the omnipotence of Allah, of the unity of their community, and of their equality.

The Kaba is linked also with Ibrāhīm (Abraham), revered not only by Muslims but also by Jews and Christians. In the context of the Muslim-Christian violence which was occurring at the time Sirojuddin prepared his work (and which is an ongoing theme in Indonesia), this might be another message for reader-viewers. It is a reminder that Judaism, Christianity, and Islam share a common tradition of monotheism through Ibrāhīm/Abraham and it emphasises that in the sight of Allah/God all humans are equal. The visual messages, or trigger images, suggest diverse ways of analysing and understanding the Quranic words. The primary aim of Sirojuddin's 'visual Quranic knowledge' is to create a work of beauty that will stir reader-viewers to reflect on the meanings of the Quranic words. The images support the sacred words through the affective senses of memory and feeling. The decision about whether to act (*'amal*) on the advice of the Quran and live according to its ethics (*akhlāq*) lies with the individual reader-viewer.

CONCLUSION

For Sirojuddin and other Quranic calligraphers, the performative aspect of their calligraphic knowledge — that is, shaping each sacred letter and bringing the Quran to life by revealing its metaphysical as well as its physical aspects — is an act of worship (*'ibāda*). Inspired by the beauty of the words, the letters, and the signs of Allah in the created world, the calligrapher is drawn to Allah spiritually and emotionally. That connection motivates the calligrapher and all believers to attend also to the needs of fellow humans in social interaction or *mu'āmalāt*. *'Ilm* must be made manifest in the form of 'good deeds', in actions which mirror Allah's attributes. The LEMKA engagement with time and place, the here and now, is unequivocal. LEMKA's message is that Allah's knowledge is infinite, and that the Quran teaches that it is beyond human capacity to match it ('Above everyone who has knowledge there is the One who is all knowing' (*Yūsuf* 12:76)). But individuals who acknowledge Allah's powers and attributes, through their awareness of His creative powers manifest in the beauty of nature, will make every effort to reflect that beauty and the values of the Quran in their daily lives and their calligraphic works.

Indonesian Muslims, including Islam-inspired artists, responded to the particular socio-political conditions of Indonesia during 1966 to 1998 to deepen the understanding of Islam among mainstream Muslims who wanted to be better Muslims. Among the artists, Sirojuddin chose to dedicate his calligraphic talents to *dakwah bi'l-qalam* (teaching Islam through the pen). He says:

> I want to bring forth people of the Quran who will make the Quran manifest through their calligraphic skills. This will awaken awareness of the need to study aesthetics as one of the teachings of the Quran, something which is insufficiently understood by the majority of Muslims. 'Truly Allah is beautiful and loves beauty' (HR Muslim). With the knowledge of beauty, we can know the beauty of God's creation and become closer to the Creator who is the Most Beautiful.[64]

In the contemporary world of 21st-century Indonesia, through Quranic calligraphy and the latest forms of IT communication, Sirojuddin and his colleagues and students give new life to the traditional sources of Islam to motivate the practical application of *'ilm* in individual lives and in Indonesian society.

NOTES

1 The Quranic quotation in the title is from *al-Qalam* 68:1. All English translations of the Quran are from MAS Haleem, 2004, *The Quran: A New Translation* (Oxford: Oxford University Press). It is a pleasure to acknowledge Emeritus Professor Anthony Johns whose thoughtful responses to this chapter are deeply appreciated. Special thanks to my colleague Amrih Widodo, expert on contemporary Indonesia, who has contributed much to the way this chapter is framed. Indonesian spelling follows the official Indonesian 'New Spelling' adopted in 1972 except for personal names which follow the individual's preferred form and titles of books published before 1972. All translations from Indonesian are my own.

2 Ibn Muqla was born in Baghdad 885, and died in prison 940 CE. Sheila Blair, 2006, *Islamic Calligraphy* (Edinburgh: Edinburgh University Press) notes that although Ibn Muqla is credited with recording the rules of calligraphy, his treatise is yet to be published (157-60). The calligraphic styles in the order they are taught in Indonesia are Naskh, Thuluth, Fārisī, Dīwānī, Ruqa'a, and Kūfī.

3 There are about 11,000 *pesantren* in Java, most of which teach some Arabic script, but this is the only one devoted purely to Quranic calligraphy. In 2007, Indonesian academic Dr Ismatu Ropi arranged for my husband and me to visit Pesantren Kaligrafi al-Quran LEMKA to commission Sirojuddin to copy verses of the Quran about gardens. Since our initial contact with him, I have visited Sirojuddin at his south Jakarta 'city' home and gallery three times. He has been most generous in sharing his knowledge, copies of his books and articles, and permissions to reproduce and show his works. I am greatly indebted to him.

4 *Mengenal Pesantren Kaligrafi Alquran LEMKA*, school handbook, 2002, 9.

5 The authoritative source is Annabel Teh Gallop, 2015, 'A Jawi Sourcebook for the Study of Malay Palaeography and Orthography', *Indonesia and the Malay World* 43(125): 13-171. See also the works of AH Johns, a pioneer in this field, as listed in Peter Riddell, 2001, *Islam and the Malay-Indonesian World: Transmission and Response* (London: C Hurst & Co.), 332.

6 See Azyumardi Azra, 2004, *The Origins of Islamic Reformism in Southeast Asia: Networks of Malay-Indonesian and Middle Eastern Ulama in the Seventeenth and Eighteenth Centuries* (Crows Nest, NSW: Asian Studies Association of Australia), and Riddell, 2001.

7 Copies of Qurans and other handwritten works in Arabic and in Malay in Arabic script are still stored in the mosque where Raja Ali Haji worshipped and probably also taught. For descriptions of some of these manuscripts, see Ali Akbar, 2013, *Manuskrip Al-Qur'an di Pulau Penyengat* (Jakarta: Lajnah Pentashihan Mushaf Al-Qur'an). My special thanks to Dr Akbar for sharing his knowledge of Indonesia's Islam-based manuscripts and sending me materials from Indonesia.

8 Raja Ali Haji, 1982, *The Precious Gift (Tuhfat al-Nafis): An Annotated Translation by Virginia Matheson and Barbara Watson Andaya* (Kuala Lumpur: Oxford University Press), 274, and notes on 400.

9 Some *pesantren*, though, especially in Aceh, still have collections of pre-20th-century handwritten texts and commentaries. See Henri Chambert-Loir, 1996, 'Keeping the Faith: A Qur'an School Library', in Ann Kumar and John H McGlynn, eds., *Illuminations: The Writing Traditions of Indonesia* (Jakarta: The Lontar Foundation), 38-9; and Annabel Teh Gallop and Ali Akbar, 2006, 'The Art of the Qur'an in Banten: Calligraphy and Illumination', *Archipel* 72: 57-194.

10 Martin van Bruinessen, 1990, 'Kitab Kuning: Books in Arabic Script Used in the Pesantren Milieu', *Bijdragen tot de Taal-, Land- en Volkenkunde* 146: 253, 254.

11 The 'classic' account of this school (during the 1960s when Sirojuddin was a pupil) is that of Lance Castles, 1966, 'Notes on the Islamic School at Gontor', *Indonesia* 1: 30-45.

12 See Aboebakar Atjeh, 1948, *Sedjarah al-Qoeran* (Jogjakarta: Kementerian Agama), with a sixth edition published in 1989. I thank Tieke Atikah of the National Library of Australia for my copy of the 1948 edition, which is the one used here.

13 Aboebakar, 1948, 9.

14 Aboebakar, 1948, 321.

15 Haleem, 2004; see chapter 3, *Al-'Imrān*: 103.

16 Aboebakar, 1948, 53.

17 See AH Johns, 2016, '*Surat al-Mu'minun*: A Reading and Reflection', *Journal of Qur'anic Studies* 18(3): 74-5, for an analysis of how the Quran's language and arrangement conveys the magnificence of divine transcendence to awaken in readers emotions of awe and wonder.

18 Sirojuddin, email correspondence with the writer, 6 June 2016. The Indonesian reads: 'Jadi, ketika seseorang itu berilmu-pengetahuan, pada saat bersamaan dia sedang diangkat derajatnya (karena manusia yang paling tinggi derajatnya adalah yang berilmu-pengetahuan), apalagi kalau diajarkan nabi SAW sendiri bersabda, "Sesungguhnya aku ini diutus untuk menjadi guru." Nabi sebagai guru utama adalah "al-Quran yang berjalan" (seperti diakui Siti Aisyah, istrinya), yang menjadikan Al-Quran sebagai way of life. Al-Quran adalah sumber ilmu pengetahuan'.

19 The text of the talk appears in a privately published collection of Sirojuddin's writings; see Didin Sirojuddin AR, 2005, *Nuansa Kaligrafi Islam: Kumpulan tulisan sekitar ide-ide pengembangan seni kaligrafi Islam di Indonesia* (Islamic Calligraphy: Collected Writings about the Development of Islamic Calligraphy in Indonesia), (Jakarta: Studio Lemka), 287-92.

20 The Attributes (*ṣifāt*, sing. *ṣifa*) of Allah are the abstract qualities which lie behind His Names. The Names themselves are the epithets applied to Him as descriptives in the Quran; see HAR Gibb and JH Kramers, eds., 1991, *Shorter Encyclopaedia of Islam* (Leiden: Brill), 545.

21 The references for both these well-known Hadiths are not given.

22 Sirojuddin, 2005, 290-1. See also al-Ghazālī, 1992, 1995, *The Ninety-Nine Beautiful Names of God: al-Maqṣad al-asnā fī sharḥ asmā' Allāh al-ḥusnā*, trans. with notes David B Burrell and Nazih Daher (Cambridge: The Islamic Texts Society), 30, where al-Ghazālī's title of Chapter 4 reads, 'Explaining how the perfection and happiness of man consists in conforming to the perfections of God most high, and in adorning himself with the meanings of His attributes and names insofar as this is conceivable for man'. For more details on the 'Beautiful names of God', see Samer Akkach, 2015, 'Beautiful Names of God,' in *The Encyclopaedia of Islam Three* (Leiden: Brill) 54-7.

23 Franz Rosenthal, 1970, *Knowledge Triumphant: The Concept of Knowledge in Medieval Islam* (Leiden: EJ Brill), 95.

24 Rosenthal, 1970, 246.

25 Rosenthal, 1970. Rosenthal refers to the Prophet's belief in 'the necessary relationship of religious knowledge with good deeds and proper action', 247-8.

26 Quoted in Kenneth M George, 2010, *Picturing Islam: Art and Ethics in a Muslim Lifeworld* (London: Wiley-Blackwell), 95.

27 Didin Sirojuddin AR, 2012, *331 Goresan Hitam Putih Kaligrafi Islam: 'Melukis Hidup dengan Amal Saleh'* (331 Black and White Islamic Calligraphies: 'Paint Life with Good Deeds'), (Jakarta: LEMKA), quotation on back cover.

28 Quoted in Sirojuddin, 2005, 279. 'Yang penting pesan-pesan ayat yang mulia itu yang diharap menciptakan sensasi psikologis, sehingga penonton terpengaruh dan jadi orang baik-baik.' See also Anna M Gade, 2004, *Perfection Makes Practice: Learning, Emotion, and the Recited Qur'an in Indonesia* (Honolulu: University of Hawai'i Press), 41, 49, 270-3, for her arguments concerning changes in moral states through direct and affective engagement with the Quran.

29 WM Abdul Hadi et al., 1995, 'Pengantar Tim Curator (Curators' Comment) in Festival Istiqlal Foundation', *Seni Rupa Kontemporer Istiqlal: Istiqlal Contemporary Art* (Jakarta: Yayasan Festival Istiqlal), 12, my translation.

30 *'Innā lillāhi wa-innā ilayhi rājiʿūn'*, *al-Baqara* 2: 156.

31 At the 1995 event, President Suharto and his wife launched the massive hand-copied *Quran Istiqlal*, designed by Pirous and a team of artists and calligraphers. Indonesia claimed that it was the largest hand-copied Quran in the world. See George, 2010, 74-8.

32 MC Ricklefs, 2012, *Islamisation and Its Opponents in Java: A Political, Social, Cultural and Religious History, c. 1930 to the Present* (Singapore: NUS Press), chapters 5 and 6.

33 Quoted in Ricklefs, 2012, 165-6.

34 See Greg Fealy and Sally White, eds., 2008, *Expressing Islam: Religious Life and Politics in Indonesia* (Singapore: Institute of Southeast Asian Studies); and Greg Fealy and Virginia Hooker, eds., 2006, *Voices of Islam in Southeast Asia: A Contemporary Sourcebook* (Singapore: Institute of Southeast Asian Studies).

35 Julian Millie, 2008, '"Spiritual Meal" or Ongoing Project? The Dilemma of *Dakwah* Oratory', in Greg Fealy and Sally White, eds., *Expressing Islam: Religious Life and Politics in Indonesia* (Singapore: Institute of Southeast Asian Studies), 80.

36 But see Millie, 2008, for other forms.

37 Anne K Rasmussen, 2010, *Women, the Recited Qur'an, and Islamic Music in Indonesia* (Berkeley: University of California Press), 51, 58.

38 Rifki Rosyad, 2006, *A Quest for True Islam: A Study of the Islamic Resurgence Movement among the Youth in Bandung, Indonesia* (The Australian National University: ANU Press), 95.

39 Rasmussen, 2010, 258, note 11. For individual examples of the 'thirst' for religious knowledge, see Fealy and Hooker, 2006, 118-20.

40 For publishing, see CW Watson, 2005, 'Islamic Books and their Publishers: Notes on the Contemporary Indonesian Scene', *Journal of Islamic Studies* 16(2): 177-210. For mass media and popular culture, see Andrew N Weintraub, ed., 2011, *Islam and Popular Culture in Indonesia and Malaysia* (New York: Routledge).

41 See Gade, 2004, and Rasmussen, 2010. Winners of the national level represent Indonesia at international Quranic recitation competitions, where they shine.

42 For a path-breaking and impressive study of performed Islam and the transformative power of emotion in religion, see Gade, 2004.

43 Gade, 2004, 233.

44 His teachers were two of Indonesia's most respected calligraphers: Salim Fachry (then in his 80s), calligrapher of Indonesia's first national Quran, and Razzaq Muhili (then approaching 70), who was regarded as Indonesia's greatest living calligrapher. See <www.lemka.net>, Tab 'Tentang LEMKA, Sejarah Pendirian Lembaga' (7 May 2016).

45 Founded in 1959 with the motto 'A Magazine to Spread Culture in the Struggle to Reform and Modernise Islam', it published articles by leading religious scholars and intellectuals. It was closed down in 1960 for criticising Sukarno's anti-democratic policies. It was allowed to publish again in 1967 with a slightly different motto, 'Spreading Knowledge and Culture for the Guidance (*dakwah*) and Development of the *Umat*' (my translation); see H Harun Nasution, et al., eds., 2002, *Ensiklopedia Islam Indonesia*, 2nd ed., vol. 3 (Jakarta: Djambatan), 881-2.

46 For a selection of Sirojuddin's print media articles, see Tim 7 LEMKA, 2006, *Pak Didin Sirojuddin AR Menabur Ombak Kaligrafi: Catatan Media* (Mr Didin Sirojuddin AR spreads the waves of calligraphy: Media clippings), 6th ed. (Jakarta: Studio LEMKA).

47 See Didin Sirojuddin AR, 1987, *Seni Kaligrafi Islam* (Jakarta: Multi Kreasi).

48 See <www.lemka.net>, Tab 'Tentang LEMKA, Sejarah Pendirian Lembaga' (15 September 2016): 'Mempercepat proses pemasyarakatan seni menulis khat atau kaligrafi kepada seluruh lapisan masyarakat, khusunya masyarakat muda, di tanah air'.

49 See <www.lemka.net>, Tab 'Tentang LEMKA, Sejarah Pendirian Lembaga' (15 September 2016): 'Al Quran sebagai sumber etika, ketika seorang khatttat menggoreskan kaligrafi Arab. Jadi olahannya adalah kaligrafi Arab, etika pengolahannya bersumberkan kepada akhlak Al Quran. Dengan demikian, seorang khattat atau kaligrafer akan selalu dikontrol dan di bawah perlindungan gagasan, ilham penciptaan, estetika dan ajaran-ajaran yang terpantul dari bias keinginan Al Quran. Dalam ungkapan yang lebih sederhana lagi: Seorang khattat atau kaligrafer haruslah berakhlak baik, berbudi pekerti luhur, saleh dan berkarya untuk keagungan agama sesuai ajaran-ajaran yang tertuang dalam Kitab Suci Al Quran.'

50 As described in Rosenthal, 1970, 95. Also more generally, Rosenthal, 1970, 316, 318.

51 I owe this point to Gade's research; see Gade, 2004, 41. The Quranic verses are *al-Najm* 53:61-2.

52 The statement is featured on LEMKA's website, <www.lemka.net>.

53 Sirojuddin, email correspondence, 6 June 2016.

54 See quotes in Ilham Berlian, 2011, 'Peran Lembaga Kaligrafi al-Qur'an (LEMKA) dalam dakwa melalui seni Kaligrafi Islam' (The role of the Institute of Qur'anic Kaligrafi [LEMKA] in spreading Islam through Islamic Calligraphy). Unpublished Honours thesis, Universitas Islam Negeri Syarif Hidayatullah, Jakarta, 55, 59, 71.

55 Berlian, 2011, 66.

56 LEMKA publishes its own textbooks; see for example Didin Sirojuddin AR, 1997, *Khat Naskhi untuk Kebutuhan Primer Baca Tulis* (Naskh Script for Basic Reading and Writing), (IAIN Syarif Hidayatullah Jakarta Selatan: Lembaga Kaligrafi AlQuran); and Didin Sirojuddin AR, 2007, *Koleksi Karya Master Kaligrafi Islam* (Collected Works by Master Islamic Calligraphers), (Jakarta: Darul Ulum Press). Sirojuddin also translates Arabic works on calligraphy into Indonesian — for example, Kamil al-Baba, 1992, *Dinamika Kaligrafi Islam* (The Dynamics of Islamic Calligraphy), trans. Didin Sirojuddin AR (Jakarta: Darul Ulum Press).

57 Sirojuddin's success was reported in a lead editorial in *Panji Masyarakat* 550, 10 September 1987, 7.

58 He has been a member of judging panels in the Middle East, Turkey, Pakistan, Malaysia, and Brunei Darussalam.

59 In 1996, a group of religious leaders in Bandung, West Java, supported the establishment of a *Pesantren Kaligrafi* outside Jakarta. Six attempts were made to find a suitable site before the present site was located and purchased through *waqf* (religious endowment) donations.

60 Aboebakar, 1948, 119, 123. Sirojuddin is proud of the *pesantren*'s small but well-stocked library.

61 Haleem, 2004; chapter 10, *Yūnus*: 108; chapter 3, *Al-ʿImrān*: 191.

62 See for example LEMKA's website, <www.lemka.net>; blog, <http://lemkaonline.blogspot.com/>; Youtube clip, '*Aksi-aksi shoting di pesantren kaligrafi Alquran LEMKA*'; and Youtube video <https://www.youtube.com/watch?v=ZB3uqLyseW8>. (Thanks to Amrih Widodo for the last reference.)

63 Haleem, 2004, 36; chapter 3, *Al-ʿImrān*: 26.

64 Sirojuddin, email correspondence, 6 June 2016.

CHAPTER 6

THE ISLAMISATION OF *'ILM*: IDEALS AND REALITIES IN A GLOBALISED WORLD

SYED MEHBOOB BUKHARI

ABSTRACT[1]

Eminent contemporary scholars Seyyed Hossein Nasr and Ziauddin Sardar have endeavoured to rethink modern science within a theoretical framework that has come to be known as 'Islamisation'. Though their basic conceptions of what 'science' is may differ, both sought to define and develop, through the notion of *ʿilm*, an approach to scientific thinking that is distinctly 'Islamic'. 'Islamic science', as they have envisioned it, is a form of scientific undertaking that is intellectually and economically progressive, inherently ethical, and environment friendly. Most important, however, they have presented their version of 'Islamic science' as being fundamentally in opposition to 'Western science', thereby rejecting the reductionism and scientism engrained in the Western approach to knowledge. Thus conceived, 'Islamic science' is able, in their view, to overcome most, if not all, of the perceived material and spiritual maladies of the Muslim world. This chapter argues that the Islamisation of *ʿilm* project, while theoretically plausible, is impractical, utopic, and simplistic, as 'Islamic science' cannot be divorced from Western science and is vulnerable to the practical controls of the global capitalist system. The chapter begins by outlining the principles underlying Nasr's and Sardar's Islamisation of science thesis, and then considers the 19th-century Islamisation discourse that informed their own approach, before discussing the similarities and differences of the two discourses. It concludes by showing how the Islamisation of *ʿilm* approach remains vulnerable to the commodifying hegemony of capitalism, the very force that the Islamisation process was attempting to escape in the first place.

ISLAMISATION OF *'ILM*

Encounters with Western imperialism throughout the Muslim world in the 19th century forced many Muslim scholars to reconsider their traditional approach to knowledge. While some wondered whether there was something wrong with their understanding of the world, others realised that modern science had much to offer, and they reflected on how to appropriate modern science for their own needs. These unsettling encounters generated many questions: Is modern science compatible with the Islamic tradition? How should Muslims understand the post-Enlightenment developments of modern science? And can any space be generated that allows for the integration of modern science with the Islamic world view? These and other related questions assume the superiority of modern science over traditional Islamic sciences.

The Muslims' responses to these complex questions were myriad: some advocated the innate compatibility of modern science with Islam; others disagreed.[2] For the 19th-century Indian Muslim philosopher and reformist Syed Aḥmed Khān (d. 1898), both the 'word of God' (revelation) and the 'work of God' (nature) unfold and describe reality in complementary ways. At the same time, for Khān, proper understanding of the 'word of God' should conform with the correct interpretation of the 'work of God' or nature, which he thought was evident in modern science[3] — while almost a century later, the French surgeon Maurice Bucaille (d. 1980) famously proclaimed that many of the findings of modern science are in fact in conformity with the Quran.[4] Although such approaches are motivated by a desire to establish a sense of unity between Islam and science, they tend to subject *ʿilm*, as a special form of Islamic knowledge, to the empirical standards of modern science. They also assume and indirectly emphasise the universality of modern science.

Some Muslim intellectuals have refuted the positivistic analyses of Bucaille, and sought a reconstruction of the scientific study of nature. They aimed to introduce a better integration between modern and Islamic sciences, while maintaining the Islamic world view. Ismail Ragi al-Faruqi (d. 1986) argues that *ʿilm* is essentially divine, and that it thus encompasses modern science but does not remain limited to it.[5] Modern science can be embraced within the broader framework of *ʿilm*, provided that modern science does not violate the core values of the divine-inspired Islamic knowledge. This approach has become known as the 'Islamisation of *ʿilm*'. Reversing Bucaille's approach, which subjected Islam to modern science, Faruqi preferred to subject modern science to the measures and precepts of the Islamic world view.

The Islamisation of science discourse has focused, on the one hand, on exposing the ethical and environmental shortcomings of modern science, and, on the other, on delineating modern science as a distinctly Western approach to knowledge. This has led many Muslim scholars to deplore the uncritical accommodation of modern science into the Islamic world view, while allowing for the conditional 'integration' or 'synthesis' of modern science with the Islamic world view. Seyyed Hossein Nasr (b. 1933) and Ziauddin Sardar (b. 1951) are two leading contemporary representatives of the conditional approach to the Islamisation of science.[6] The following summarises their views and positions.

NASR: SCIENCE AND THE SACRED

For Seyyed Hossein Nasr, *ʿilm* is inherently religious. The Quranic revelation, one of the key sources of Islamic *ʿilm*, is 'dominated by its sacred quality and nature'.[7] God has created both the objects of knowledge and the intelligence — the gift of God — with which man cognises objects of knowledge. Accordingly, the nature of Islamic science is different from modern science because Islam has a different metaphysics and epistemology from that of the West.[8] In Islamic metaphysics, *ʿaql* (reason) is seen to be 'always attached to' and always to have 'derived sustenance from' revelation, and *ʿilm* (knowledge) is seen to be essentially both sacred and rational.[9] The Prophet Muhammad famously instructed Muslims to seek *ʿilm*, thus understood, from the cradle to the grave, and to travel as far as China to achieve this noble goal.[10] The continuity of the sacred nature of *ʿilm* in the Islamic tradition has given Islamic civilisation a unique character. According to the Islamic world view, Nasr asserts, humans must obtain 'supreme knowledge of the divinity' in order to actualise their hidden potentialities and talent and to be able to unlock 'the manifest in relation to the One'.[11]

In contrast to the Islamic world view, Nasr posits, modern Western epistemology presupposes a different metaphysics. It studies the material world quantitatively and mathematically. It measures the primary qualities (such as weight, height, length, and so on) of nature and tends to explain 'all physical reality in terms of the movement of atoms', an approach that has become known as scientific reductionism.[12] Modern physics was born out of this world view, which subsequently gave birth to other sciences. In short, modern science emanates from a metaphysics that is significantly different from Islamic metaphysics.[13]

Nasr argues that scientific reductionism combined with scientism (an ideology to test the legitimacy of everything on scientific parameters) has resulted in the 'disenchantment' of the world.[14] Enchantment, for Nasr, encompasses the spiritual and sacred aspects of reality. Thus, while attempting to understand the work of God, to use Khān's terms, modern science has promoted a disregard of God. Without this metaphysical outlook, Nasr claims, modern Western science would have been impossible. In response, Nasr strives to separate scientism from 'pure science', accusing scientism of cultivating and promoting an exploitative attitude towards nature. In doing so, Nasr believes he can extract 'pure science' from Western metaphysics and then re-employ this pure science to create a legitimate space for new 'Islamic science'.

In this process, the presence in the Muslim world of a sophisticated technological knowledge that has not been integrated into Islamic knowledge presents a complicated challenge for Nasr. To address this challenge, Nasr proposes a twofold approach: first, to 'create a paradigm drawn from Islamic sources and develop a chapter in the history of Islamic science based upon earlier Islamic tradition'; and, second, to 'criticize the premises and the conclusions of this [modern Western] science in the light of teachings of Islam'.[15] Nasr's Islamic science would, accordingly, 'integrate all that is positive [from] modern sciences into the Islamic world-view'.[16] The word 'positive' refers, in Nasr's view, to the scientific aspects that align with the Islamic tradition and should therefore be integrated into the Islamic world view. Thus, Nasr's Islamic science aims to synthesise Islamic spirituality and sacredness with the 'positives' of Western science.

Muslims, Nasr strongly believes, are ethically and religiously bound to act as 'protectors' of Allah's world of nature, and to strive to live 'in harmony with the natural environment'.[17] Islamic science should pursue equilibrium between humankind and nature through what Nasr describes as the Islamic principle of the 'interdependence and interrelation of all things in the Universe'.[18] In particular, Nasr thinks that Islamic science is helpful to the industrialised world 'in solving its energy problems by providing guidelines on the wise use of wind and solar energy'.[19] Energy can effectively be used by preserving 'as much energy as possible in any process and [by using] the most easily available form of energy requiring the minimum amount of disturbance of the environment'.[20] In this way, Islamic science can protect nature from 'aggressive destruction and the unilateral reaping of resources'.[21] And Muslims are empowered by science to 'put the rights of nature and all of the creatures of Allah including animals and plants in their place'.[22] To show Muslims living in diaspora the benefits of his approach, Nasr highlights the strengths of Islam by comparing the potentialities of Islamic sciences with the problems of Western capitalism. In short, 'Islamic science' that is achieved through integrating 'the positives' of modern science with Islamic morality and spirituality is, in Nasr's view, capable of overcoming the maladies of modern industrial capitalism.[23]

SARDAR: SCIENCE AND MORALITY

A contemporary of Nasr, Ziauddin Sardar has furthered the discourse on *'ilm* by advocating a pragmatic approach to Islamic science.[24] For Sardar, civilisations realise their values by producing distinct sciences. Without 'an objective problem-solving system', he posits, no civilisation can maintain its autonomous identity.[25] Science produced within a particular culture is necessary to negotiate people's day-to-day affairs and problems. Thus, in Sardar's view, science is instrumental for resolving mundane needs as well as 'the attainment of a higher [civilisational] goal'.[26]

For Sardar, Islam has established a civilisation as autonomous as any other in the world. Throughout Islamic history, Muslims have developed their distinct science 'subservient to the eternal values of Quranic revelation'.[27] Sardar states that *'ilm*/science is essentially 'a form of *'ibāda* (worship)'[28], and as such its pursuit cannot be 'in open transgression of Allah's commands ... at the expense of nature'.[29] Accordingly, Muslims are answerable to Allah for all their deeds. The unity of reality, knowledge, and ethics in Islam can prevent the unfair exploitation and domination of nature, which have been undertaken in the West in the name of modern science.

Sardar sees Islamic science as being 'subjectively objective' — that is, it pursues normative goals by resolving objective problems within Muslim societies.[30] The 'subjective' aspect has produced 'polymathy', a traditional system that promotes multiple methods of inquiry, rather than 'the method', which he describes as 'an institution that is largely unique to Islam'.[31] He considers this uniqueness to be predicated on a form of rationality that complies with Islamic ethical values. Unlike Western science, Islamic science advocates integration and synthesis of scientific empiricism and religious morality. It approaches reality holistically without breaking it into parts, while relying on its normative side to shape its objective inquiry and research.

From Sardar's perspective, Western science appears to be of no help to Muslims. He argues that reductionism of scientific inquiry has increased the gulf between ethics and knowledge. This has assisted global markets to cultivate the instrumental nature of modern science by funding projects which maximise capital accumulation but compromise ethical obligations. In addition, the anthropocentricity engrained in Western epistemology has caused Western science to exploit the natural world. In addition to being destructive and regulative, Sardar argues, Western science has also been 'labour-saving' and 'capital intensive'.[32] By contrast, Muslims have a shortage of capital and an excess of labour. Sardar accordingly thinks that the priorities and needs of Muslims are fundamentally different from Western civilisation, and thus that Western science is incapable of resolving Muslim issues. Muslims must 'express their individuality and meet their needs according to their wishes and resources' by reconceptualising and redesigning the 'Islamic science' that has 'always existed' in their long and rich tradition.[33]

Sardar works with a holistic framework of thinking known as *ijmālī* (from the root *j-m-l* denoting wholeness and beauty), which comprises diverse, yet interconnected, concepts, such as *tawḥīd* (divine unity), *khilāfa* (the caliphate), *'ibāda* (worship), *'ilm* (science/knowledge), *amāna* (trust), *ḥalāl* (that which is permissable), *ḥarām* (that which is forbidden), *'adl* (justice), *ẓulm* (injustice), *i'tidāl* (righteousness), *istiḥsān* (the ability to approve or to sanction), and *istiṣlāḥ* (public interest), the term we shall return to below. With reference to the *ijmālī* framework, Sardar attempts to synthesise 'pure knowledge' with 'moral knowledge'. The *ijmālī* approach has a dual function. On the one hand, it allows for the scientific exploration of the natural world, and, on the other, it regulates these explorations in terms of the ethical values of Islam. For instance, the concept of *tawḥīd* (divine unity) recognises that Allah is the creator of the universe and humankind, and people's attempts to understand aspects of His creation (such as nature) are synonymous with worship. This understanding entails ethical obligations: humans must deal with the 'world of creation' (*'ālam al-khalq*) in accordance with the will of Allah as dictated through the 'world of command' (*ʿālam al-amr*). It follows that the Islamic holistic approach to morality and knowledge or science (*ʿilm*) will render un-Islamic any exploitation of nature and humankind. In addition, the Quranic concept of *khalīfa* (trustee) makes every Muslim accountable to Allah for all his or her thoughts and deeds. Accordingly, every Muslim is ethically bound to treat natural resources with care in their use for the *istiṣlāḥ* (betterment) of human conditions, which should be for the wide benefit of all of humankind rather than for the gain of the individual or of small groups.

ISLAMISATION AND THE ORIENTALIST CHALLENGE

Nasr's and Sardar's Islamisation of *ʿilm* thesis mirrors a similar line of thought that emerged in the 19th century as a result of the Islamic encounter with Western modernity. The 19th-century Islamisation discourse evolved in a confrontational context against Western ideas and the Orientalist construction of Islam during the colonial expansion. The nature of this confrontation changed with the growth of the Islamisation discourse. In its earlier phase, Muslims felt threatened by European scientific theories that questioned the traditional relationship between God, humans, and nature. Here it is important to note that the Western challenge was construed and articulated within the Orientalist construction of Islam and in particular the question of '[w]hether religion and reason accommodate each other'.[34]

19th-century Orientalist thinkers tended to represent Islam as a dogmatic, static, legalistic identity, in distinction to the dynamic, rational, and autonomous West. Orientalists like Sir William Muir (d. 1905) and Ernest Renan (d. 1892) attempted to explain Islam's backwardness by emphasising how Islam and reason were inherently incompatible. Islam was condemned to prohibit the private use of reason and judgment. Renan, for example, in his 1883 lecture on 'Islam and Science' at the Sorbonne in Paris, proclaimed that Islam and science or modern civilisation (he equated modern science with civilisation) were incompatible with one another. For him, 'science was the form in which reason expressed itself ... in the modern world'.[35] On these premises, he prophesied that Islam would perish soon whereas European science would prosper and spread. He further claimed that Muslim minds were opened by their exposure to European ideas and people, rather than by, say, their inherent concern for *ʿilm* and love of reason.

Needless to say, the Orientalist construction of Islam was simplistic and, as Rahman claims, incorrectly 'overemphasized and exaggerated' different aspects of Islam.[36] Moreover, Rahman thinks that the Orientalists' assessment was based on 'superficial logic and inner poverty' of Western thought itself.[37] For instance, when Renan wrote of Islam, he was reductively comparing it to Catholicism, and thinking of religion in general terms. Moreover, the Orientalist perspective presupposed an unproblematic relationship between Enlightenment ideals and instrumental reason.

The Orientalist perspective overlooked how Muslims sought to integrate the social and political benefits of Western science and technology in a way that did not negatively influence their faith. In other words, they were looking for a form of synthesis that permitted Muslims to fully benefit (socially and politically) from Western science without requiring any minor compromise on faith. In synthesising religion and science, Muslims have encountered similar theological concerns and intellectual challenges to those that European proponents of science encountered, the key difference being that Muslims have been 'pressed to resolve overnight what had taken centuries in Europe'.[38] Earlier efforts for synthesis overlooked the fact that Western ideas of science were produced in certain 17th- and 18th-century European historical, social, and political conditions. In addition, the Islamisation discourse does not aim to reject the West as such. Rather it focuses on how the best of the West can be integrated into Islam.

19th-century Muslim thinkers sought to activate the idea of *ijtihād* (innovative reasoning) in order to integrate Western science with Islamic science. In the process, they delegitimised *taqlīd* (imitative reasoning) and opened primary sources for reinterpretation in adaptation with the dictates of modern European institutions, which appeared in the Islamic world during colonisation. Interestingly, 19th-century Muslim thinkers were willing to adopt the social benefits of modern science, but postulated that supposedly 'value-neutral' Western science could help Muslims to overcome their material deficiencies on their own terms. Thus, in the 19th-century Islamisation process, *ijtihād* was adopted as a tool to show the potential of Islam to overcome its foreign nature (as painted in the Orientalist construction), yet in its own way.

The thinking of the Azhar scholar Rifāʿa al-Ṭahṭāwī (d. 1873) epitomises the early-19th-century Islamisation trend. Rather than systematically analysing modern science and Islamic belief, he is more concerned with the partial induction of modern science into the Egyptian-Islamic national education policy. He sees himself acting in the role of a guardian to preserve the *sharīʿa*, which, according to him, guarantees social justice. If Islam is to maintain a central social and paedagogical role, then Muslims have to induct modern science into Islamic education.[39] He views modern science as being able to resolve existing problems, provided that it works under the supervision of *sharīʿa* law. Moreover, if science is adequately funded and if governments allow it to function independently, then the induction of science will empower modern Muslim states to resolve many of their civilisational problems.

For Ṭahṭāwī, the pursuit of science, rather than being a valid realm of metaphysical speculation, is imperative for what it can produce. He celebrates the socio-human benefits that modern science bestowed on European society, and positively identifies modern science with power and development, thereby idealising the beneficial side of Western science in his writings. To induct science, Ṭahṭāwī proposed a 'repossession argument'. Whatever knowledge a civilisation has lost in the past, he wrote, remains that civilisation's property, and it is imperative that they repossess their lost heritage, even if it has been revised and incorporated into other civilisations.

Notably, Ṭahṭāwī is more at home with Enlightenment ideals than with Western science. The growth of modern science presupposes freedom. The Enlightenment values of liberty, equality, and progress are evident in the Quran, and therefore, he maintains, Muslims are justified to idealise these values in their life. At the beginning of the 19th-century Islamisation discourse, Muslim scholars thought that the Enlightenment was value-neutral and consistent with the beliefs of the Islamic faith.

Jamāl al-Dīn al-Afaghānī (d. 1897) responded to the Orientalist construction of Islam with the same language. Inspired by François Pierre Guillaume Guizot (d. 1874), he redefined Islam as a civilisation rather than as a religion. Under the direct influence of 19th-century Europe, Afaghānī viewed civilisation as an 'active, willed progress, of a people who are pressing forward ... to change ... their condition'.[40] Afaghānī accordingly translates the 19th-century Islamisation discourse into 'worldly' terms. For him, the aim of human actions is not just the service of God alone, but also the creation of human civilisation. Muslim faith in transcendental Islam must be expressed through modern humanism, meaning a concern for humankind as such. A person's concern for his or her worldly conditions must be privileged on his or her concern for the hereafter. Here, concern for the hereafter is not denied; rather, its place and worth is redefined. In short, transcendental faith must uplift the 'socio-moral' life of the individual and the community in this world.[41] Here Islam is identified with civilisation, which is nothing but a will to change one's worldly conditions.

Defining Islam in terms of European civilisation leads Afghānī to idealise the 'fruits of reason, the sciences of modern Europe'.[42] He views modern science as an adequate methodology to change one's material conditions, and wishes to show that Renan's criticisms do not apply to Islam. He identifies philosophy with prophecy, saying that what prophets received through revelation was the same as what the philosopher thought by use of reason. The only distinction the two have, Afghānī argues, is their way of communication: philosophers disseminate the truth by clear concepts in complex language to 'the few', whereas prophets spread their truth through religious symbols to the 'many'. The essence of Islam is the same as that of modern rationalism, and thus it is in complete harmony with scientific reason. Thus, Afghānī urges Muslims to improve their society by following Enlightenment ideals and using instrumental reason.

Afghānī seems to be convinced that the Muslim civilisational crisis was internal rather than external, and that the power and pressure of European colonisation only gave the internal problems a new urgency. In reply to Renan, Afghānī admits that Muslims have failed to practise reason in the right (Enlightenment) spirit. If they had exercised reason correctly — that is to say, if they had exercised private judgment in the form of *ijtihād* — Afghānī believes that Muslim countries would necessarily be strong. Afghānī thus persuaded the Muslim community to understand their religion aright and live in accordance with its teachings.

After the ideological defence of Islam against Orientalist objections, a new strategy was developed. It was thought that if Islam failed to be reconciled with sciences today, Islam would become extinct in the world.[43] To counter static and legalistic representation of Islam, the aforementioned Muslim reformer and philosopher Syed Ahmad Khān, who was influenced by 'European rationalism and natural philosophy', contended that Islam is a religion of nature and reason.[44] To solve civilisational problems, he, too, activated the idea of *ijtihād*. Khān's Islamisation program is both ideological and institutional. His 'ideological Islamisation' seeks to reinterpret the foundational sources of Islam within his 'conformity to nature' methodology. He applies the contents of Islam to this principle and concludes that Islam justifies itself with this principle. Without reformulation, Khān uses the basic tenets of mediaeval Muslim philosophers to 'integrate the modern scientific worldview with the Islamic doctrine'.[45] Reason is the overriding standard. In order to assert the autonomy of nature and natural laws, Khān drew on the emancipationist spirit in Muslim thought. The institutional aspect of his program involved establishing institutions in accordance with the spirit of his ideological program. To institutionalise his program, he established Muhammadan Anglo Oriental College. Besides teaching, it had a scientific society and a translation house. The translation house was responsible for translating Western texts published in Europe into Urdu language. All institutions aimed to integrate Western disciplines with Islamic heritage.

Following Afghānī, Muhammad 'Abduh (d. 1905) restated that Islam is the only religion compatible with reason. Reason (science) and religion aid human development at different levels. 'Abduh accentuates Islam's presentation 'in terms that would be acceptable to [the] modern mind'.[46] For the acquisition and understanding of modern knowledge, 'Abduh suggests that doors for the influence of new ideas should be opened. Thus, he opens the closed doors of *ijtihād* in order to welcome new ideas. For this, he divides Islamic law into two realms: people's religious duties to God, and their social duties and regulations. The former are eternal and unchangeable; however, the latter are open to new interpretations as socio-political conditions change. 'Abduh used this distinction to great effect and brought the traditional social realm of Muslims into capitalist hegemony.

In summary, Western science serves as a relevant and authentic model to overcome problems in the Muslim world. This is true for both discourses of Islamisation. The 19th-century discourse had a limited success. It aimed to convince Muslim leadership to inculcate scientific thinking and culture among common Muslims. The direction of intellectual revolution was top-down: no leader has succeeded in establishing legitimacy within the various groups and institutions that possess the power and authority to influence and implement policy decisions.

ISLAMIC SCIENCE IN THE POSTCOLONIAL WORLD

In the mid-20th century, most of the Muslim world was liberated from colonialism, and Muslim populations started living in comparatively more autonomous conditions. Yet these altered conditions did not help Muslim thought to transcend so-called Western science. Rather, science was given a new role and meaning encompassed by the new term 'Islamic science'.[47] Many of the themes and patterns of earlier discourses on the role and place of science in the Muslim world reappear in Nasr's and Sardar's Islamic scientific enterprise. Nasr's and Sardar's contributions may accordingly be viewed as continuing the previous themes of adaptation and synthesis. In line with their forerunners, Nasr's and Sardar's arguments revolve around the relevance and ability of Islamic science to solve contemporary civilisational problems. Further, in relation to this, they also consider the relevance of Islam in the modern world. Their arguments for Islam's relevance are premised on Islam's self-sufficient and universal character, and, like their 19th-century precursors, Nasr and Sardar return to the foundational sources of Islam, the Quran and Sunnah, to explain these characteristics.

However, unlike the 19th-century Islamisation scholars, contemporary scholars like Nasr and Sardar are critical of Western science. They consider Western science both inadequate for understanding, and incapable of resolving, problems in the Muslim world, because Western science adheres to a different world view from that of Islam. In addition, they consider Western science to be part of the problem rather than solution, in view of its relationship to global exploitation and environmental degradation. Both accordingly advocate the construction of a new form of Islamic science based on 'authentic Islam'. While they are both optimistic that new 'authentic' Islamic science will be relevant to the problems of the Muslim world, and while both use Islamic epistemological principles to establish their conception of Islamic science, they struggle to define the idea of 'authentic Islam'. Sardar grounds authentic Islam in orthodox Islamic tradition. For Nasr, it is rooted in aspects of Sufi mysticism. The most pressing question is: how far has the proposed Islamic science come out from behind the shadow of Western science? Both authors are content to import from external sources, provided the import is fully integrated into Islamic epistemology. Does integration of the 'positives' of Western science into Islamic epistemology establish the autonomy of Islamic science from its Western counterpart?

The criticism of Western science has also overshadowed the practical program of Islamic science.[48] Accordingly, how can Islamic or sacred science operate to revolutionise Muslims in contemporary global society? Sardar and Nasr do not have clear answers, besides a few general and ideal statements. For this reason, the discourse on Islamic science is heavily criticised for being 'rhetorical', 'overambitious', and 'non-practical'.[49] It has failed to 'solve the particular problems that were initially attributed to western science'.[50] Furthermore, the Islamisation of science discourse has been critical of capitalist exploitation, yet it has surprisingly ignored the influences of hegemonic capitalist regimes within the context of which the proposed 'Islamic science' is thought to be produced and functionalised. When critiquing Western science, both Nasr and Sardar have presupposed its relationship with the state and the market. They have accused the Western state and market of manipulating modern science and leading it down dangerous pathways that often result in systemic environmental and human catastrophes. In their theorisation of Islamic science, Nasr and Sardar have disregarded the contemporary vital nexus between science, modern state, and the global market.[51] The state and the market are important institutions for shaping ideas and practices, and for cultivating individual and public interests in contemporary societal conditions. The conditions in which 'Islamic science' is produced and practised thus deserve rigorous examination.

In the process of actualising Islamic science, two steps may be gleaned from the works of Nasr and Sardar. First, Islamic scientific policy should be developed independent of the state because the modern state has a complex bureaucratic structure and is dominated by practical interests.[52] The policy must move towards 'strong objectivity' — that is, objective problems of the Muslims should be resolved within the *ijmālī* framework of values. As Sardar puts it, both 'the ends and means of science' as well as Muslim society are 'dictated by the ethical system of Islam'.[53] He further says that'[t]he needs of the community' (that is, the 'basic problems of everyday living') should be isolated objectively.[54] The policy must reflect 'both *istiṣlāḥ*, that is public interest, as well as public participation' of a well-informed public.[55] Moreover, the interconnection between *ʿilm* and *istiṣlāḥ* ensures that knowledge is pursued 'to promote equality, social justice, and values that enhance the well-being of Muslim society and culture'.[56] This abstract policy, however, is, according to Sardar, 'given practical shape in the objective framework of Sharia', which is a 'methodology for solving problems' that provides both the ethical norms and the legal structure within which actual decisions can be made.[57] *Sharīʿa* provides the 'universal common good of all created beings encompassing both our immediate welfare and our future in the hereafter'.[58] Put simply, to solve the problems of Muslim society within the bounds of Islamic ethics, the genuine needs of Muslims should be determined objectively, independent of the state interests.

It is necessary to consider the language that Nasr and Sardar use to develop their discourse on Islamic science, and how that language intersects and diverges from the preceding 19th-century Islamisation discourse. One can argue that Nasr and Sardar ground their sciences in the abstract principles of Islamic ethics, which are directed to integrate or adjust with contemporary changes that are, in fact, nothing but global capitalism.

SCIENCE AND PUBLIC INTEREST

While the 19th-century Islamisation discourse tended to emphasise the idea of *ijtihād* (innovative reasoning) in dealing with the benefits of modern science, the contemporary discourse of Nasr and Sardar shifts the emphasis towards the notion of *istiṣlāḥ* (public interests). Nasr and Sardar consider 'Western science', in its globally circulated forms, to be of no help to Islam, and in this they differ from their 19th-century predecessors. Nasr and Sardar call for a return to the primary sources in search for 'authentic Islam', within the frame of which 'Islamic science' can be revived, taking advantage of modern developments. Muslim thought thus shifts from adaptation to the construction of a new Islamic science based on orthodox Islamic epistemological grounds.

Sardar's work, as already mentioned, promotes the approach of *istiṣlāḥ,* which is concerned primarily with reform and improvement in the 'public interest'. Historically, the Arabic word *istiṣlāḥ* (from the root *s-l-ḥ*) meant 'to seek the best public interest', and was often used interchangeably with *maṣlaḥa,* meaning 'interest', public or private. In its semantic development, however, the term has acquired diverse meanings at different times and in different Muslim cultures. For the renowned mediaeval theologian Abū Ḥāmid al-Ghazālī (d. 1111), *istiṣlāḥ* was among one of the fundamental 'purposes' of Islamic law (*maqāṣid al-sharīʿa*), which aimed at protecting public and individual interests, including one's religion, reason, and justice. Ghazālī argued against the utilitarian interpretations of *istiṣlāḥ* on the grounds that such an interpretation would undermine the purposes of *sharīʿa*.[59] It is one of the purposes of *sharīʿa* to protect genuine benefits that fulfil genuine needs, and science should serve genuine Islamic purposes to receive the protection of the *sharīʿa*.[60] This serving of Islamic interests would imbue science with an Islamic identity.

The concept of 'public interest' has its origins in mid-17th-century Europe, when it was constructed in contrast to the concept of 'common good', which did not sit well with the rising capitalist values of the state at the time.[61] 'Common good' was associated with the selfish, paternalistic, and unjustified demands of the monarchies.[62] While the concept of public interest does not signify the aggregate interests of individuals, it nonetheless places the individual at its centre and seeks to protect his or her capitalist interests. The English philosopher Thomas Hobbes (d. 1679) stipulated that humans are essentially selfish beings, and that to pursue individual material interests is a legitimate and moral course of action for humans.[63] It is the individual capitalist interest that develops the foundations for, and defines, public interest. When the interests of a variety of individuals match the interests of others, the shared interests are defined as public interests, against which private interests are identified. It was this public interest, or what Jean Jacques Rousseau (d. 1778) calls 'the General will', that would legitimate the governance of the modern state. Thus 'public interest' and the modern state are defined and maintained together.

In the Islamic context, the 19th-century reformist scholar Muhammad Rashīd Riḍā (d. 1935) advocated the liberation of *istiṣlāḥ* from the bounds of *sharīʿa*, and subjected the traditional approach of *maqāṣid al-sharīʿa* to reformation (*istiṣlāḥ*) in order to 'make adaptation more flexible' within the growing dominance of capitalist order.[64] Riḍā doubted the ability of traditional 'deductive analogy' (*qiyās*) to cope with modern changes. Appropriate for classical and mediaeval legal methodologies as it might have been, for Riḍā Islamic deductive analogy became impractical and unfit for dealing with 'civil transactions' and 'worldly interests (*maṣāliḥ dunyawiyya*)'.[65] Riḍā strove to free Islamic thinking from the grip of classical religious theory and to introduce a methodology that focuses on public interest 'where considerations of human needs, interest and necessity would reign supreme in elaborating a legal corpus'.[66]

Sardar, following Rida, privileges *istiṣlāḥ* methodology for reconstruction. For him, the democratic participation of well-informed people formulates public interest. He seems to postulate an ideal 'public sphere' where people can discuss matters of need without being influenced by various power groups. However, in practice, no sane Muslim will 'accept such [a] level-playing field where everyone has (equal) rights to participate in the debate'.[67] Discussions are complicated and stressful, and topics might be complex and not easily handled. It is unlikely that public welfare and good can be determined democratically in the way that Sardar suggests. Not only would it be hard to effect in practice, but also the concept of 'public interest' relies on the conception and use of power.[68]

Indeed, Sardar aims to *construct* rather than uncover the true needs and interests of Muslims in order to adjust to the dominant capitalist order. Sardar accordingly decontextualises the concept of *istiṣlāḥ* from its historical association with *sharīʿa* and makes it serve future solutions for troubled Muslim societies. In doing so, *istiṣlāḥ* is made abstract, having no value tied to Islamic history, and thus now being ready to be manipulated and controlled. Indeed, it is important to note that two competing concepts, namely *istiṣlāḥ* (which has religious bearings) and public interest (which is a secular idea), have evolved in two different histories for different objectives and have now been subsumed under capitalist discourse and practice. Both of these terms have first been decontextualised from their life worlds respectively and then reassembled for the benefits of the capitalist system.[69]

ISLAMIC SCIENCE IN A GLOBALISED WORLD

Muslim societies today are integrated into the global capitalist system, which is indifferent and impersonal. Global capitalism constructs and shapes everyone's desires regardless of whether the recipient is Muslim or non-Muslim. Both Nasr and Sardar tend to underestimate the power of dominant institutions of the globalised world in shaping human consciousness, interests, values, desires, and ideas. Their proposed Islamic scientific policy should, they urge, receive 'encouragement' and 'strong support from Muslim states'.[70] In so doing, they hesitate to give any account to ensure that Islamic scientific policy is constructed independent of the control of capitalist hegemony. Capitalist institutional influence receives little attention from them. Invisible though it might be, institutional influence is so forceful that it can lead people to follow, like members of a chorus. In contemporary capitalism, desires, wants, and needs are continuously constructed and shaped by transnational and multinational branding advertisements and numerous other practices. Needs may to some degree remain stable, but desires are constructed and reconstructed ceaselessly. Moreover, needs are constantly filtered through the global market for definition and satisfaction. In the contemporary capitalist society, to separate genuine needs from speculated desires is becoming harder.

The scientific policies of most contemporary Muslim countries are accordingly subservient to their economic or military problems. Indeed, the current practices of Muslim states is to instrumentalise science for their arbitrarily defined national interests. Consequently, the question of whether scientific policies should be developed independently from state interests, at both national and transnational levels, and directed to the immediate welfare of the people remains at the margins. The success of the kind of Islamic science conceived of by Nasr and Sardar requires intellectual revolution from the ground up. To achieve it, they criticise the priorities of Muslim states and try to convince them that they should privilege the welfare of common people rather than the superficial interests of the states. The states must only fund and implement Islamic scientific policies. Muslim states, they insist, must allow ample space for the growth and development of traditional knowledge, and must exploit untapped reservoirs of indigenous knowledge of and experience in medicine, agriculture, and natural resources.

If a single Muslim state cannot resolve all of its issues by employing local resources, Sardar argues, it can effectively do so by collectively identifying common problems and pooling resources together at the level of *umma* (the transnational Muslim community), because the Muslim world as a whole possesses enough resources to tackle and solve such problems.[71] In this case, the states can turn their attentions to the intellectuals and scientists: their strategies and policies should be funded and implemented democratically. In order to support his argument, Sardar gives the example of the industrialised Islamic state of Malaysia, which has shown, according to him, seriousness about science and development. Malaysia has poured 10 per cent of its Gross National Product into science and education, and the results have been impressively transformative.[72] Interestingly, there does not seem to be anything impressive in the case of Malaysia besides the fact that it has been subsumed in global capitalist hegemony.

In this way, Nasr and Sardar do not deviate from their 19th-century predecessors, who wanted to suggest their ideological agenda to their respective states. They seem to believe that if science is adequately funded by the governments, and is allowed to function freely and independently, it will revolutionise common Muslims, who will consequently change their socio-political conditions. Once governments are convinced, Nasr and Sadar argue, transformation of Muslim societies is not too far off. This belief presupposes that the success of any Islamic scientific development policy entirely depends on modern sovereign Muslim states designing their own policies and modes of implementations without interference from transnational actors. The belief further presupposes that Islamic scientific enterprise is thought and practised in tandem with the modern state of which they speak quite little. Modern states are becoming less sovereign and increasingly part of global capitalist hegemony.

This chapter concludes that such presuppositions reflect ideal thinking that is divorced from the dominating forces and constraints of global realities. The Islamisation of science discourse has evolved in relation to Western science and cannot effectively come out from its shadows. As contemporary representative voices of the Islamisation of science discourse, Nasr's and Sardar's interventions are hinged predominantly on the criticism of Western science. Islamic science, for them, is meant to transcend the domination of Western science as well as the capitalist system that supports it. Their vision of the possible ways to achieving this, while taking into account the essential role Western capitalism has played in the development of modern science, tends to avoid testing its workability against the conditions of global capitalist hegemony.

This chapter has placed and examined the Islamisation of science discourse in the context of the global capitalist system in order both to understand its tentative potentials and to expose its limitations. This examination has shown that the Islamic parameters or concepts around which the arguments for 'Islamic science' are constructed are rather abstract and vague. Contemporary capitalism via its transnational paradigm institutions reduces classical Islamic concepts, on which Islamic science is constructed, to mere abstract ideas by first decontextualising them from their history and then reassembling them with capitalist ideals without any resistance. Furthermore, *istiṣlāḥ* methodology, on which contemporary scholars rely, is inherently weak because determining the interests and needs of Muslims objectively in the realm of 'public interest', though ideal, is in practice difficult in contemporary capitalist conditions. Hegemonic capitalism restricts the possibilities of picking up 'positives' from Western science. Accepting the positives whilst rejecting the negatives is not as simple and straightforward an exercise as Nasr suggests, and 'Islamic science' thesis remains vulnerable to the commodifying hegemony of capital.

NOTES

1 I would like to acknowledge a travel grant from HEC Pakistan, without which my presentation of an earlier version of this work at the *'Ilm* conference at the University of Adelaide might not have been possible. I also appreciate the comments of the reviewers, editor, and publisher on earlier versions of this chapter, which have improved the quality of this work.

2 Issa J Boullata, 1990, *Trends and Issues in Contemporary Arab Thought* (Albany: SUNY), 4.

3 John L Esposito, 1984, *Islam and Politics* (Syracuse: Syracuse University Press), 54.

4 Maurice Bucaille, 1978, *The Bible, the Quran and Science* (Paris: Sehers).

5 Clinton Bennett, 2005, *Muslims and Modernity* (London: Continuum), 107-28.

6 Christopher A Furlow, 1996, 'The Islamization of Knowledge: Philosophy, legitimation, and politics', *Social Epistemology* 10(3/4): 267.

7 Seyyed Hossein Nasr, 1994, *Ideals and Realities of Islam* (London: The Aquarian Press), 123.

8 Nasr is an Iranian-born Muslim thinker currently based at George Washington University. As manifested in his corpus, he was influenced spiritually and intellectually by Frithjof Schuon (d. 1998) in his early career.

9 Nasr, 1994, 102.

10 Seyyed Hossein Nasr, 1990, *Traditional Islam in the Modern World* (London: Kegan Paul International), 120-36.

11 Nasr, 1994, 150, 133.

12 Seyyed Hossein Nasr, 1998, *A Young Muslim's Guide to the Modern World* (Lahore Pakistan: Suhail Academy), 186.

13 Nasr, 1998, 188.

14 Max Weber borrows the concept of 'disenchantment' from Friedrich Schiller to describe the character of capitalist society which is oriented on scientific understanding and rational processes, as opposed to the traditional society where 'the world remains a great enchanted garden'. In this view, the bureaucratised capitalist society devalues spiritual and mystical aspects of life.

15 Seyyed Hossein Nasr, 2010, 'Islam and The Problem of Modern Science', *Islam and Science* 8(1): 69.

16 Nasr, 2010, 69.

17 Nasr, 1998, 192.

18 Seyyed Hossein Nasr, 1976, *Islamic Science: An Illustrated Study* (England: World of Islam Festival Publishing Company Limited), 228.

19 Nasr, 1976, 231.

20 Nasr, 1976, 233.

21 Nasr, 1976, 227.

22 Nasr, 1998, 191.

23 Nasr, 1990, 130.

24 Sardar is a Pakistani-born Muslim intellectual educated and brought up in Britain. His intellectual interest lies in the future of Muslim societies. For this reason, he spends considerable time in some Muslim countries, particularly Saudi Arabia and Malaysia, where he surveys the state of science and technology in those regions, and helps to modernise some aspects of Islamic life there (for example, the Hajj in Saudi Arabia).

25 Ziauddin Sardar, 2006, *How Do You Know?* (London: Pluto Press), 106.

26 Sardar, 2006, 137.

27 Sardar, 2006, 133.

28 Sardar, 2006, 134.

29 Sardar, 2006, 134.

30 Sardar, 2006, 146.

31 Sardar, 2006, 145.

32 Sardar, 2006, 157.

33 Sardar, 2006, 159. See also Ziauddin Sardar, 1989, *Explorations in Islamic Science* (London: Mansel), 21.

34 Fazlur Rahman, 1979, *Islam*, 2nd ed. (Chicago: University of Chicago Press), 215.

35 Quoted in Albert Hourani, 2013, *Arabic Thought in the Liberal Age* (Cambridge, UK: Cambridge University Press), 121.

36 Rahman, 1979, 214.
37 Rahman, 1979, 215.
38 John Livingston, 1996, 'Western Science and Educational Reform in the Thought of Shaykh Rifa al-Tahtawi', *International Journal of Middle East Studies* 28(4): 548.
39 Livingston, 1996, 547.
40 Quoted in Hourani, 2013, 115; see also Rahman, 1979, 216.
41 Rahman, 1979, 216.
42 Quoted in Hourani, 2013, 115.
43 Rahman, 1979, 217.
44 Rahman, 1979, 218.
45 Rahman, 1979, 218.
46 Rahman, 1979, 217.
47 It is interesting that both discourses evolved in conjunction with the development of the Western discourses.
48 Nidhal Guessoum, 2015, *Islam's Quantum Question* (London: IB Tauris).
49 Andrew Jamison, 1994, 'Western Science in Perspective and the Search for Alternatives', in Jean-Jacques Salomon et al., eds., *The Uncertain Quest: Science, Technology and Development* (Tokyo: United Nations Press).
50 Jamison, 1994, 131-67.
51 I have in mind Gilles Deleuze's small article 'Postscript on the Societies of Control', in *Negotiations* (1995, New York: Columbia University Press), in which he articulates his ideas about the society in which we all are living today. Contemporary society, Deleuze writes, inherently controls human beings, their desires, their ideas, and so on. His concept of the controlling society was refined by Michael Hardt; see 'The Global Society of Control', *Discourse* 20(3): 139-52. See also Michael Hardt and Antonio Negri, 2000, *Empire* (Cambridge M.A: Harvard University Press) for a further development of these ideas.
52 Sardar, 2006, 188; Nasr, 2010, 63-75.
53 Sardar, 2006, 160.
54 Sardar, 2006, 137, 157.
55 Sardar, 2006, 188.
56 Sardar, 2006, 134.
57 Sardar, 2006, 100.
58 Sardar, 2006, 100.
59 Abu Ishaq al-Shatabi (d. 1388) has signalled that '*maslaha* is the only overriding objective of *shar'iah* securing genuine benefits for the people in this world and hereafter'. See Muhammad Khalid Masud, 1977, *Islamic Legal Philosophy: A Study of Abu Ishaq al-Shatibi's Life and Thoughts* (Isamabad: Islamic Research Institute), 221.
60 Mohammad Hashim Kamali, 1988, 'Have We Neglected the Shariah Law Doctrine of Maslaha?', *Islamic Studies* 27: 287-304. In order to be valid, public interest (*maṣlaḥa 'āmma*) must fulfil certain conditions, one of which is being genuine (*ḥaqīqiyya*) and not false or fictitious (*wahmiyya*).
61 JAW Gunn, 1969, *Politics and the Public Interest in the Seventeenth Century* (London: Routledge & K Paul).
62 Virginia Held, 1970, *The Public Interest and Individual Interests* (New York: Basic Books).
63 Bruce Douglass, 1980, 'The Common Good and the Public Interest', *Political Theory* 8(1): 107.
64 Vikør S Knut, 2005, *Between God and Sultan: A History of Islamic Law* (Oxford: Oxford University Press), 234-5.
65 Wael B Hallaq, 1998, *A History of Islamic Legal Theories* (United Kingdom: Cambridge University Press), 217.
66 Hallaq, 1998, 219. As Islamic legal and intellectual historian Hallaq has noted, to 'accept the revealed texts' affirmation of the cause of welfare, interest and necessity and to reject all other stipulations of rules and precepts, without proper theoretical justification amounts to nothing less than sheer arbitrariness' and makes 'law nominally Islamic' and dominantly capitalist: 224.
67 Guessoum, 2015, 138.
68 According to the German philosopher Jürgen Habermas (1989), the public sphere is coextensive with the state. Public interests are determined at the top of the official political hierarchy, non-democratically implemented in a strongly controlled manner by the executive authorities. Public interest is synonymous with 'state interest'.

69 I have in mind Gilles Deleuze's (1926-95) thinking here. Deleuze argues that capitalism in its contemporary operation decontextualises non-capitalist concepts from their history and then reassembles and subsumes them under capitalist domination; see Gilles Deleuze and Felix Guattari, 2005, *Anti Oedipus* (India: Viva Books Private Limited), 242-60.

70 Nasr, 2010, 71; Sardar, 2006, 188.

71 Sardar, 2006, 189.

72 Sardar, 2006, 188.

Chapter 7

In between the mind and the heart: Kātip Çelebi's concept of ʿilm

Selen Morkoç

ABSTRACT

Kātip Çelebi (1609-57) was a distinguished and prolific 17th-century Ottoman scholar, whose works exhibit openness towards the 'new science' of the early modern period. His geographical work *Cihannüma* (Displaying the World) shows his awareness of the new geographical knowledge and discoveries unfolding in Europe during his time. Meanwhile his major bibliographical work *Kashf al-ẓunūn* (Dispelling Doubts) presents a lengthy and sophisticated engagement with the Islamic concept of *ʿilm* in an attempt to reconstruct its theoretical foundations, to demonstrate its progressive nature, and to emphasise the necessity and usefulness of its rational and philosophical dimensions, which have come under attack in recent years. This chapter examines Kātip Çelebi's last work, *Mīzān al-ḥaqq* (The Balance of Truth), which captures his inner uncertainty about the significance of *ʿilm*. Its aims are, first, to show how Çelebi's conceptualisation and definition of *ʿilm* oscillated between the heart and the mind. Second, the chapter shows the way in which he understood and approached the relationship between reason and faith as complementary rather than opposing instruments of knowledge and elements of belief. In this intertwined conception, rational sciences and philosophy were considered as necessary to religious understanding. Third, the chapter discusses Çelebi's rational approach to answering the 21 controversial issues generated by the Kāḍīzāde and Sivāsī antagonism that were hotly debated within Ottoman circles. These included the legality of music and dance in religious practices and worship, and the morality of social habits new to the times, such as smoking, opium, and coffee drinking.

DREAM AND TRUTH

In his last work, *Mīzān al-ḥaqq* (The Balance of Truth), the celebrated 17th-century Ottoman scholar and bibliophile Kātip Çelebi (1609-57) presents a chronologically ordered biographical account of his life and works.[1] The account reveals his oscillation between rational and religious sciences (*ʿaklī* and *şerʿī ʿilimler*) at various stages of his short yet prolific career, pointing to the deep sense of uncertainty he felt concerning the right approach to truth. At the end of this biographical account, Çelebi relates the story of a significant dream he had, which seemed to have delivered him out of the state of uncertainty and showed him the correct path to truthful knowledge. Referring to the dream as 'Glad tidings', Çelebi wrote:

> While I was beginning the fair copy of the present treatise on the eve of Sunday 24 Muharram 1067 [22 November 1656], the Glory of the World (Peace be Upon Him) appeared in a dream to my unworthy self. He was in an open field, garbed as a warrior, girded for battle and wearing a sword. He was in a remote spot, surrounded by his aides and helpers. I stood in his august presence and asked him about certain problems of the sciences, and he answered me. The one thing I clearly remember is that he was standing and I was half standing, half sitting. In the course of my questioning him, I kissed his blessed knees and said, 'O Prophet of God, suggest a name with which I may occupy myself'. He replied, 'Occupy yourself with the name of the Prophet', in a great voice, so my ears were full of it and I awoke with it still ringing in my head.[2]

Çelebi's dream occurred at a late stage in his career when he was preoccupied with pursuing and teaching rational sciences (*ʿaklī ʿilimler*) and mathematics, and hence he interpreted the Prophet's message as a call to return to focusing on traditional or religious sciences (*şerʿī ʿilimler*). The Prophet's advice to Çelebi to occupy himself with the Prophet's name meant to confirm to Çelebī that the only way for attaining truthful knowledge of God was through God's Messenger himself. At that critical moment, it became clear to Çelebi that the rational and philosophical sciences alone were inadequate means for attaining truthful knowledge of God, and that rational understanding must be complemented with transmitted religious wisdom if one was to be able to 'fly' towards the truth. 'Because two wings are necessary to fly', he wrote, 'one cannot take a distance with one wing. Rational and religious sciences are comparable to two wings'.[3]

Çelebi's oscillation between reason and tradition, the mind and the heart, in his pursuit of truth is reflective of a wider debate at the time concerning the right approach to truthful knowledge. His dream might have represented a decisive moment that revolved around his personal dilemma, yet his views can be taken to represent a prevailing current among various intellectual circles in Ottoman society. This study considers Çelebi's experiences to be an important 'barometer' for understanding intellectual developments in the early modern period. It examines his multiple engagements with the polarity of rational and religious sciences, in an attempt to unravel his complex understanding and articulation of the concept of *ʿilm*. At that time, *ʿilm* began to take on new dimensions, especially with the emergence of a new mode of knowing that was to become known later as 'modern science'. Çelebi was among the first Ottoman scholars who actively engaged with early modern sciences and attempted to incorporate their findings and methodology into the Islamic perspective. His attempts to expand the meaning of *ʿilm* beyond its traditional bounds while oscillating between his mind and his heart is the focus of this study.

EARLY MODERN OTTOMANS

Kātip Çelebi is viewed by many Ottoman historians as one of the leading supporters of the emerging rationalism and new intellectual trends that changed Europe in the 17th and 18th centuries.[4] Born in Istanbul, Kātip Çelebi was also known as Hacı Khalīfa, yet his proper name was Mustafa bin Abdullah. As the title Çelebi in his name suggests, he came from a well-established Istanbul family of the upper middle class.[5] His father was a member of the cavalry of the Porte (*silāḥdār*) as well as a scribe in the fiscal administration (*Anadolu muḥāsebesi*). These official posts afforded him the financial means to hire private tutors for his son's education outside the traditional *madrasa* system.[6] Early in his career in the chancery, Çelebi spent considerable time travelling as he joined the Hemedan,

Erzurum, Tercan, Revan, and Baghdad campaigns. He spent most of his later life, however, in his native city of Istanbul working as an accountant and a clerk in the Ottoman bureaucracy. After inheriting a considerable amount of wealth from his family later in life, Çelebi was able to leave his official job and devote himself entirely to his intellectual pursuits.[7] His exceptional skills in categorising and cataloguing might have been a result of his occupational background.

Çelebi was a polymath as well as a scholar, genuinely concerned with both the status of knowledge and the socio-religious problems of the Ottoman society. In addition to being an author, he was an avid collector of books. Ottoman historian Gottfried Hagen estimates that Çelebi had the largest private library in Istanbul in his time.[8] In his short life of 48 years, Çelebi managed to write 21 books, the largest and most important of which was his massive seven-volume catalogue of Islamic books and sciences entitled *Kashf al-ẓunūn* (Dispelling Doubts). The fact that he came from outside the traditional *madrasa* system might explain his broad perspective and tendency to synthesise knowledge from the many sources and disciplinary fields available to him. He explained the wide horizon of thinking which his works reveal by describing '[t]he supreme zeal he owned', which 'did not allow him to suffice with one single scientific field'.[9]

Çelebi lived in a period of significant change which presents contrasting characteristics according to the viewpoint from which it is considered. From the politico-economic and military perspectives, the 17th century was a period of social confusion, economic crises, and military stagnation in Ottoman history. It is identified with the start of the decentralisation of the Ottoman Empire, which is presumed to have taken place between the death of Süleyman the Magnificent in 1566 and the Treaty of Karlowitz in 1699. These changes, as Karen Barkey argues, can be seen as a result of an international crisis that was omnipresent across Eurasia and was due to changing economic and military relations between the East and the West.[10]

The pre-modern Ottoman perception of history, as Hagen argues, was built on the dynastic myth supporting holy war against the infidel, which promoted expanding physical territories for the spread of the Islamic faith. Its premise was that ultimate justice leads to a stable rule. This world view was very much in contrast with the social realities of the 17th-century Ottoman context. The Celali uprisings in Anatolia, the downfall of young Sultan Osman II in 1622, the series of wars with Venice over Crete (1645-69), and the failed siege of Vienna of 1683 were some of the events that signalled political problems.[11] The dynastic myth gave way to an alternative view of history influenced by Ibn Khaldun's sociology, which compared states with the human body and its developmental stages (birth, growth, death).[12] Historians such as Muṣṭafā Naʿīmā (d. 1716) adopted this view. Although the end of the state was never a matter for discussion, the age of Süleyman the Lawgiver was perceived as the golden age of the Ottomans. The self-centred view of the state gave way to the perception of Ottomans as one polity among many within the empirical geography of the world. Ottoman scholars of the 17th century offered advice literature for the statesmen, suggesting ways to restore peace to the society.[13] Hagen proposes that famous literary figures of the 17th century, such as Evliya Çelebi (the author of the *Seyaḥatnāme*) and Kātip Çelebi (a clerk with privately acquired education), represent a shift of class in the intellectual activities.[14] These upper-middle-class scholars contributed to the emergence of 'secularist and modernist tendencies' in the society through their work.[15] Çelebi penned his last work, *Mizān,* within this context.

From a socio-cultural and intellectual perspective, however, Çelebi's period appears somewhat different. In *Early Modern Ottomans: Remapping the Empire*, Virginia Aksan and Daniel Goffman propose 'early modernity' as a historical framework for understanding the socio-cultural and intellectual developments of the period. They understand 'modernity' broadly as a mode of self-consciousness which manifested at the individual, social, and state levels and defined the early modern Ottoman period, from the fall of Constantinople to the establishment of *tanẓīmāt*. These two events are taken to mark two important moments of change in Ottoman history: one 'when the Ottoman state began consciously to envision itself as a world-conquering empire', the other 'when the Ottomans began consciously and deliberately to emulate the west'.[16]

Problematic as this projection might be, viewing Ottoman history within the 'early modern' framework introduces different preoccupations and conditions that bring Ottoman history closer to the Europeans. Thus, Aksan and Goffman's edited volume attempts to show that during this period the Ottomans were active agents who contributed to the construction of the early modern European world. The multi-ethnic and multireligious structure of the Ottoman Empire allowed utilisation of commercial and cultural diasporas of communities for economic and political purposes. New genres of writing, the renewal of political, diplomatic, and legal strategies, and the emergence of an upper-middle-class aristocracy mark the distinctive outcomes of the early modern Ottoman context.[17] Earlier historian Rifaʿat Abou-El-Haj also argued, like Aksan and Goffman, that the 17th century was a period of increasing complexity and positive changes in the social structure and could be appropriately characterised as the 'early modern period' of the Ottoman Empire.[18]

Çelebi, with the rich diversity of his scholarship that is characterised by open-mindedness and desire for change, can be seen to represent the intellectual milieu of early modernity in the Ottoman context. His *Mīzān al-ḥaqq*, in particular, contains textual evidence of the social-cultural and intellectual dynamics of the period. Viewing his work from this perspective, both republican historian Adnan Adıvar and Hagen consider Çelebi and his work as a turning point in Ottoman intellectual history, with his 'worldly' interest towards systematising and categorising information. Adıvar goes so far as to consider Çelebi to be a forerunner of Westernisation. In fact, Çelebi is one of the few Ottoman scholars whose works have been translated into Western languages after the Classical Period of Islam.[19] However, Hagen rightly interprets Çelebi's quest for useful knowledge as a utilitarian effort to address economic, military, and political problems of the Ottoman State.[20]

'ILM: THE MIND AND THE HEART

In his preface to the *Mīzān*, Çelebi explains the main reason for writing the book:

> Since the beginning of creation it has been acknowledged among the wise that intelligence and tradition are like a pair of twins, while the reports of intelligence and tradition are like two race-horses, and that logical proof is a staircase and a ladder to the heights of certainty, so that in matters of inquiry and speculation it is the basis of all men's speech and the referee of all things. Some men there are who, seduced by the Slinking Whisperer, have laid aside proof and through ignorance and folly have deliberately set up surmise and conjecture as a rival to proof. In more questions than one they have fallen victim to the diseases of contention and vain bigotry. Like the fanatical wars in olden time, the futile wrangling of these stupid people has well-nigh led to bloodshed. For this reason these few lines have been drafted in order to demonstrate the method of proof in the questions at issue, and the name *Mīzān al-ḥaqq fi'khtiyār al-aḥaqq* ('the Balance of Truth in Choosing the Most True') has been given to them, so that ordinary people may know what the matters of strife and dispute are, and what manner of fruit they yield.[21]

Mīzān was Çelebi's last work, in which he shed light on various aspects of his life and presented insights from all of his previous works. His preface reveals his deep concern about a prevailing trend that was dismissive of rational sciences and led to religious division and social turmoil. Çelebi strongly defended rational sciences and their indispensability in truth seeking. He considered reason and tradition as being not only two complementary modes of acquiring knowledge but also inherent in human make-up. He perceived the science of logic (*manṭiq, mīzān*) and proof (*burhān*) as offering viable ground for solving issues of contention. He saw logic as an instrumental science that helps scholars assert the truth: it is the balance and measure of all other sciences and is thus highly valued in critical judgement. Through the science of logic and proof scholars can achieve more rigorous and respectful works.[22]

Çelebi's zealous defence of the use of reason resulted from complex events. In 1629, the 20-year-old Çelebi started attending Kāḍīzāde Mehmed Efendi's (d. 1635) sermons and lectures on Islamic theology (*kalām*) and jurisprudence (*fiqh*). Kāḍīzāde was at that time leading a puritanical movement against religious innovations, especially Sufi thought and practices, and the degree of influence Kāḍīzāde's fundamentalist ideas had on the young impressionable Çelebi is not clear. Although later in life Çelebi and Kāḍīzāde took seemingly opposing paths to knowledge, Kāḍīzāde's ideas must have played a role in Çelebi's oscillation between the mind and the heart, the rational and traditional approaches to knowledge.[23] One of the motivations behind Çelebi's *Mīzān* was indeed the social turmoil the Kāḍīzādeli movement had generated. The movement arose from the fiery Friday sermons Kāḍīzāde delivered as the preacher at Hagia Sophia Mosque and gained strong momentum over the years. Across the road at the nearby Sultan Ahmed Mosque, his opponent preacher, Abdülmecīd Sivāsī Efendi (d. 1639), delivered his own provocative sermons. Sivāsī Efendi and his followers defended a tolerant Sufi understanding of Islam, while Kāḍīzāde and his followers promoted an intolerant, fanatical approach against all innovations in religion (*bidaʿ*, sing. *bidʿa*), and called for a revival of traditional Islam, as lived and practised during the time of the Prophet Muhammad. For nearly 20 years between 1630 and 1650 the acrimonious sermons raged on, often resulting in violent clashes between the followers of both preachers in the streets of Istanbul.[24]

This social and religious division had a lasting impact on Çelebi's thought and approach to both religion and knowledge. In his critical edition of *Mīzān*, Uludağ argues that what differentiates Çelebi from the Ottoman scholars of his time was his devotion to reconciling Islamic law (*sharīʿa*) with Sufism (*ḥikma*), rationality (*ʿaql*) with tradition (*naql*), and religion (*dīn*) with philosophy (*falsafa*). This is to say, it was Çelebi's self-appointed mission to find a harmonious ground for reconciling what he recognised as contrasting yet valid claims to truth, in order to bring together knowledge of the mind and knowledge of the heart, the *ʿulamāʾ*, the philosophers, and the Sufis.

Çelebi saw ignorance and misunderstanding as the main sources of the deepening religious division and escalating violence in Ottoman society. He also saw truthful knowledge (*ʿilm*) as a powerful tool to overcome this division. If people were truthfully informed, he thought, they would overcome their differences. In the introduction to *Mīzān*, he set out to demonstrate the benefits of rational sciences, including philosophy (*falsafa*), logic (*manṭiq*), geometry (*handasa*), geography (*jughrāfiya*) and astronomy (*nujūm*), in an attempt to find solutions to the problems of his period. He pointed to the fact that rational and natural sciences were not valued in the Ottoman *madrasas*, arguing that ignoring these branches of knowledge could only result in misunderstandings, false teachings, and wrong decisions in the social realm.[25] He suggested that in order to make accurate decisions and sustain justice (*ʿadāla*) high-ranking officials should have sound understanding of rational sciences (*maʿqūlāt*) and mathematics (*riyāḍiyyāt*).[26]

The productive duality of the heart (*qalb*) and the mind (*ʿaql*), traceable in the *Mīzān* as well as other Çelebi's works, especially in the introduction to *Kashf al-ẓunūn,* is not unique to Çelebi's approach.[27] It is strongly present in one of Çelebi's key sources on the nature, subjects, and classification of *ʿulūm*, *Miftāḥ al-saʿāda* (The Key of Happiness), by eminent 16th-century Ottoman scholar Taşköprülüzāde. This duality can be traced back to the influential Muslim theologian and Sufi master Abū Ḥāmid al-Ghazālī (d. 1111). In his widely celebrated work *Iḥyāʾ ʿulūm al-dīn* (Reviving the Sciences of Religion), al-Ghazālī presented a parable which narrates the story of an artistic competition between Chinese and Byzantine artists, held to demonstrate the superiority of their artwork to a king. The king gave each group one side of a portico to decorate and separated the two sides by a veil. While the Byzantine artists used their exquisite colours and painterly skills to decorate their side, the Chinese artists worked diligently on polishing up their side. When the veil was lifted, the Byzantine artists' work was stunning, yet the polished side of the Chinese reflected the Byzantine painting with all its beauty, adding depth and shine to its lustre and glamour. The king was equally impressed with both sides.[28] In this well-known example, which was quoted by many Muslim scholars, the Chinese side represented knowledge of the heart, while the Byzantine side represented knowledge of the mind. In the Islamic tradition, the heart became the Sufi's instrument of acquiring knowledge through polishing and purifying, whereas the mind became the other scholars' means of building knowledge through deliberate thinking, studying, reasoning, and reflecting. In the *Mizān*'s 21 chapters, Çelebi strove to demonstrate the values of both rational and revelatory modes of knowing, as he repeatedly cross-examined the discoveries of his rational thinking with the intuitive revelations of his heart.

Çelebi's uncertainty and oscillation between the mind and the heart can be attributed to his complex exposures to local and foreign sciences. Locally, around 1639, at the age of 30, Çelebi attended Kadı Mustafa Efendi's lectures (d. 1653), whom he viewed as a master in both rational and transmitted sciences. He also studied with and attended the classes of Kürt Abdullāh Efendi (d. 1654), Keçi Mehmed Efendi (d. 1644), Veli Efendi, and ʿAbdürrahīm Efendi (d. 1656). Broadly, his wide scope of interest shows exposure to early modern European sciences, and an awareness of both its technological and social benefits.[29] He attempted to use the emerging new approach to knowledge to rethink traditional approaches, and warned his traditionalist colleagues against their growing dismissive attitude, narrow scope, and close-mindedness. This is particularly evident in two of his major works: *Cihannüma* (Displaying the World) and *Kashf al-ẓunūn* (Dispelling Doubts). Due to this exposure, Çelebi's approach to *ʿilm* developed an eclectic and reconciliatory nature. Uludağ explains that Çelebi's approach to *ʿilm* was deductive in nature; he was interested in major and general principles more than in details and particulars. Although Çelebi regarded tradition and transmitted knowledge highly, he was also critical of the notion of authority in religious science, with sometimes even an uncompromising stance toward traditional views on *ʿilm*.[30]

Through his writings, Çelebi shows a conscious recognition of the indisputable neutrality of *ʿilm* and its function in promoting harmonious religious understanding and social cohesion. This appreciation of the nature and function of *ʿilm* as indubitable truthful knowledge reflects the early modern understanding of science. Yet, in contrast to the rational understanding of *ʿilm* in the *Mīzān's* introduction, Çelebi's epilogue presents a more reconciliatory understanding of *ʿilm* as a moral disposition that binds the intuition of the heart (*kashf*) with the deliberation (*nazar*) of the mind. What is discovered by the mind must, for Çelebi, be confirmed by the heart. The mind and heart duality gradually became synonymous with the polarity of science and religion, and early modern European intellectual history was marked by the emergence of this polarity. Despite the pronounced distinction between the rational and transmitted approaches to knowledge in the Islamic tradition, the boundary between the two remained obscure in the 17th-century Ottoman context. To further explore Çelebi's interest in the mind and the heart and to probe his attitude towards the emerging trends of acquiring *ʿilm*, we need to examine his writings demonstrating his engagement with *ʿilm* as science, as religion, and as moral values.

ʿILM: SCIENCE, RELIGION, AND MORALITY

Çelebi's interest in emerging early modern sciences is most evident in his massive geographical work *Cihannüma* (Displaying the World), which was motivated by his scientific curiosity to have up-to-date information on Europe and the new world.[31] In this unique work, Çelebi's approach to dealing with new geographical knowledge, as Hagen argues, brought innovative strategies to the Ottoman perception of science. Çelebi perceived geography as a scholarly pursuit that is different from the personal impressions or experiences of a traveller (including his own).[32] His engagement with geographical science aimed at changing the social function of geographical knowledge from being an educational and entertaining interest of the elite to a practical and popular understanding of the world.[33] Presented to Sultan Mehmed Khān IV (r. 1648-87), *Cihannüma* stands as an exemplary work displaying Çelebi's interest in the developments of Western sciences. In this work, a serious rift between scientific and religious modes of *ʿilm* begins to show. For example, with reference to the certainty of geographical knowledge, Çelebi explicitly argues that the earth is round in the shape of a globe, and not flat, as reported in a popular prophetic Hadith widely acknowledged at the time.[34] Çelebi sees that the significance of geography lies in the way it enables people to learn about the world in a short span of time. Going through the pages of a geography book, as he puts it, saves more than 1000 years of travel. Scholars and statesmen, he asserts, should have accurate information of the world in order to guide their subjects wisely.[35]

Cihannüma was an ambitious project that pushed the limits of Çelebi's geographical knowledge. Admitting the incompleteness of information available in Asian sources, he interrupted his writing to consult Mercator's *Atlas Major,* which he interpreted with the help of a Christian convert named Sheikh Mehmed Ikhlāṣī Efendi (d. 1639). Çelebi resumed his work on *Cihannüma* in 1654, and included additions from *Atlas Major*, but was unable to complete the work due to his premature death in 1657.[36] Although unfinished, Çelebi's *Cihannüma* paved the way to a new geographical understanding in the Ottoman context. His ambitious project work was later completed by Ibrāhīm Müteferriqa, who published it in the first state-sponsored printing press of the Ottoman Empire, the Müteferriqa Press, which he established in 1732. At that time geography and astronomy were closely related sciences, and new discoveries in both fields were changing Ottoman understanding of the shape of the universe. In the original text of *Cihannüma,* Çelebi did not delve into Copernicus's new theory of heliocentrism; in his addition, Müteferriqa did. He presented Copernicus's heliocentrism as another school of thought along with Ptolemy's geocentrism. He acknowledged its validity cautiously as a point of view; however, he considered it wrong.[37] His cautiously dismissive attitude towards heliocentrism reflected the official Ottoman position on the new theory.

Generally, Ottoman scholars showed little or no interest in the new astronomy. The historian of science Ekmeleddin Ihsanoğlu suggests that Müteferriqa's expressed interest in heliocentrism might have been due to his Christian background and his awareness of the religious debates unfolding in Europe. Ihsanoğlu argues that Ottoman astronomers were capable of following the developments in Europe with short gaps in time, but that they chose not to because their interests were confined to practical matters, such as timekeeping and the cycles of the calendar.[38] The general apathy towards heliocentrism among Muslim scholars in the early modern period remained unexplained. Despite his attempt to undermine the religious view concerning the shape of the earth by arguing for its spherical form, Çelebi did not show much concern for heliocentrism in *Cihannüma*. There he kept his focus on technical and practical earthly matters.[39]

Against the wide scope of Çelebi's preoccupations with big intellectual and scientific issues, he reveals deep concerns with narrow socio-religious debates. New social habits that flourished among early modern Ottomans, such as smoking, coffee drinking, social outings, listening to music, and dancing, generated unsettling debates, which often resulted in violent confrontations. The 17th-century Ottoman approach to religion can be described, as Hagen suggests, as 'a return to piety' in the form of a purification of religious thoughts and practices. Hence, the issue of *bid'a* (pl. *bida'*, innovation in religion) was central to the negotiation and making of 17th-century religious sensibility. In this sensibility, *'ilm* took on new moral and religious dimensions which can be seen in Çelebi's engagement with the raging controversies.

The concept of *bid'a* includes, in principle, all innovations in, or unpresented changes to, religious thoughts and practices that occurred after the times of Prophet Muhammad and his companions. In dealing with this issue, Çelebi considered innovations to be of two kinds, good and bad (*bid'at-i hasene* and *bid'at-i seyyi'e*), and recognised the variation in moral positions on innovations among various groups in the society. At that time, new trends were becoming widely appreciated and accepted as social habits. Çelebi recognised the currency of these new social habits (good or bad, depending on one's point of view) and warned against futile attempts to ban them as they became deeply embedded in the Ottoman culture.[40]

Çelebi introduced a moral criterion based on human nature to determine the acceptability of new social practices: *mülāyemet ve münāferet* (harmony and contrast). *Mülāyemet* means being suitable for, or in harmony with, one's human nature, whereas *münāferet* means being against or in opposition to it. One kind of practice can lead to gentleness and positive social interaction, the other to agrivation and disgust. In his search for social and religious harmony, Çelebi articulated his position with reference to this polarity. On the issue of smoking, for example, he explains that the reason behind its ban in communal spaces, such as *madrasas* and mosques, is its discordance with human nature, a discordance which results in harmful effects. However, if a person is addicted to smoking, he adds, it would be harmful for this person to quit, as smoking ultimately becomes second nature. Thus he endeavours to show the difficulty of taking a categorical position (permissible/not permissible, *ḥalāl/ḥarām*) on such social habits, concluding that people should be left to make their own moral decisions concerning their choices.[41] The limits to this moral freedom, in his view, lie in the communal moral commitment to preserving the integrity and healthiness of the body and the soul. In contrast to his tolerant view on smoking, however, Çelebi's view on the use of opium for pleasure is strict. He supports its ban because it destroys human nature, and it is an Islamic attribute not to compromise the healthy primordial human nature (*fiṭrat-i selīme*). Accordingly, per Çelebi, one should never accept an invitation to take up this addictive habit.[42]

Similarly, Çelebi argues that coffee might be useful for one person and harmful for another, depending on the disposition of their nature. Originating from Yemen, Çelebi writes that Sheikhs and Sufis alike consumed coffee with the conviction that it was appropriate for their religious training, mental alertness, and suppression of sensual desires. He provides a historical account of the consumption of coffee in the Ottoman Empire from its discovery until the opening of coffee houses around Istanbul. He has reservations about the wide spread of this new social culture, noting that coffee houses breed laziness and immorality among members of the public, which resulted in the closing down of these places and the final ban on the consumption of coffee during his time.[43]

Listening to music and religious dance were also two critical social phenomena that were hotly debated during Çelebi's time. In the first half of the 16th century, Taşköprülüzāde commented on the powerful effect of music on humans, noting its capacity to evoke different thoughts and emotions, both positive and negative. He explained the core reason behind the influence of music on humans as being the remembrance of heavenly tunes that coincided with the origination of the soul (*al-mabadaʾ al-awwal*) in the act of creation. He interpreted the Pythagorean idea of the music of the spheres created by their ordered harmonious movements as a celestial expression of the reverence these objects pay to the creator, and believed that humans tend therefore, as a part of their inherent disposition, to admire and respond to order and harmony.[44] Çelebi reiterates Taşköprülüzāde's thoughts on music to emphasise its perennial significance but also argues that the ban on music according to the *sharīʿa* has sound rational grounds. According to him, every human being has a soul that is different from their ego. Virtuous people are those who are able to supress their ego: they tend to perceive music as a tool to recall the *al-mabadaʾal-awwal*. By contrast, for those who are unable to supress their ego, and whose ego dominates their soul, music can only provoke animal instincts and sensual pleasures. The impact of music on ears is similar to the impact of dance on sight, Çelebi adds. And for this reason, he finds the religious ban on dancing and music to be reasonable despite their popularity amongst the members of the upper class of Ottoman society.[45]

The Sufi practice of *samāʿ* as a coming together of music and dance, according to Çelebi, following Taşköprülüzāde, can be acceptable or banned depending on its effect on the heart. In the execution of *samāʿ* the appropriateness of time, space, and people is crucial. The *samāʿ* ritual should not interfere with people's daily chores; the space used should be calming and peaceful; and the *samāʿ* community should consist of religious folk.[46] Çelebi believes in the usefulness of *samāʿ* in the *zikr* (remembrance) ceremony of the Sufis. A Sufi Sheikh using *samāʿ* is like a doctor using poison as medicine to cure a patient, according to Çelebi; rhythmic body movements help organise thinking, while music helps organise the body movements. He concludes that the appropriateness of *samāʿ*, therefore, depends on its visible (*ẓāhir*) and invisible (*bāṭın*) motives.[47] Despite his sophisticated evaluation of music, dance, and *samāʿ* in the Ottoman context, Çelebi admits that debates for and against them would not come to an end, as their sensitive nature is open to immoral exploitation.

Visiting graveyards and tombs of saints is another innovation upon which Çelebi touches. As much as he warns about the danger of falling into polytheist inclinations (*shirk*), he believes that pantheism has its own degrees, and those who belong to lower levels may use the mediation of a saint in their prayers as long as they do not worship the mediator. He believes that, as the relationship of the soul (*rūḥ*) with the body (*badan*) continues after death, according to Islam, there are signs of spirituality at the graves of the saints, and that praying at such places has more merit than praying elsewhere.[48] Çelebi continues his moderate attitude by adding that he dislikes the lowly attitude of people who expect curative remedies from graves. He adds that such people are open to exploitation, as some others make a living out of their weaknesses. He finally submits that the science of medicine is the only place to seek cure.[49]

Çelebi concludes his remarks on morality by stating that the principle of enjoining right and forbidding wrong is a necessity according to the followers of the *sunna*. However, he complains that in his period everyone tries to impose their opinions and moral criteria on others. As this has resulted in social divisions, endless debates, and violent confrontations, he suggests that it should be done only by knowledgeable people of religion, with the caution that Muslims should not disclose the faults of their religious fellows.[50]

CONCLUSION

In summary, Çelebi, through his open-mindedness and multifaceted works, represented the early modern enlightened Ottoman scholar, who recognised the healing merit and uniting power of *'ilm* in a rapidly changing society witnessing serious religious divisions. He explored the scientific, religious, and moral dimensions of *'ilm* and its agency in restoring peace, justice, and tolerance to Ottoman society. He saw himself as an enlightened individual capable of both inspiring social change and introducing better ways for restoring order in his society, through engagements with the various facets of *'ilm*.[51] Oscillating between his heart and his mind, he recognised the merits of both religious and rational sciences as two complementary and necessary paths to truthful knowledge and social harmony.

NOTES

1 For the Arabic titles cited in the chapter, I have used the Arabic convention of transliteration. Other Ottoman-Turkish terms follow the convention of Ottoman-Turkish transliteration. This work appears in an epilogue entitled 'Utterance of the Blessing and a Couple of Advices' (*Nimete şükür ve bir kaç öğüt*). Kātip Çelebi, 2007, *Mizānü'l-Hakk fi İhtiyari'l-Ehakk*, trans. Orhan Şaik Gökyay and Süleyman Uludağ (Istanbul: Kabalci), 222. For all quotations from the Turkish text of *Mīzān al-ḥaqq*, I used the most recent (2007) critical edition.

2 I made slight changes to Geoffrey Lewis's English translation based on the 2007 critical edition. Çelebi, 2007, 222; and Geoffrey Lewis, 1957, *The Balance of Truth* (London: Allen and Unwin), 145-6.

3 '*Çünkü uçmak için iki kanat lazımdır, bir kanatla menzil alınmaz. Aklī ve şer'ī ilimler iki kanat mesabesindedir.*' Çelebi, 2007, 229-30.

4 This view is first purported by the early republican Turkish historian Adnan Adıvar (2000) in his *Osmanlı Türk'lerinde İlim* (Istanbul: Remzi).

5 In Ottoman Turkish the word '*çelebi*' meant a person of letters, a courteous and civilised person; see *Osmanlice Turkce Sozluk*, 2017, <http://www.osmanlicaturkce.com/?k=çelebi&t=%40>, accessed 23 January 2017.

6 Gottfried Hagen, 2007, 'Kātip Çelebi: Mustafa b. Abdullāh, Hācı Halīfe (b.1609; d. 1657)', *Historians of the Ottoman Empire*, <https://ottomanhistorians.uchicago.edu/en/historian/katib-celebi>, accessed 25 January 2017.

7 Adıvar, 2000, 138.

8 'Parts of his library were sold in 1069, presumably after the death of his wife. Several volumes were purchased by Levinus Warner and today constitute a part of the Legatum Warnerianum at Leiden Library.' Hagen, 2007.

9 *Mīzān al-Ḥaqq* embodies an autobiographical section in which Çelebi narrates important events of his life in the third person: '[Y]ek fenle kanaate ulüv-i himmet rıza vermemişti'. Çelebi, 2007, 127.

10 Karen Barkey, 1994, *Bandits and Bureaucrats: The Ottoman Route to State Centralisation* (New York: Cornell University Press), 48.

11 Gottfried Hagen, 2004, 'Afterword: Ottoman Understandings of the World in the Seventeenth Century', in Robert Dankoff, ed., *An Ottoman Mentality: The World of Evliya Çelebi* (Leiden: Brill), 237-8.

12 See Mustafa Na'īmā, 1967, *Tārīḫ-i Na'īmā* (Naima Tarihi), ed. Zuhuri Danisman (Istanbul: Zuhuri Danisman Yayinevi).

13 Cornell Fleischer, 1983, 'Royal Authority, Dynastic Cyclism and "Ibn Khaldunism" in Sixteenth-Century Ottoman Letters', *Journal of Asian and African Studies* 18: 198-220.

14 Hagen, 2004, 253-4.

15 Hagen, 2004, 254.

16 Virginia H Aksan and Daniel Goffman, 2007, 'Introduction: Situating the Early Modern Ottoman World', in Virginia Aksan and Daniel Goffman, eds., *The Early Modern Ottomans: Remapping The Empire* (Cambridge: Cambridge University Press), 6-12.

17 Aksan and Goffman, 2007.

18 See Rifa'at Ali Abou-El-Haj, 1992, *Formation of the Modern State: Ottoman Empire from the 16th to 18th Century* (Albany: SUNY).

19 *Jihannüma* is his most widely translated work. See Joseph von Hammer, 1812, *Rumeli und Bosna Geographisch Beschrieben von Mustafa Ben Abdalla Hadschi Chalfa* (Vienna: Kunst- und Industrie-Comptoirs); M Norberg, 1818, *Gihan Numah. Geographia orientalis ex Turcico in Latinum versa* (Göteborg: Londini Gothorum, literis Berlingianis); Jean-Louis Bacqué-Grammont, 1996, 'Les routes d'Asie centrale d'après le Cihān-Numā de Kātib Çelebi', *Cahier d'Asie Centrale* 1(2): 311-22; and Jean-Louis Bacqué-Grammont, 1997, 'La description de Chypre dans le Cihān-nümā de Kātib Çelebi', *Epetērida tou Kentrou Epistēmonikon Erevnōn* 23: 189-214.

20 Adıvar, 2000, 151; Hagen, 2007.

21 The translations provided here and below are based on Gökyay and Uludağ's work (Çelebi, 2007, 145), with minor modifications. The original Turkish reads: 'Ta yaratılışın başlangıcından bu yana, ilim erbabı arasında akıl ile naklin ikiz, akla uygun olan naklin rahvan bir at olduğu herkesçe müsellemdir. Lakin zirvesine çıkmak icin delil ve burhan mesleği bir merdiven ve basamak olarak, bahs ve nazar, araştırma ve inceleme vadilerinde cumhur ona dayanmış ve her hususta ona başvurmuştur'.

22 'Onun için muhakkik olan alimlerin coğu bu ilmin farz oldugu kanaatine varmışlardır.' Çelebi, 2007, 147.

23 Çelebi, 2007, 224.

24 Madeline C Zilfi, 1986, 'The Kadızādelis: Discordant Revivalism in Seventeenth-Century Istanbul', *Journal of Near Eastern Studies* 45(4): 252-5.

25 'Here I translated "eşyanın hakikatine dair olan ilim [science concerning the truth of things]" as "natural sciences"'. Çelebi, 2007, 150.

26 His attitude in the introduction towards ignorant people of high rank (who are opposed to the rational sciences) is very harsh: he compares them to asses or cows, as both lack the capacity to think and speculate. Çelebi, 2007, 150, 152.

27 '*Qalb*' in Turkish is spelt as '*kalp*'. '*Aql*' in Turkish is spelt as '*akıl*'.

28 Al-Ghazālī, 2010, *Kitāb Sharḥ 'ajā'ib al-qalb* (The Marvels of the Heart), trans. Walter James Skellie (Louisville: Vons Vitae), 57-62. Al-Ghazālī was among the scholars Kātip Çelebi regarded highly and frequently quoted in his works. To illustrate, Ghazzali's *TTahāfut al-falāsifa* is one of Çelebi's major sources in *Mīzān*. Çelebi, 2007, 148-9.

29 Hagen notes that Celebi certainly knew prominent Western and Ottoman intellectuals of his time such as Antoine Galland (d. 1715), Ferdinando Marsili (d. 1730), Levinus Warner (d. 1665) and historian Hüseyin Hezārfenn (d. 1691). He further writes that 'K.Ç. shows great sympathy for political figures associated with attempts at political reform … He knew Kemānkeş Qara Mustafā Paşa (executed in 1644) and expressed sympathy for Tarhūncu Ahmed Paşa (d. 1653). *Mīzān* includes a cryptic homage to Köprülü Mehmed Paşa (d. 1661)'. Kātip Çelebi, 2007, 225; Hagen, 2007.

30 Çelebi, 2007, 132-3.

31 During the first Ottoman campaign to Crete Island (1646), Çelebi developed an interest in map-making by marking land and sea. Several following campaigns to conquer the island as well as the competition with the Venetian rivals also prompted Çelebi to rethink Ottoman naval strategies and their geographical knowledge of the seas. Çelebi, 2007, 226.

32 Hagen, 2004, 227-9.

33 Hagen, 2004, 230-1. His translations from Western geographers in this regard were a matter of concern for Westerners: Venetian colleagues worried that Ottomans could use geographical information against them in their efforts towards state expansion.

34 This Hadith was attributed to Prophet Muhammad's companion, Ibn Abbas, who stated that the earth was flat, resting on the horns of an ox. Çelebi argues that the 'ox' should in fact be understood as the zodiacal sign of Taurus and contests its contemporary literal interpretations without dismissing the Hadith itself. See Kâtip Çelebi, 2013, *Kitāb-ı Cihannüma* (Displaying the World), ed. Fuat Sezgin (Istanbul: Boyut Yayınları).

35 Çelebi, 2013, 16.

36 Adıvar, 2000, 144-5.

37 Çelebi, 2013, 34-45. Müteferriqa took a neutral stance against all models and mentioned that Ptolemy's proposal had been accepted widely by Muslim scholars in the past. He perceived models of the universe as a convention depicted by concentric circles; putting the Earth or the Sun in the centre, for him, was a matter of representation.

38 Ekmeleddin İhsanoğlu, 1992, 'Introduction of Western Science to the Ottoman World: A Case Study of Modern Astronomy (1660-1860)', in Ekmeleddin İhsanoğlu, ed., *The Transfer of Modern Science and Technology to the Muslim World* (Istanbul: Research Centre for Islamic History, Art, and Culture), 108.

39 Hagen, 2004, 229, 233.

40 Çelebi, 2007, 192.

41 Çelebi, 2007, 44.

42 Çelebi, 2007, 174-6.

43 Çelebi, 2007, 45, 46.

44 Taşköprülüzāde, 1975, *Mevzuat'ül-Ulüm* (Istanbul: Er-tu), 304.

45 Çelebi, 2007, 31.

46 Taşköprülü-zāde, 1975, 1187.

47 Çelebi, 2007, 31.

48 Çelebi, 2007, 194-5.

49 Çelebi, 2007, 196.

50 Çelebi, 2007, 202-3.

51 I agree with Gottfried Hagen and Ethan L Menchinger (2014, 'Ottoman Historical Thought', in Prasenjit Duara et al., eds., *A Companion to Global Historical Thought*, New Jersey: John Wiley & Sons, Ltd, 98) that '*adālet*' means more than justice and can only be translated insufficiently into English: '*[A]dālet* means both the moderation of personal temper and the administration principle of balancing the different social classes in a permanent equilibrium'.

Chapter 8

ʿ*Ilm* and the human body: Al-Suhrawardī's concept of the illuminated temple

Faris Hajamaideen

Abstract

Islam places strong emphasis on the relationship between knowledge (*ʿilm*) and light (*nūr*). The Prophet Muhammad is reported to have said, '[K]nowledge is light' (*al-ʿilmu nūrun*), and to have described the omniscient God as dazzling light. This relationship took new dimensions in the 12th century with the work of the renowned philosopher-mystic Shihāb al-Dīn al-Suhrawardī, who founded what has become known as the 'philosophy of illumination' (*falsafat al-ishrāq*). In his works, Suhrawardī uses two architectural metaphors to explain the human body's relationship to light: one is the body as temple (*haykal*), the other is the body as fortress (*ṣīṣiyya*). Through these two metaphors, Suhrawardī presents an understanding of reality based on gradation of illumination in contrast to the then prevalent Greek understanding which was based on the polarities of form and matter and the sensible and intelligible. In this understanding of reality, the relationship between knowledge, illumination, and the human body is invested with a new horizon of possibilities. Focusing on Suhrawardī's two key works, *Hayākil al-nūr* (Temples of Light) and *Ḥikmat al-ishrāq* (The Philosophy of Illumination), this study examines the cosmological significance of the concepts of *haykal* and *ṣīṣiyya* to show how the architecture of the human body plays a key cognitive-illuminative role in the process of transformation from a fortress of darkness into a temple of light. In this process, the body and the mind work as a unified 'structure' or 'temple', wherein 'form' and 'space' work together in an integral manner as 'architecture' to enable the infusion of light to dematerialise the body and erase its opacity.

ʿ*Ilm* as light: Suhrawardī's illumination

The conceptual connection between knowledge, light, and mental and spiritual enlightenment is universal; it can be found throughout history in many pre-modern and modern traditions. Perhaps the most well-known and enduring example of this link is Plato's 'Allegory of the Cave' in his *Republic*, wherein the search for wisdom is presented in the analogy of reaching out of darkness into light.[1] In the Christian tradition, Christ is reported to have said: 'I am the light of the world', and is accordingly presented as the coincidence between knowledge (*logos*) and light (*lux*).[2] In the Islamic tradition, the link between knowledge (*ʿilm*) and light (*nūr*) is equally fundamental.[3] The Prophet Muhammad is attributed as saying, '[K]nowledge is light' (*al-ʿilmu nūrun*), and the Quran has close to 30 verses in which the term *nūr* is used to describe the light of revelation effacing the darkness of falsehood.[4] The Quran itself is also described as that which 'bring(s) forth mankind out of darkness into light'.[5] One of the names of God is *al-Nūr* (the Light), and Muhammad is described in the Quran as a 'luminous lamp' (*sirājan munīran*).[6] The light verse in the Quran (*āyat al-nūr*) is perhaps the most pre-eminent description of light, which inspired numerous works and received sustained attention from Muslim theologians, mystics, and philosophers. Infused with mystical allusions and religious symbolism, it shows in an allegorical way how God, knowledge, and light are intrinsically interwoven:

> God is the Light of the heavens and the earth. The parable of His Light is a niche, wherein is a lamp. The lamp is in a glass. The glass is as a shining star kindled from a blessed olive tree, neither of the East nor of the West. Its oil would well-nigh shine forth, even if no fire had touched it. Light upon light. God guides unto His Light whomsoever He will, and God sets forth parables for mankind and God is the Knower of all things.[7]

The verse identifies God as the light of all things and affirms that He alone possesses the knowledge of all beings. The destination of all knowledge is therefore set to be God and the journey to this destination can only be guided by His light. The illuminated niche (*mishkāt*) described in the verse, according to most Classical commentators, including Junayd (d. 910), al-Ṭabarī (d. 923), al-Ghazālī (d. 1111), al-Rāzī (d. 1210), and al-Kāshānī (d. 1680), was said to be referring to the human reality (*al-haqīqa al-insāniyya*).[8] The casting of divine light into the human was generally understood by scholars to be a spiritual illumination gifted to the select few in order for them to be able to perceive light and grasp the knowledge of God.

Al-Ghazālī's *Mishkāt al-anwār* (the Niche of Lights) is one of the most celebrated treatises that expounded the light verse and unravelled its theological meanings and mystical symbolism. However, it was the 12th-century philosopher and Sufi master Shihāb al-Dīn Yaḥyā al-Suhrawardī (d. 1191) who provided the most sustained and profound reflections on the significance of light and its creative agency in being and becoming. His thoughts introduced a new metaphysics based on the hermeneutics of light that later inspired the School of Illumination (*ishrāq*). In the introduction to his magnum opus, *The Philosophy of Illumination* (Ḥikmat al-ishrāq), Suhrawardī stated that his objective was to pen the wisdom of illumination that he had received solely by intuition (that is, spiritual enlightenment).[9] He hoped that the reader of his works was blessed with the continuous descent of divine light from above, so that through the knowledge and practices he was imparting, the reader could ascend the ladder of the soul to draw closer to God, the Light of Lights.[10]

In broad terms, al-Suhrawardī's ideas follow the 'emanationist' models of earlier Muslim philosophers, especially the noted philosophers al-Fārābī (d. 950 CE) and Avicenna (d. 1037 CE).[11] According to their works, existentiation occurs through a series of emanations. The emanation process begins with the First Cause, God, who yields the formation of the First Intelligence, which, by interacting with the First Cause, gives birth to the first planetary sphere, Saturn, and together with it a Second Intelligence. Thereafter the Second Intelligence interacts with the First Cause and the First Intelligence, resulting in Jupiter and together with it the Third Intelligence. This process continues until the moon is created. The heavenly bodies are thus arranged in a vertical hierarchy.[12] The moon emerges at the end of this cosmological order and with it a differentiating threshold is formed. All that exists above this boundary is identified with wisdom and order, and is untainted by change. All beings that are formed below the sublunary threshold are impacted by time, change, and corruption.[13] This defines briefly the structure of the emanationist cosmos.

Suhrawardī's thought follows this structure, but with a significant difference. He imposes upon the cosmological order, described above, an overarching principle of illumination. He does this because, for him, nothing is more evident or real than light: 'Anything in existence that requires no definition or explanation is evident. Since there is nothing more evident than light, there is nothing less in need of definition'.[14] This means that Suhrawardī's ontology of all beings is determined by the structure of its illumination. He summarises this ontological structure in the following manner:

> A thing either is light and luminosity in its own reality or is not light and luminosity in its own reality ... Light is divided into light that is a state of something else (the accidental light) and light that is not a state of something else (the incorporeal or pure light). That which is not light in its own reality is divided into that which is independent of a locus (the dusky substance) and that which is a state of something else (the dark state).[15]

This passage suggests that the ontological hierarchy of Suhrawardī's world is solely based upon modes of luminosities. All beings are a result of an illuminative emanation from God, the Light of Lights.[16] Thus, the First Cause is described as the Light of Lights (*nūr al-anwār*). The First Intelligence is termed the proximate light (*nūr aqrab*); and the resultant solidification of light, which is the planetary body, is described as a connecting barrier or isthmus (*barzakh*). Resulting from this, the formation of the cosmos reveals itself as a theatre in which we find light kindled, reflected, refracted, and eventually solidified into spherical forms.[17] In this manner the study of al-Suhrawardī's philosophy of illumination postulates that everything that exists is to be contemplated and experienced as a form of light, measured in light, articulated with light, and defined as light.

In Suhrawardī's cosmological hierarchy, the vertical descent of illumination reaches the sublunary boundary that marks, as indicated above, the cosmic threshold of change. At this threshold, the descending light's pristine qualities start to become modified as light finds itself impacted by the sublunary forces of change: space and time. From this point onwards, in its continuing descent, illumination starts to lose its lustre and in its stead light starts to gain in opacity. The opaque and cloudier lights form into the beings that make up the terrestrial world, including the human being.[18] Though one is still able to experience and wonder at the extra-lunary lights and their effects from this terrestrial level, as when gazing at the stars up in the sky, for example, the purer metaphysical and incorporeal lights that belong to the eternal cosmic wisdom and order become occluded, distant, and elusive.[19] Nevertheless with divine providence, residual trace of the illumination from the vertical chain lingers; Suhrawardī calls this the celestial 'commanding light' (*nūr isfahbad*). The human being, which Suhrawardī calls 'the most noble constitution', is alone among the terrestrial bodies that can form a relationship with this illumination.[20] This human body is described by al-Suhrawardī again in terms of light as oscillating between opacity (*barzakh*) and duskiness (*ghāsiq*). This darker being desires the heavenly illumination, so that it, too, can become radiant, or as Suhrawardī puts it: '[J]ust as the poor man is desirous of freedom from want, so, too, is the dusky substance desirous of light'.[21]

This unique approach to framing the ontology of beings over a gradated illuminative scale represents a kind of reconciliation between the Platonic and Aristotelian philosophical models. While Plato privileged the metaphysical over the experiential world, Aristotle privileged the experiential over the metaphysical, arguing for the need to seek a posteriori, by investigating the fabric of the material world.[22] Such oppositional dualities — of the intelligible versus the sensible, of the mathematical versus the biological, and of form versus matter — are overcome in the philosophy of illumination. The entire cosmic fabric is considered as a seamless continuum of luminosities, as both metaphysical and physical realities are only composed of a single matter, light. This light continuum is built up of varying densities strung across a gradating rule spanning from the thick opacity of earthly matter to God, the Light of Lights.[23]

The originality of Suhrawardī's work lies in breaking with the dominant Greek philosophical tradition, which promoted an understanding of reality based on two fundamental polarities: form and matter (*ṣūra* and *hayūla*) and the sensible and intelligible (*ḥissī* and *'aqlī*). This double division created the enduring mind-body dichotomy, which attributed to the mind cognitive and intellectual abilities of which the body was deprived. Hence, knowledge (*'ilm*) became the prerogative of the mind, which assumed a superior status over the body. Knowledge as light and enlightenment concerns the mind, while the body is relegated to worldly indulgence and carnal pleasures. Both the Judaeo-Christian and Islamic traditions abhorred the body's attachments to the material world and urged their followers to transcend their bodily imprisonment through gnostic enlightenment and spiritual liberation. Suhrawardī's philosophical thoughts, as outlined above, proposed an alternative understanding of reality based on the gradation or densification of light rather than on those conventional divisions. In this understanding the body and the mind became a unified 'structure' or 'temple' (*haykal*), wherein 'form' and 'space' work together in an integral manner to construct the 'architecture' of reality.[24] He applies this model to humans, and uses it as an exemplar to illustrate the fundamental structure of reality. In this understanding of reality, the relationship between knowledge, illumination, and the human body assumes a new horizon of possibilities.[25]

HAYKAL: THE BODY AS TEMPLE OF LIGHT

Suhrawardī laid out the core ideas of his ontological model in a small yet influential work which he called *Hayākil al-nūr* (Temples of Light). In this work he introduced his conception of light gradation using the architectural metaphor of a temple (*haykal*). The Arabic term *haykal* literally means 'temple' and 'structure' and is used in connection with architecture and engineering: *haykal* is at once a place of worship and the main structural frame of a building. An animal and human 'skeleton' is referred to as *haykal 'aẓmī*, an expression borrowed from architecture and engineering which literally means the 'bone structure' of the body. With reference to this semantic scope, Suhrawardī divides the text of *Hayākil al-nūr* into seven chapters, with each identified as a temple: *al-haykal al-awwal* (The First Temple) followed by *al-haykal al-thānī* (The Second Temple) and so forth. The first temple of light is the darkest and densest: it is the three-dimensional material substance represented by the body, whereas the seventh temple of light is the lightest and subtlest: it is the human self in its most detached, spiritualised, and transcendental state. In between there are five states representing various degrees of entanglement between the body, the soul, and the mind.

In his prologue to the *Hayākil*, Suhrawardī assembles his readers at the threshold of his temple in preparation for entering the sacred portal: 'O Deity of the worlds! O eternally Subsistent! Strengthen us with (the aid of) the light, maintain us in the light, assemble us under the light ... Those who are imprisoned in darkness stand at Your Portal, awaiting mercy and liberation from captivity'.[26] This opening prayer is followed by taking the reader on a reflective journey through the seven temples in search of illumination. As an effect of this journey the body becomes overwhelmed with light and unburdened of its opacity:

> Now, when we purify ourselves from the preoccupations of the body and contemplate the grandeur of God, the Light of the Glory that spreads out and the Light that effuses from

> the Glory upon the beings, we find in ourselves shining flashes and orienting illuminations and we visualize lights and attain our goals.[27]

In the seventh temple (the final chapter), Suhrawardī returns with a conclusive architectural image. Having now been completely claimed by light, the body loses its relation to the horizontal terrestrial world. Its orientation is singular and upwards. With this in mind, Suhrawardī fuses architecture and the body. The temple structure and the human body ascend sharply and vertically, shrouded only in light:

> Thus, the beam of light draws near to the one who experiences it, as this person approaches the beam, ascending to it. Then the road to the sacred world is opened for the ascension to the elevated dwellings to which [opaque] barriers are forbidden.[28]

The renowned 15th-century scholar Jalāl al-Dīn al-Dawwānī (d. 1502), in the introduction to his commentary on al-Suhrawardī's *Hayākil,* shed valuable light on the cosmological significance of the temple metaphor through his hermeneutical explanation of the term *haykal.* He explained that while the term *haykal* can mean both 'temple' and 'body' in common usage, this was not what it originally meant.[29] The term *haykal,* he said, was used in pre-Islamic Persia to refer to the celestial bodies, and through its relation to the planetary bodies, the term then came to be associated with temples. Explaining how the interaction between the heavenly stars eventually came to describe the earthly temples, Dawwānī writes:

> *Haykal* originally meant shape or form. The ancient sages assumed that the stars constitute the shadows and forms (*hayākil*) of the incorporeal lights. They set up for each of the seven planets (stars) a theurgy (*ṭilism*) made of a metal, which was suitable to its own structure and time. They placed each of these theurgies in a house built, in conformity with a horoscope, in a location appropriate to the star. Then they went to the houses at certain times to execute certain (theurgical) activities ... Thus they would gain an advantage from the theurgical activities, and moreover they would make those houses magnificent and then call them [precisely] the Temples of Light ... because of their being the sites of these theurgies ... which were forms of the stars which themselves were the temples of the supreme lights.[30]

The temple construct described here seems to be the mirror image of the cosmos above. To prepare them as worthy microcosms, the temples are carefully constructed as astrological instruments and as talismans that ensure a connection to the heavens. Dawwānī describes how the study of horoscopes was used not only for conducting ritual theurgies, but also for selecting temple sites. He also reminds the reader of how each chapter of Suhrawardī's Temples of Light is to be imagined as a temple — a place of theurgy — through which the contemplation of incorporeal lights is made possible. Referring to Suhrawardī, Dawwānī writes:

> Therefore the author has accordingly named this treatise *Hayākil al-Nūr* ... whose purpose is to set out the modes ... of the incorporeal lights. So, each chapter of this treatise, together with the explanations as well as the terms that it contains, would resemble a place of theurgy whose contemplation would lead inevitably to the contemplation of these lights.[31]

Dawwānī's interpretations unravel the semantic scope of the word *haykal,* bringing into focus the cosmological dimensions and symbolic significance of the complex structure of the human reality which Suhrawardī conceived as constituting temples of light. Illuminating as his unravelling might be, Dawwānī did not identify the key sources of Suhrawardī's ideas, nor did he reveal to which religious community these temples belonged. The temple structures suggest that they were dedicated to the worship of the stars and that their designers and builders had a strong belief in the astrological powers of alchemy.

In *The Wisdom of the Mystic East,* historian John Walbridge examined the key sources of Suhrawardī's temple metaphor. He proposed that the metaphor may have been inspired by influential works on alchemy and talisman making which circulated in the Islamic world from around the 11th century CE.[32] The most famous of such works was the *Ghāyat al-ḥakīm* (The Goal of the Wise Sage), which was later translated into Latin as the *Picatrix*.[33] The ideas in this comprehensive manual for talisman making were largely inspired by the gnostic teachings of Hermes Trismegistus (c. 1300 BCE), whom Suhrawardī referred to as the 'father of philosophy'.[34] In his *al-Talwīḥāt* (Intimations), Suhrawardī presented a more concrete architectural description depicting Hermes Trismegistus as a pilgrim seeking light within the temple. In his depiction the experiences of the body and building are analogues of one another:

> Hermes was occupied praying before a sun of night (north star) in the temple of light. When the pillars of dawn were split, he saw a land whose villages had sunk beneath the anger of God. He fell down and called, 'Father, deliver me from the vicinity of evil.' He heard a voice, 'Cling to the cord of ray and ascend to the lofty reaches of the throne.' He went up until earth and heavens were beneath his feet.[35]

With these allusions of the ground giving way to darkness and the pillars collapsing to allow celestial light to flood in, Suhrawardī aimed to present a description of the human condition as continually oscillating between darkness and light. The temple architecture evolves from a subterranean darkness that ascends towards lightness. Yet with the ground obliterated, the body, as the temple of light, is reduced to only a vertical shard of light — what Suhrawardī described as a 'cord of ray'. With this we are presented with an image of the moment in which the human structure is comprehensively overcome with light and assumes its rightful composition as a temple of light.

Walbridge proposes that Suhrawardī's views on Hermes Trismegistus were most likely informed by the Sabians of Ḥarran in northern Syria. This ancient religious community was established in Mesopotamia around 2000 BCE, and is mentioned in the Quran, alongside the Jews and the Christians, as a community that preceded Islam.[36] According to pre-modern Muslim historians, including al-Masʿūdī (d. 956), al-Shahrastāni (d. 1153), and Ibn Kathīr (d. 1373 CE), the Sabians worshipped the stars and built temples dedicated to them 'at each of the seven gates of Damascus'.[37] They described the particular shape these temples took: 'Saturn, which was hexagonal; Jupiter, triangular; Mars, rectangular; the Sun, square; Venus, triangular in a square enclosure; Mercury, triangular in a rectangular enclosure; and the Moon, octagonal'.[38] Suhrawardī seems most likely to have developed his use of the architectural metaphor of the human temple, therefore, through the Sabians' temple model.[39] The division of chapters in Suhrawardī's Temples of Light supports this notion. Just as the Sabians responded to their adoration of the planets and stars with the seven types, Suhrawardī, too, divides his text into seven parts, with each part aptly named as a temple.

The eminent French scholar and intellectual historian Henry Corbin (d. 1978), in his attempt to interpret Suhrawardī's mystical imagery, has also found links between Suhrawardī's architectural allusions and a group of Sabian temples.[40] In a study entitled *Temples and Contemplation*

(1986), Corbin cites *Murūj al-dhahab* (Meadows of Gold), by the 10th-century Muslim historian and geographer Masʿūdī, to describe these magnificent buildings:

> The precinct wall of this Temple is pierced by seven gates, and it is capped with a seven tier dome. On the crown of the dome is set a kind of precious stone, vast in size and a brilliance that illuminates everything within range ... Inside the Temple itself is a well with a heptagonal opening; anyone who leans over it is in danger of being overcome with dizziness which drags him down into the abyss ... The Temple is built on a rock which rises out of the Earth like a high mountain.[41]

With reference to Masʿūdī, Corbin presents the idea of 'a Temple divided into seven oratories and lit by large windows, before each of which stands an Image, or statue'.[42] As mentioned, Dawwānī claimed that each temple site housed a talisman sympathetic to its planetary counterpart. In his earlier writings, Masʿūdī provided a clearer description of the talismanic artifacts. Corbin states that the statues are composed 'out of a substance and a color ... that correspond to the action of the planet represented'.[43]

In *The Man of Light in Iranian Sufism* (1994), Corbin examines Suhrawardī's allusions to the septet. While the symbolism of seven primarily alludes to the celestial orbs, and reinforces the link between the stars and the temples, Suhrawardī claims that this link is also threaded within the human body. According to his *Ḥikmat al-ishrāq*, the body is also composed of seven pathways or orbits, and it is only in traversing these interior spiritual pathways that one is able to find 'recourse to luminous inspirations'.[44] Corbin shows how within the Illuminationist circles (*Ishrāqiyyūn*), Suhrawardī's image of the human body as consisting of light pouches refers to the seven encampments of lights which are the seven subtle organs or centres (*latīfa*).[45] These centres mark out the landmarks in the interior spiritual terrain of the human being.[46] Each one of these centres is linked to its cosmic counterpart, which, in turn, is linked to a corresponding prophet and alchemical colour. This yet again recalls the sites of the statues of the Sabian temples mentioned above.[47] These talismanic regions of the body offer sectional diagrams of the human interior, its subtle organs and the ephemeral regions it is connected to.[48] These seven interior regions of the body are as follows:

subtle bodily organ (*laṭīfa qālabiyya*)
subtle organ of passions (*laṭīfa nafsiyya*)
subtle organ of the heart (*laṭīfa qalbiyya*)
subtle organ of secrets (*laṭīfa sirriyya*)
subtle organ of the spirit (*laṭīfa rūḥiyya*)
subtle organ of heavenly inspiration (*laṭīfa khafiyya*)
subtle organ of divine centre (*laṭīfa ḥaqqiyya*).

In his/her search for light, each pilgrim experiences these interior sites, which are of varying illuminative intensities that are commensurate with his/her spiritual aptitude. Each of the seven regions are spiritual waystations growing from the least to the most luminous. The *latīfa haqiqiyya* is the centre and the peak, similar to the elevated and most luminous seventh temple. It is here that all knowledge is consolidated and the most radiant light is to be found, where the cord of illuminative ray is made to extend to the pilgrim. This station belongs to Muhammad.[49] The temple mirrors the human body, which in turn mirrors the cosmos.

Suhrawardī's architectural metaphors are reinforced further in his short poetic recital entitled *Qiṣṣat al-ghurba al-gharbiyya* (The Story of the Occidental Exile). The Occidental Exile is a tale in which Suhrawardī, with a travelling partner (his rational soul), are found excursing through a strange land. The itinerant travellers are waylaid in their journey and are soon thrown into an 'infinitely deep pit' of foreboding opacity covered by 'layer upon layer of darkness'.[50] The prisoners are allowed some respite only at night. This concession is afforded so that they can ascend from the pit to see what lies above. The climb finds them emerging from deep darkness and becoming unveiled to the peaks of seven elevated towers. These towers represent the seven celestial orbs, or heavenly temples, which they can now see all at once. This ritual is repeated, reiterating the analogy of the human condition when it is offered the opportunity to emerge from darkness to ascend with, and towards, light.[51]

ṢĪṢIYYA: THE BODY AS FORTRESS OF DARKNESS

In the *Ḥikmat al-ishrāq*, Suhrawardī applies an unusual architectural term to the body. In order to describe the body as a clouded presence, he describes it as *ṣīṣiyya*, a 'fortress'. Rarely used in Arabic literature, this term is not reserved for the body of humans alone, as it also applies to all animals. All darkened beings on earth seek out the celestial 'commanding light'. But this commanding light is only attracted to the distinct light admixture which formed the human body. In its function as a fortress (*ṣīṣiyya*), the human body is said not only to receive the commanding light but also to secure those lights in pouches within itself. Invoking the spatial qualities of the fortress, Suhrawardī describes the human fortress both as a *containment* and also as an *encampment* of lights.[52] The aim of the divine light is thus to weaken the opacities of the human fortress in order to transform human beings into radiant beings. If this does not occur, then, according to Suhrawardī, the 'human fortress [has become] corrupted', and instead of the commanding light radiating through the fortress, the reverse happens: the light becomes contained, entrapped, and 'clouded by darknesses'.[53] This darkening results from the lethargy of the human fortress in striving for the gnosis of God. This being the case, the fortress becomes enamoured by the 'desire of the lowest of the low' and with this, eventually the commanding light becomes extinguished.[54]

The fortress is essentially a dark place as it conceals illumination, and a human fortress that remains stunted in darkness and opacity is no different from the fortresses of the beasts according to Suhrawardī, for it has failed to be catalysed by the incorporeal commanding lights.[55] But in fact this was not the case, as the human fortress became the 'first station of the commanding light'.[56] Thereafter, the commanding light is supposed to ignite a desire to elevate the human's 'perceptive essences [toward] the Light of Lights'.[57] Suhrawardī thinks this happens to be the case when one strives in the path of God. This strengthens the commanding light, and with that the opacities of the fortress become diluted. This leads to a link between the commanding light and other incorporeal illuminations from above. This chain is to be woven and strengthened until it reaches its origin, the Light of Lights:

> Whoso strives in the path of God as he ought and subdues the shadows beholds the lights of the all-highest world more perfectly than he beholds the objects of the vision here below. The Light of Lights and the dominating lights [*qawāhir*] are seen by vision of the commanding light and by their seeing each other.[58]

Such a body, when transformed by the illuminating lights, can no longer function as a fortress. Once the fortress becomes dissolved in light, humans, too, start to become distinguished from other beings — that is, from the other brute animal fortresses. This is when, for Suhrawardī, the human body assumes its true ontological being. It no longer remains a dark fortress; rather, it has now been transmuted into an illuminated temple. Suhrawardī elevates the human temple even further by proclaiming it to be the very talisman (*ṭilsam*) or idol (*ṣanam*) that becomes an object of worship. With this also occurs a notable shift as the once descending heavenly light is able to reconnect and ascend towards its origin. When returning to the temple, the commanding light claims the opacity of the building. This process is intended to illustrate al-Suhrawardī's views on the resultant effect of gnostic knowledge, the experience of *maʿrifa*. He writes:

> [L]ights of sundry kinds shine upon the brethren of incorporeality: a flashing light descending upon the beginners ... a stronger flashing light descending upon others ... a light extremely pleasant, shining from the soul upon the entire spirit of the soul, in which it seems as though something armors the body, and the spirit of the entire body might almost seem to have a luminous form.[59]

For Suhrawardī, the human has to transcend the 'fortress' and be transformed into a 'temple'. Only through this transformation does the human become like a microcosmic mirror.[60] As the illumination becomes pronounced, the architectural project shifts from fortress to temple and opacity turns to light. In fact, the intensity of the light could become 'so great as to nearly tear asunder the joints' and eventually it bears the structure away from its earthly confines altogether.[61] While Suhrawardī's use of architectural terms in *The Philosophy of Illumination* is limited, as the foregoing demonstrates, it does establish a spatial vocabulary in order to describe the intensity of, or lack in, one's knowledge of God.[62]

In one of his shorter treatises, entitled *Ṣafīr-i Sīmūrgh* (The Song of the Griffin), Suhrawardī appears to be in agreement with his august predecessors with regards to knowledge and light. He, too, argues for the path of the Sufis, and tells the reader that he agrees with the great al-Junayd that '*maʿrifa* is nobler than all sciences'.[63] After stating this, Suhrawardī delves into the resultant effect of this knowledge — that is, the experience of *maʿrifa*: 'The first lighting that comes to the souls of the Seekers from the presence of Divinity is accidents and flashes; and those lights dawn upon the soul of the (mystic) traveller from the world of Divinity; and it is delightful'.[64] The body now beheld by varying modes of light is made aware by experiences of time and space which oscillate between the states of wakefulness and dreams.[65] In his writings, Suhrawardī was interested to describe the types and effects of light upon the body. Uniquely in *The Philosophy of Illumination*, Suhrawardī describes how the body is cast with this light of God and is transformed into an illuminated temple (*haykal*). With this important claim, a nexus of relation is formed between light, knowledge, body, and building.

MESOCOSM: THE BODY IN PROXIMITY TO THE LIGHT OF LIGHTS

Suhrawardī's conceptualisation of the body metaphorically as a 'temple of light' aims to reveal the capacity of the human to become a mirror for cosmic luminosity.[66] He imagined that model to be in the form of illuminated architectural temples. These temple structures, with their various morphologies, materiality, alchemical symbolism, and ritual programs, offer us a sophisticated perspective on how the Islamic notion of 'knowledge is light' was understood and developed within the Illumination school. In this perspective, the martial and enclosed architecture of the body becomes porous and modified through its encounters with heavenly luminosities. For Corbin, the architectural imageries of the temple act as mediating tools capable of folding the macrocosm into the microcosm, through which the temple functions as an imaginal middle ground, a 'mesocosm'. The 'mesocosm', Corbin explains, is 'a sacred cosmos [which] is the place and instrument of the spiritual [r]itual; its heavens are neither the heavens of astronomy nor yet the inner heavens of pure subjectivity, but the esoteric heavens, rising in tiers to form the dome of the ideal Temple'.[67] In these mesocosmic pilgrimages, human beings may recover their own presence and potential as a microcosm. The actualisation of the human, as an illumined body, is only realised when it mirrors the illumination of the cosmos, resides in proximity to God, and thus becomes an appropriate site for the inhabitation of the Light of Lights.

Corbin's insights into Suhrawardī's thoughts are further enhanced by those of Hossein Ziai, who summarises succinctly the four stages that define the structure of knowledge in Illuminationist epistemology.[68] The first stage, Ziai states, involves the abandonment of the world, which is then followed by experiences of illuminative visions in the second stage. The third stage is the 'acquisition of unlimited and unbound knowledge', while the final stage involves the dissemination of acquired knowledge.[69] Given that the experiences are visionary and mystical, they can, in Ziai's view, only be described using 'symbolic portrayals'.[70] As an example, Ziai makes references to Suhrawardī's evocative descriptions of light and the human body.[71]

Ultimately, through conceiving of the human body as an illuminated temple and presenting the body as a mediating instrument, Suhrawardī presents the human body as an avenue for the gnostic journey aimed at acknowledging that true knowledge is only God, viewed as the Light of Lights. This journey, made to mediate through a unique architecture of gradated lights, the temple, reveals the 'noble constitution' of the human and its hidden metaphysical dimensions. In fact, it is with this knowledge and its light that one is able to trace the path from the darkness of the fortress in order to arrive at the radiant threshold of the temple of lights where we saw Suhrawardī praying earlier: '[W]e find in ourselves shining flashes and orienting illuminations and we visualize lights and attain our goals'.[72]

NOTES

1 Plato, 2003, *The Republic*, trans. D Lee (London: Penguin Books), 240-8. The 'Allegory of the Cave' is an archetypal tale which Plato uses to illustrate his Theory of Forms. In this tale, we find humans chained in a cave and facing a wall, projected upon which are shadows, which are the only reality they can see. This experience refers to the temporal world of changes. Eventually, one of the prisoners manages to escape and climbs upwards and out of the cave where he finds himself exposed to light. Initially, he is blinded, but after a while with the aid of light he is able to discern things as they truly are. Finally, he also sees the source of the light, the sun itself. For more on this allegory, see Eric Voegelin, 2000, *Plato* (Columbia: University of Missouri Press), 115; and Peter Adamson, 2014, *Classical Philosophy: A History of Philosophy without any Gaps*, vol. 1 (Oxford: Oxford University Press), 155-6.

2 Christians saw the meaning of both the light, with which God creates the world in the opening verses of the Old Testament, and the 'Word' (logos), with which God creates the world as mentioned in the Gospel of John in the New Testament, as one and the same in referring to Christ; see Jaroslav Pelikan, 1985, *Jesus Through the Centuries: His Place in the History of Culture* (New York: Harper and Row), 59.

3 Sabiha Khemir's (2014) monograph to the exhibition she curated on light in Islamic art and science, *Nūr: Light in Art and Science from the Islamic World* (Seville: Focus-Abenoga Foundation), is an excellent introduction in explaining the comprehensiveness of this relationship. Khemir discusses in this text how scriptural underpinnings of light formed an inspirational and enduring influence within the Islamic intellectual and aesthetic practices over a vast expanse of time and space. See also Franz Rosenthal's comprehensive review of the relationship between knowledge and light, especially in Sufi tradition within Islam: 2007, *Knowledge Triumphant: The Concept of Knowledge in Medieval Islam* (Leiden: Brill).

4 This saying, which is attributed to the Prophet Muhammad, is cited in Seyyed Hossein Nasr, 2006, *Islamic Philosophy from its Origin to the Present: Philosophy on the Land of Prophecy* (New York: SUNY), 161. Examples of Quranic verses describing light as revelation include the following: 'O mankind! Verily there has come unto you a proof from your Lord! And We have sent down unto you a clear light'. Quran 4:174. 'Thus those who believe in [Muhammad] honor him, and follow the light that has been sent with him; it is they who shall prosper.' Quran 7:157. 'Say, "Are the blind and the seer equal, or are darkness and light equal?"' Quran 13:16. 'We indeed sent Moses with our signs, "Bring thus people out of darkness into light, and remind them of the Days of God."' Quran 14:5. 'He for whom God has not appointed any light has no light.' Quran 24:40. Unless otherwise stated the translations of the Quran are from Seyyed Hossein Nasr et al., eds., 2015, *The Study Qur'ān: A New Translation and Commentary* (New York: Harper Collins).

5 Quran 14:1. See also Quran 4:174.

6 See Tosun Bayrak, 2000, *The Name and the Named* (Kentucky: Fons Vitae), 199-201; Quran 33:46.

7 Quran 24:35.

8 For a study of the review of this verse by the key Quranic exegetes see Nasr et al., eds., 2015, 878-80. Amongst separate treatises written on this verse see al-Ghazālī, 1998, *The Niche of Lights* (Mishkāt al Anwār), trans. D Buchman (Utah: Brigham Young University Press); and Mullā Ṣadrā Shīrāzī, 2004, *On the Hermeneutics of the Light Verse of the Qur'an* (Tafsīr Āyat al-Nūr), trans. LP Peerwani (London: ICAS Press).

9 Al-Suhrawardī, 1999, *The Philosophy of Illumination* (Ḥikmat al-Ishrāq), trans. J Walbridge and H Ziai (Utah: Brigham Young University Press), 4. Marcotte writes that the intuition al-Suhrawardī discusses here does not refer to what is usually understood in Aristotelian thought, which is the reasoned philosophical intuition that is used to distinguish the universals from the particulars. Rather, for al-Suhrawardī intuition is almost synonymous with revelation that arrives by way of 'mystical perception or vision': Roxanne Marcotte, 2005, 'Reason (*'aql*) and Direct Intuition (*Mushāhada*) in the Works of Shihāb al-Dīn al-Suhrawardī (d. 587/1191)', in T Lawson, ed., *Reason and Inspiration in Islam: Theology. Philosophy and Mysticism in Muslim Thought* (London: IB Tauris with The Institute of Ismaili Studies), 222-3.

10 Suhrawardī, 1999, 4.

11 See al-Fārābī, 1998, *On the Perfect State* (Ārā' ahl al-Madīna al Fāḍila), trans. R Walzer (Chicago: Kazi Publications), 89-163; Avicenna, 2005, *The Metaphysics of the Healing (Al-Shifā'): A Parallel English-Arabic Text*, trans. M Marmura (Utah: Brigham Young University Press), 326-38. For an understanding of the comparisons between the emanationist cosmological models of Al-Fārābī and Avicenna, see Herbert Davidson, 1992, *Al-Fārābī, Avicenna and Averroes on Intellect: Their Cosmologies, Theories of Active Intellect, and Theories of Human Intellect* (New York: Oxford University Press), 44-73.

12 Al-Suhrawardī, 1999, 99-106. See also Mehdi Amin Razavi, 1997, *Suhrawardī and the School of Illumination* (London: Curzon), 79-81.

13 For a clear explanation of this cosmological model see Seyyed Hossein Nasr, 1993, *An Introduction to Islamic Cosmological Doctrines: Conceptions of Nature and Methods Used for its Study by the Ikhwān al-Ṣafā', Al-Bīrūnī, and Ibn Sīnā* (New York: SUNY), 202-12.

14 Al-Suhrawardī, 1999, 76.

15 Al-Suhrawardī, 1999, 77 (parentheses in original). See Razavi's (1997, 78-81) excellent attempt to categorise the various lights referred to by Suhrawardī.

16 'The ontological status of all beings, therefore, depends on the degree in which they approach [God] and are themselves illuminated.' Seyyed Hossein Nasr, 1964, *Three Muslim Sages: Avicenna, Suhrawardī, Ibn 'Arabi* (Cambridge, Mass.: Harvard University Press), 69.

17 Al-Suhrawardī, 1999, 95-114; See also Seyyed Hossein Nasr and Amin Mehdi Razavi, eds., 1996, *The Islamic Intellectual Tradition in Persia* (London: Curzon), 139-40.

18 For the account of al-Suhrawardī's cosmological description and the differentiated experience of the pure lights, see Seyyed Hossein Nasr and Amin Mehdi Razavi, eds., 1996, *The Islamic Intellectual Tradition in Persia* (London: Curzon), 99-114. Al-Suhrawardī's overlaying of Illuminationist terms over the emanationist cosmological model makes for a rather complex and technical read. Both Razavi and Nasr in their writings not only help unpack the Illuminationist cosmology but also reveal its Zoroastrian and Islamic influences. See Razavi, 1997, 78-84; Nasr, 1964, 69-76.

19 Al-Suhrawardī, 1999, 104 and 107-11.

20 Al-Suhrawardī, 1999, 142.

21 Al-Suhrawardī, 1999, 141.

22 For a succinct presentation of how Aristotle sought to distinguish his philosophical approach from his teacher Plato, see Christopher Shields, 2007, *Aristotle* (London: Routledge), 8-15.

23 For a detailed elaboration of the various gradations of the lights in al-Suhrawardī's cosmology, see Razavi, 1997, 78-9.

24 The use of architectural models to articulate abstract ideas was well established in the Classical period. Examples include Plato's description of the perfect city in the dialogue *Critias*, and Aristotle's advice on how practical wisdom should be demonstrated in the layout of a city's defences in his *Politics*. Plato, 1977, *Timaeus and Critias*, trans. D Lee (London: Penguin Books), 138-42; Aristotle, 2009, *Politics*, trans. E Barker (Oxford: Oxford University Press), 276-8.

25 In recent times, spatial modalities have been used to interrogate philosophical ideas in the works of Michel Foucault (d. 1984), Henri Lefebvre (d. 1991), Jacques Derrida (d. 2004), and Peter Sloterdijk. An excellent example of how philosophy uses the architectural program and modalities can be found in Neil Leach's (1997) edited collection of essays *Rethinking Architecture: A Reader in Cultural Theory* (London: Routledge). The collection includes the writings of various 20th-century philosophers such as Martin Heidegger, Henri Lefebvre, Gilles Deleuze, Jacques Derrida, and Michel Foucault. In his introduction, citing both Andrew Benjamin and Derrida, Leach concludes that '[p]hilosophy inhabits architecture, no less than architecture inhabits philosophy' (xx). Peter Sloterdijk's *Spheres Trilogy* (2009) is a massive enterprise to cast his philosophical project in spatial terms. To better understand this project see Peter Sloterdijk, 2009, 'Talking to Myself about the Poetics of Space', *Harvard Design Magazine*, <http://www.harvarddesignmagazine.org/issues/30/talking-to-myself-about-the-poetics-of-space>, accessed 23 April 2017. Hubert Damisch describes this enterprise as the 'architectonic dimension of the workings of thought' in which architectural vocabulary is used to make present ideas in a tangible and phenomenologically experiential manner: 2016, *Noah's Ark: Essays on Architecture*, trans. J Rose (Cambridge, Mass.: MIT Press), 27-8.

26 Bilal Kuşpinar, 1996, *Ismail Ankravi on the Illuminative Philosophy: His Izhu'l Hikem: Its Edition and Analysis in Comparison with Dawwānī's Shawakil al-Hur, Together with the Translation of Suhrawardī's Hayākil al-Nūr* (Kuala Lumpur: ISTAC), 77.

27 Kuşpinar, 1996, 185.

28 Kuşpinar, 1996, 233.

29 While *haykal* refers to bodies in general, in *The Philosophy of Illumination* Suhrawardī uses it exclusively to refer to humans. Kuşpinar, 1996, 89.

30 Dawwānī, cited in Kuşpinar, 1996, 88-89 (parentheses in original).

31 Cited in Kuşpinar, 1996, 89.

32 John Walbridge, 2001, *The Wisdom of the Mystic East* (New York: SUNY), 17-50. Hermes Trismegistus is identified as an ancient font of knowledge. While his actual existence is contested, Hermes experienced a grand revival in the Renaissance, when he was thought to be real and to have existed around the time of Moses. Hermes is identified to be a most important and significant source of Gnosticism, alchemy, and magic. He is ascribed authorship of the *Hermetica*, a source book for talisman making and magic. Frances Yates's detailed study of Hermes Trismegistus remains an important source in understanding his importance in the revival of magic, alchemy, and talisman making in the Renaissance: 2002, *Giordano Bruno and the Hermetic Tradition* (New York: Routledge), 1-89.

33 Yates, 2002, 52-65.

34 Al-Suhrawardī, 1999, 2. For further reading on the Sabians see al-Birūnī, 1879, *The Chronology of Ancient Nations (Āthār-ul-Bākiya)*, trans. CE Sachau (Pall Mall: William H Allen and Co), 186-88. Yates (2002) describes the Arabic origins of *Picatrix* to be around the 12th century. The text is a manual of talisman making, yet it claims to describe the wisdom of Hermes which was derived through the influence of the Sabians. For a discussion of Hermes in Islamic thought see Walbridge (2001, 23), who, commenting on the importance of Hermes to Suhrawardī, writes: 'Hermes' importance seems to lie first in his antiquity, "the father of the sages," he is the common ancestor of the Greek, Egyptian and Persian philosophical traditions that are reunited in Suhrawardī [sic]'. Per Yates, the dating of Hermes Trismegistus in the Christian tradition situates him as a contemporary of Moses: 2002, 12-15. Walbridge (2001, 22-3) writes that in the Islamic tradition he is identified with the prophet Idris. According to Nasr et al., eds. (2015, 779, fn. 56-7), Idris is said to have lived between the ages of Adam and Noah. Accordingly, this would place the Islamic version of Hermes to have existed around 4000 BCE.

35 Suhrawardī, cited in Walbridge, 2001, 48-49. See also Henry Corbin, 1994, *The Man of Light in Iranian Sufism*, trans. N Pearson (New York: Omega Publications), 45.

36 Walbridge, 2001, 37-42; Quran 2:62, 5:59, and 22:17. On a brief discussion of the Islamic view of who the Sabians were, see Nasr et al., eds., 2015, 31, fn. 62.

37 Ibn Kathīr, 2014, *From the Beginning to the End* (al-Bidāyah wa al-Nihāyah): *The Story of Creation, Ummahs of the Past, The Life of Muhammad up to 9 AH*, vol. 1, trans. RA Rahman (Karachi: Darul Ishaat), 239.

38 Walbridge, 2001, 39. See also Corbin, 2013, *Temple and Contemplation* (London: Routledge), 140.

39 However, it must be made clear that none of these temples existed during his time. Walbridge, 2001, 40.

40 Corbin, 2013, 133.

41 Corbin, 2013, 132.

42 Corbin, 2013, 133.

43 Corbin, 2013. Compare this with the description of the construction of man-made gods in the *Hermetica* cited in Yates, 2002, 39.

44 Al-Suhrawardī, 1999, 4 and 158.

45 Corbin (1994), in his study of al-Suhrawardī's spiritual heirs, amongst others, introduces Najmoddīn Kobra, Najmoddīn Rāzī, and 'Alāoddawleh Semnānī.

46 Corbin, 1994, 12 and 121.

47 Corbin, 1994, 126.

48 Corbin, 1994, 124-5.

49 Corbin, 1994, 125-6.

50 Al-Suhrawardī, 1982, 101.

51 Al-Suhrawardī, 1982, 100-2. See also Nasr and Razavi, 1996, 132; Corbin, 2013, 133; and Corbin, 1994, 43-6.

52 Al-Suhrawardī, 1999, 141-2.

53 Al-Suhrawardī, 1999, 142.

54 Al-Suhrawardī, 1999.

55 Al-Suhrawardī, 1999, 142-3.

56 Al-Suhrawardī, 1999, 141.

57 Al-Suhrawardī, 1999, 145.

58 Al-Suhrawardī, 1999, 139.

59 Al-Suhrawardī, 1999, 159-60.

60 Al-Suhrawardī, 1999, 141-2. See also Nasr and Razavi, 1996, 141: 'Man as the microcosm contains in himself the complete image of the universe … This body in turn is the theurgy for the [incorporeal] light which governs each man'.

61 Al-Suhrawardī, 1999, 160.

62 Al-Suhrawardī, 1999, 111. This ambition in journeying towards God, conveyed solely in light, is best summarised by his prayer: '[God,] I ask Thee by the light of Thy countenance, which fills the pillars of Thy throne'.

63 Al-Suhrawardī, 1935, *Three Treatises of Mysticism*, trans. and ed. Otto Spies and SK Khattak (Stuttgart: W. Kohlhammer), 32. Al-Junayd is cited in Ali Hassan Abdel-Kader, 2013, *The Life, Personality and Writings of Al-Junayd: A Study of a Ninth Century Mystic with an Edition and Translation of his Writings* (Selangor: Islamic Book Trust), 96-103. Al-Qushayrī defined *ma'rifah*, divine gnosis, as the goal of *'ilm*, by saying that 'all knowledge is gnosis and all gnosis is knowledge'. Abu 'l-Qāsim al-Qushayrī, 2007, *Al-Qushayrī's Epistle on Sufism* (Al Risāla al-Qushayriyya fī 'ilm al-taṣawwuf), trans. AD Knysh (Reading: Garnet), 320. See also Rosenthal, 2007,166.

64 Al-Suhrawardī, 1935, 32. See also Razavi, 1997, 65-78. Here Razavi discusses the symbolism deployed by al-Suhrawardī in describing his gnostic visions.

65 Al-Suhrawardī, 1935, 36.

66 See n. 61 above. Of the human capacity to be the receptacle of knowledge of the cosmos, al-Ghazālī wrote: '[God] gave [Adam] an abridged form that brings together every sort of thing found in the cosmos'. See Al-Ghazālī, 1998, 31.

67 Corbin, 2013, 137.

68 Hossein Ziai, 2004, 'Suhrawardī on Knowledge and the Experience of Light', in M Kapstein, ed., *The Presence of Light: Divine Radiance and Religious Experience* (Chicago: University of Chicago Press), 28.

69 Ziai, 2004, 29.

70 Ziai, 2004. Al-Suhrawardī himself (1999, 4) makes it clear in the introduction of his Philosophy of Illumination that his work only contains symbols.

71 See Ziai, 2004, notes 21, 49 and 68.

72 See n. 28 above.

PART III

‘ILM AS ART

CHAPTER 9

ʿ*ILM* AND THE 'ARCHITECTURE OF HAPPINESS': THE OTTOMAN IMPERIAL PALACE AT EDIRNE/ADRIANOPLE, 1451-1877

SUSAN SCOLLAY

ABSTRACT

This chapter considers the imperial palace built by the Ottoman sultan Murat II (r. 1421-51) at Edirne in Thrace and its aesthetic context. The city had been the Ottoman seat of government for almost a century but it was not until the final years of Murat II's reign that the dynasty commissioned a palace of any significance. The built form of the royal complex appeared to have no precedent in the Ottoman realm and, although little studied, has been interpreted by scholars as being a key articulation of the emergence of a new imperial vision. Likely sources of inspiration for key structures of the Edirne Palace include Seljuq and Timurid architectural precedents. According to the *Encyclopedia of Islam*, the term *ʿilm al-jamāl* (knowledge or science of beauty) describes the concept of aesthetics in modern Arabic usage. Yet, as Doris Behrens-Abousief has noted, it is a term missing from historical Islamic civilisation. Architecture, for example, had pre-eminent status as an art form throughout the Islamic world, yet there were no theoretical writings on architectural design or construction. This chapter proposes that palaces of the imagination described in illustrated manuscripts, such as the Persian *Shāhnāma* (Book of Kings) and other Persianate poetic tales, were likely models for the Edirne Palace. It concludes that poetic ideals of beauty connected to *ʿilm*, understood here as knowledge of literature and cultural models from elsewhere in the Islamic world, played a large part in the artistic evolution of the House of Osman.

INTRODUCTION

Many recent studies of the visual culture of the Ottoman Empire take as their starting point Mehmet II's (r. 1444-46, 1451-81) successful siege of the crumbling eastern Roman capital, Constantinople.[1] The reshaping of a new and final capital for the young sultan and his successors, with the introduction of distinctive architecture and sophisticated court culture, dominates research in Ottoman art history. Leslie Peirce has called for wider recognition of the impact of global styles and fluid boundaries in the years leading up to what has been seen as a critical shift in the Ottoman articulation of imperial authority. Such acknowledgement, she argues, would assist in dispelling the tendency to portray the early years of Ottoman rule in Istanbul as a 'kind of miraculous virgin birth'.[2]

This chapter is a step towards filling the gap that Peirce so accurately identifies. It considers the way in which the House of Osman 'visualised' its emerging state in the form of the imperial palace at Edirne in Thrace, begun in 1451.[3] The city was known to Europeans as Adrianople and had been the second capital of the Ottomans, after Bursa, since 1361. However, it was not until almost a century later, in the final year of the reign of Murat II (r. 1421-44, 1446-51), that the dynasty commissioned a palace of any significance. The appearance of the royal complex appeared to have no precedent in the Ottoman realm. Sometimes described as a crucial period of preparation for the empire of Mehmet II, Murat II's reign began in disunity and rebellion, was punctuated by his brief abdication from 1444 to 1446, and concluded with a period of expansion and renewed vision of a centralised empire.[4] In nearly all the capital cities of the Islamic world in the early modern era, writes Sussan Babaie, a major reworking of the urban fabric 'marks a political transition toward centralization and absolutism' and begins with either the building of a new palace or extensive remodelling of previous royal compounds.[5]

The new imperial residence at Edirne was a conglomeration — a complex of freestanding buildings — spread over an extensive site at the confluence of three rivers, a few kilometres northeast of the town. The complex was modified and expanded by successive sultans until its eventual destruction in 1877.[6] Murat II oriented the key buildings of the palace complex towards the southeast, facing the direction of Mecca at 45 degrees southeast.[7] The old palace at Edirne had been built with a north-south orientation on a hill inside the Byzantine city walls along the lines of an urban citadel.[8] Little is known of the mix of tents and pavilions previously used by the court at Bursa.

When Murat II conceived the idea for his new palace, there were no treatises on Ottoman architecture. These were to come later, with Ca'fer Efendi's *Risāle-i Mi'māriyye* in the early 17th century and an 18th-century work by Ahmed Efendi being among the best known.[9] In early modern Europe an architect was recognised as an artist, with wealthy patrons, allowing for a high degree of professional autonomy. However, in the emerging Ottoman realm at this time, an architect was regarded as a servant of the state. Architectural know-how (*'ilm*), often gained through the palace system as a form of apprenticeship, included surveying, engineering, and various building techniques. There was little distinction between art and craft, and principles of architectural proportion and aesthetics were not codified as a scholarly discipline, although practitioners were well aware of Byzantine and Islamic building heritage (Figure 9.1).[10]

Likely sources of knowledge and inspiration for the appearance of Murat II's new palace include Seljuq and Timurid Persian architectural precedents. The spatial layout at Edirne that required a visitor to enter the palace at the main gate and move across the first court to the second gate was classically Iranian. This first courtyard was the outer zone of the palace, the *birun*; the second courtyard was a more restricted inner zone, the *endurun*, which led into the protected zone around the third courtyard, the *harem*. It was a sequence that reflected the boundaries and gated entrances of the riverside paradise gardens described in the Quran, through which only the faithful could enter.[11] Court poets sometimes described the ruler as being 'like the sun' in the 'seventh sky', and compared royal 'paradise' gardens to 'God's heaven'.[12] Such progression from the periphery of the palace gardens through courtyard space and paired gateways was drawn directly from Ilkhanid models, which in turn drew on the 12th-century palaces of the rulers of Ghazna.[13] There was an ongoing interplay between the geographic reach of Persianate culture and the evolution of Ottoman imperial self-representation during the lifespan of the Edirne Palace. Persian-language scientific, religious, and literary culture, along with shared knowledge, circulated freely and easily along the robust trade networks that linked Ottoman territories with the rest of the eastern Islamic world.[14]

Figure 9.1 Detail: Architectural reconstruction of the central buildings, courtyards and gardens of the Edirne Palace drawn by Orhan Çakmakçıoğlu (1923-2003). Photograph by S Scollay, 2007.

In the manner of the great Persian kings of the past, and in keeping with his carefully constructed image as a *gazi* ruler[15], Murat II chose a bucolic riverside setting for his new palace. A notable precedent was a royal complex begun by the founder of the Ghaznavid Dynasty, Mahmud of Ghazna (r. 998-1030), and completed by his son, Masʿud I (r. 1031-41).[16] Two of the main structures at Edirne serve as examples of the palace's Persianate inspiration. The first, the Cihannüma Kasrı (Belvedere or View of the World Pavilion), the most important building of the palace, was conceived and begun by Murat II and completed by his son and successor, Mehmet II, after Murat's death soon after construction began.[17] The second is a pleasure pavilion, known as Saʿdabad (Abode of Happiness), built by Mehmet IV (r. 1648-87) during the 17th century.[18] Saʿdabad was constructed during a period of increased building activity at the Edirne Palace in the years from 1661 to 1703, when Mehmet IV and his successors chose to live and rule from Edirne in preference to the Topkapı Palace in Istanbul.

THE CIHANNÜMA KASRI

The first building begun on the site was the Cihannüma Kasrı, an imposing seven-storey tower, facing the Tunca River due southeast. Its design merged elements of the palaces of the Persianate literary imagination with reinvented antecedents closer to home. In keeping with established Islamic palatine practice, the building was positioned at the centre of the complex, deep inside the second precinct, the ceremonial space that the public were not permitted to enter. From the upper level of the building, the panorama of the outer domains of the new palace and flowing rivers

Figure 9.2 Detail: Architectural reconstruction of the Cihannüma Kasrı at the Edirne Palace drawn by Orhan Çakmakçıoğlu (1923-2003). Photograph by S Scollay, 2007.

could be admired in all directions, and the constellations of the heavens observed at night. Such centrally placed structures overlooking garden vistas were a key element of the Persian palatine tradition and an unmistakable statement of royal power (Figure 9.2).[19]

Before the rise of the Ottomans, the Seljuq rulers of mediaeval Anatolia had built themselves royal compounds outside their capital, Konya, with park-like gardens whose central structures were freestanding pavilions, often with more than one storey. Interiors were tiled and painted with Persianate themes of hunting, feasting, and drinking. Couplets of verse from the *Shāhnāma* (Book of Kings) and other works of Persian literature carved in stone were also used in their decoration.[20] It was a palace scheme typically employed by Persianate dynasties such as the Timurids in Central Asia from 1396 to 1510, and also later used by the Safavid dynasty in Iran from 1501 to 1736.

The appearance and uses of traditional Persianate palaces, as depicted in literature, metaphorically in the text, and pictorially in the illustrations, were an important source of inspiration for Seljuq and Ottoman palace design. Palaces of the imagination were described in illustrated manuscripts such as the *Shāhnāma* and other embellished poetic tales that had been popular in the Islamic world since the 12th century. Like other Muslim rulers keen to extend the appearance of legitimacy and power, Murat II and Mehmet II collected luxury editions of the *Shāhnāma* and other classic Persian poetic works.[21] In 848/1450-51, the same year he began the Edirne Palace, Murat II commissioned the first known translation of the *Shāhnāma* into Ottoman Turkish.[22] As well as being active patrons, both sultans also wrote poetry in the Persian-language cultural tradition, with Murat II being the first Ottoman sultan known to compose and circulate his own verse.[23] Under Murat II's patronage, Edirne was a centre of literary and artistic production.[24] His court was filled with poets whose literary credentials were their common grounding in, and veneration for, the Persian classics.

Many of the illustrated manuscript copies of the *Shāhnāma* included architecturally accurate images of palatial structures in the Persianate manner — interior throne chambers, double-storey towers, and the type of garden pavilion that characterised palace complexes, such as that of Edirne, built on the outskirts of urban centres. By the time Murat II began building the Edirne Palace, the Ottomans had also collected copies of the *Khamsa* (Quintet) of the Persian poet, Nizami Ganjavi (d. 1209). One of these five tales, *Haft Paykar* (Seven Portraits, or Seven Pavilions), told the story of the Sasanian king Bahram Gur V (r. 420-38 CE), who, in the grounds of his hunting palace, built private pavilions for seven princesses from different regions of the world, so that after he married them all he could visit them, one by one, every day of the week.[25] These pavilions, each a different colour in accordance with the symbolism taught by many schools of Sufism[26], were often illustrated in manuscript copies of the *Khamsa* as multi-level towers; as were illustrations of the story of the ancient Persian king Khusrau, who loved a Christian princess, Shirin, who lived in a towered palace. This latter story was a favourite of Mehmet II, who commissioned poets at court to produce versions inspired by an illustrated copy of Nizami's *Khamsa*, commissioned by his father, and dedicated to him in Edirne in 846/1440 when he was a boy.[27]

Murat II's fanciful tower, completed by Mehmet II, was built as a solid rectangle over seven levels, accessed by a stone staircase that led to a marble terrace.[28] The structure was built in wood and rectangular blocks of stone (a technique known as *aşlar*) and bricks. It included a throne room for less formal occasions, rooms for storage of the holy relics and other treasures, an armoury, and the palace library.[29] The top level consisted of an octagonal room that was cantilevered and detached from the building's solid square base. A 16-sided, enclosed and shuttered arcade wrapped around it, allowing for extensive views.[30] As well, an ornamented pool was built in the centre of the upper room, octagonal in form and highly symbolic. According to the historian Günküt Akın, the octagonal shape of the interior pool and of the upper level of the tower itself had a twofold purpose. It represented 'world sovereignty for the ruler' and the 'unity with the divine'[31] pursued in the mystic beliefs and practices of the various Sufi orders, to which Murat II and Mehmet II owed allegiance.[32] Throughout its lifetime, the imperial complex, like all Islamic palaces, symbolised more than just its material form, linking human and cosmic concerns.[33] When the Ottoman traveller Evliya Çelebi visited Edirne in the early 17th century, he described the Cihannüma Kasrı as aspiring to 'the highest level of the skies', with a large marble terrace enhanced by a central pool. It was, in his estimation, 'a paradise kiosk ... with many cubicles, balconies, jets, and ponds in each of its seven levels'.[34]

There is no firm evidence that any architect was consulted to oversee the planning and building of the Cihannüma Kasrı. Since Murat II's building program had not been extensive during his reign to this point, and the mosques he had commissioned were not monumental, it is likely he co-operated with various master builders at Edirne and did not use a specific architect. In Gülru Necipoğlu's detailed discussion of the Topkapı Palace constructed soon after the conquest of Constantinople/Istanbul in 1453, she stressed the active role that Mehmet II played in the project he had commissioned. In the absence of sources that name a specific architect/designer, Necipoğlu suggested that the Edirne Palace served as a model for the building of the Topkapı, and concluded, along with a chronicle of Kemalpaşazade, that the sultan himself conceived the Topkapı building program, 'inspired by the architect of his mind'.[35] In an earlier paper, Necipoğlu made an argument for the existence of plans and models during the 15th century as a means of communication and dissemination of abstract architectural ideas, although there are none extant. On the basis of the evidence provided by 16th-century plans, she also concluded that Ottoman builders adhered to the conventions of manuscript illustrations with their lack of perspective and two-dimensionality.[36] Until Murat II decided to build the new palace at Edirne, the most significant building he had previously commissioned was the Uç Şerefeli Mosque, completed in the centre of the city in 1447. According to Doğan Kuban, this mosque, with its large interior space, balconied minarets in Persianate style, and the first large courtyard in all Ottoman mosque architecture, is proof that 'Ottoman architecture had commenced creating the products that demonstrated ... its capacity to conceive novel typologies'.[37]

If, as the writer Alain de Botton claims, 'every architectural style speaks of an understanding of happiness'[38], then the novelty of the Cihannüma Kasrı suggests that happiness for the elite of the emerging Ottoman empire was to be found in structures redolent with spiritual and literary symbolism set within gardens whose earthly features were reflections of divine beauty and the paradise gardens promised in the Quran. These were the overarching themes and settings of the poetry that was the main cultural pursuit of the court at Edirne, with many of the poets being initiated into Sufi orders, like the sultans. In 1435-36, Murat II paid for the upgrade of a Mevlevi dervish house in Edirne and added a mosque to the complex. From 1444 to 1446, he abdicated the throne in favour of his 13-year-old son, Mehmet, in order to live a contemplative life with the Mevlevi order in Manisa.[39]

THE *DILSUZNĀMA*

A rare manuscript copied and dated in Edirne in 860/1455-56, before Mehmet II's court had completely moved to the new capital in Constantinople/Istanbul, further demonstrates the connections of the Ottoman elite to Sufism. The illustrated story is one of the earliest known literary works of Ottoman production.[40] It is written in Persian and assumes an understanding and appreciation of its Quranic references, Sufic meanings, and its classical Persian poetic parallels and puns. The manuscript is the only known copy of the *Dilsuznāma* (Book of Compassion)[41], a work composed by replace with Badī' al-Dīn Manūchihr al-Tajirī al-Tabrīzī, a relatively unknown 14th-century Persian poet from Tabriz. Badi' al-Din is known to have travelled from Iran to Anatolia assisting his merchant father in 1391. He spent time in Konya, where he was associated with Mevlevi dervishes; a manuscript attributed to him remains in the archives there.[42] While the scribe and illustrator of the Edirne manuscript copy are not identified and the exact circumstances of its production in Edirne are not known, the text and five illustrated folios provide insight into the physical and cultural context of the Edirne Palace (Figure 9.3).

The *Dilsuznāma* relates the popular story of the 'rose and the nightingale' and is charmingly illustrated, with parallels drawn between the sweet singing soul bird who loves the beautiful flower and a human couple, she named 'Rose' and he named 'Nightingale'. They are illustrated alongside each other in a garden pavilion in a version of the extensive rose gardens planted by Mehmet II soon after the Cihannüma Kasrı was built. The roses are drawn and coloured in an exact rendition

Figure 9.3 Detail: Rose gives Nightingale a handkerchief as a keepsake. From a manuscript of Badī' al-Dīn Manūchihr al-Tajirī al-Tabrīzī, *Dilsuznāmah*, dated 860/1455-56, Edirne. The Bodleian Libraries, The University of Oxford, MS. Ouseley 133, fols 49r, 62r.

of the variety of many-petalled damask roses that perfumed the palace grounds.[43] The garden pavilion in which the protagonists sit is not shown in its entirety but frames the seated pair in their enclosed world of early-Ottoman decoration. Their pose is that of the Persianate princely elite: seated cross-legged on a slightly raised dais, with a large, figured-fabric bolster (*yastık*) on which they recline only slightly. Above the backrest, the pavilion wall is rendered in the hexagonal tiles known in Edirne from the decoration of the Muradiye Mosque and other buildings from the era of Murat II.[44] A curtain drawn in the manner of Byzantine miniature painting is suspended ready to be lowered as a screen, protective of the side of the pavilion open to the garden and the sightline of any onlooker. Rose passes Nightingale the handkerchief that symbolises her love for him, but their eyes do not meet, nor do they meet the gaze of the viewer.[45] These suggestions of privacy and interior space — the enclosed pavilion, the curtain, their posture and decorous gestures — all accentuate the layers of sensuous and mystical meaning in the story and the mental images its language evokes. Like almost all Persian and Ottoman poetry describing the theme of love, the tale presents human attachment as acting as a bridge to the love of, and union with, the divine, which was the goal of all Sufis.[46] At the same time, the spatial and decorative details and the lovers' robes and headgear are all accurate representations of Ottoman material culture of the time. While the themes and illustrations are drawn from Persian models, they have been reworked within the Ottoman context and act as a visual 'translation'.

SA'DABAD, THE 'ABODE OF HAPPINESS'

This knowledge of aesthetic, cultural, and spiritual ideals, conveyed through Persianate literary texts and illustrations, continued to underpin the architecture of the Edirne Palace complex as it expanded and responded to changes in political power over the years. This was especially so in the flurry of building activity carried out by Mehmet IV after the court moved to Edirne in 1661, until he was dramatically removed from the throne in 1687. Portrayed by later chroniclers as an inept sultan, more interested in hunting than affairs of state, the young Mehmet IV left Istanbul to escape court factionalism and restore political authority. His powerful mother, Turhan Hatice Sultan, and her court advisors were instrumental in the move.[47] In contrast to his predecessors, whose lives were secluded in the Topkapı Palace, Mehmet IV created an image of himself as a mobile, active, and visible ruler, like the models of monarchy described in the Islamic 'Mirrors for Princes' literature.[48] From the outset, individual structures within the palace compound were given Persianate names, and Mehmet IV continued this practice, calling his main pleasure pavilion Sa'dabad.

Unlike Cihannüma Kasrı, nothing remains of Sa'dabad, but its appearance may be understood from eyewitness accounts and plans drawn by the Austrian Baron Gudenus in 1741.[49] Soon after the court had made its permanent move to Edirne in 1661, the Valide Sultan built her son a new pavilion called Dolmabahçe (Filled Garden). It was situated on the northeast edge of the inner section of the palace complex close to the grand curve of the Tunca River, near the gate that Mehmet IV used to depart on his regular hunting expeditions. The residence had a large audience chamber and reception rooms to be used according to the seasons, plus a treasury and a bathhouse. The reception rooms were richly decorated with gilded plasterwork and ceramic tiles painted with floral motifs that echoed the paradisiacal flower gardens that could be glimpsed through the two rows of stained-glass windows. From the outside, the half-timbered building was shaped like a tent, with a leaden roof topped by a golden finial (*alem*) that denoted imperial authority, just as in the imperial tent complex that was often set up in the gardens of the Edirne Palace and mobilised when the sultan was hunting or on campaign.[50] Jasmine, honeysuckle, and roses perfumed the terraced gardens that sloped down to the riverbank, where marble steps and gateways gave access to the water.[51]

Later, Mehmet IV constructed a cross-shaped pavilion nearby, with several rooms and a large enclosed living area that opened onto an enormous pool of about 133 square metres that was called *Şehvar* (Worthy of a King). This new pavilion was built very quickly, using a lighter and faster method of construction, with a combination of *aşlar* and an increased quantity of timber, a technique known as *çatma*.[52] Its interiors were flooded with light, which played in the water jets thrown by the fountain in the centre of the main room and produced moving reflections in the mirrored and faceted wall panels used throughout. This is the pavilion he called Sa'dabad, a name that evoked direct associations with palace structures of the same name in the Persian tradition (Figure 9.4).

After hostilities with the Ottomans in Tabriz in 1544, the Safavid Shah Tahmasp (r. 1524-76) transferred his capital to Qazvin, building on its northern outskirts a complex of buildings and gardens for his court. He named his garden city Sa'databad, a variation of Sa'dabad. The name derived from *sa'āda*, a Persian/Arabic term that corresponded to the Greek *endaimonia*, meaning

Figure 9.4 Detail: Architectural reconstruction of the Sa'dabad Pavilion at the Edirne Palace drawn by Orhan Çakmakçıoğlu (1923-2003). Photograph by S Scollay, 2007.

'happiness' or 'wellbeing' achieved through the pursuit of the divine.[53] In a lengthy, five-part poem, *Jannat-i 'Adn* (Garden of Eden), 'Abdi Beyk Shirazi described the 'transparency' of the octagonal pavilion that stood at the centre of Shah Tahmasp's complex, with its arched openings and columns, and the 'unity' of its interior and the vast gardens that surrounded it.[54] These incorporated spaces that were set aside as promenades for the enjoyment of the public[55] and mansions for princes and court officials.[56] Later, Shah Abbas II (r. 1642-66) built a pleasure palace complex just outside Isfahan on the southern banks of the Zayande River and gave it the same name. Its cluster of pavilions included an octagonal structure built in the 1630s by the previous Safavid Shah, Safi (r. 1629-42). Here in the restorative atmosphere of the *Ayenehane* (Hall of Mirrors), as it was known because of its mirrored interior, Shah Safi chose to spend the last years of his life.[57]

Meanwhile, in Edirne in 1687, Mehmet IV flanked his Sa'dabad Pavilion with another that he, too, called the Aynali Kasrı, the 'Mirror Pavilion'. One side faced the pool and was an open summer room screened from the outside with shutters or curtains. It was divided from another large room that faced the river by a marble fountain that acted as a transparent and decorative partition. The water of the fountain fell into a container and overflowed into a channel carved into the floor, and then, in turn, flowed into the pool of another fountain in the middle of the summer room. The excess water flowed out through three marble channels under the window openings to the large pool outside. The interior walls and ceiling were covered with large mirrors inscribed with lines of mystical poetry.[58] Mirrors played an important part in the symbolism of Sufi poets, evoking images from the philosophy of the great master Ibn 'Arabī (1165-1240), who had travelled extensively and lived in Seljuq-ruled Anatolia in the early 13th century. In his mystical vision, the Sufi universe was God's hall of mirrors, every facet reflecting an aspect of God. 'Every known thing has a relation with the Real, for the Real is Light', he wrote. 'It follows that nothing is known but God.'[59] The Mirror Pavilion was the last of the major structures built at the Edirne Palace. It continued the much more open and airy style of architecture that Mehmet IV's unprecedented building program had introduced to the imperial precinct.

Sa'dabad remained the centre of this architectural trio at Edirne and the focus of what also became a more open and visible way of life for the Ottoman court: a promotion of its authority, but also a pragmatic sharing of the pleasures of its idyllic surrounds, which functioned not only as a military staging post but also as a place of rest and retreat, of gatherings where local wine was served, and musicians and poets entertained the royal entourage. In 1674, the head gardener at the palace, Aşık Ali Ağa, wrote in his chronicle that Mehmet IV

> was the first to allow the public to come and enjoy the outer gardens of the palace. The members of the royalty, the viziers, and other men of the state could enter the private gardens and their families could spend time beside the *Şehvar* pool. At the same time the Valide Sultan and the princes and their mothers could spend time together on their boats over and around the pool. Sweets and other treats would be sent from the Harem to be given to the children of the public in the outer gardens.[60]

RE-PRESENTING SA'DABAD

One of Mehmet IV's sons, who played in the boats on the pool and who hunted alongside his father along the riverbanks and deep into their wooded surrounds, was the future Ahmet III (r. 1703-30).

He was made sultan after a violent rebellion at Edirne in 1703 and was forced to bring the court back to Istanbul and restore the image of Ottoman sovereignty. Even then he shunned the Topkapı Palace in favour of a series of pleasure palaces he developed along the shores of the Bosphorus and the Golden Horn. Ahmet III's building program was unprecedented in Istanbul, opening up the city to novel architectural styles, social practices, and patterns of consumption.[61] The most famous of his pleasure palaces was begun in 1721 outside the established imperial centre in an area known as Kağithane (Paper Mill), where two rivers flowed together in the upper reaches of the Golden Horn. The course of one of the rivers was reshaped as a canal, more than 1000 metres long, with the palace buildings clustered around a series of cascades and fountains where the canal met the natural course of the stream. The imperial pavilions and extensive gardens were built on one side of the waterway, with some parts open to the view of the promenades and equally extensive gardens built for the public on the other side. Ahmet III called this palace, with its fountains, mirrored interiors, flower gardens, treed walkways and grassy meadows, Saʿdabad. Its main pavilion, the Waterfall Pavilion, built beside the canal at the point where it opened into a pool, shared most of its architectural features with the Saʿdabad pavilion he had known as a child at Edirne (Figure 9.5).[62]

Ahmet III's Saʿdabad complex was such a radical departure from previous palace architecture in the Ottoman capital that European observers compared it favourably to Louis XIV's late-17th-century palaces at Versailles and Marly. The Saʿdabad palace has generally been held by Europeans as proof of the increasing Westernisation in Ottoman politics and culture during a

Figure 9.5 Saʿdabad Palace, engraving by WH Bartlett (1809-54), c. 1836. From Miss Pardoe, *Beauties of the Bosphorus: Views of Constantinople and its Environs*, 1839, plate facing page 6. Reproduced from *Travelogues,* http://eng.travelogues.gr. Courtesy of Aikaterini Laskaridis Foundation Library, Greece.

period of dynamic change in the capital, a period that later became known disparagingly as *Lâle Devri*, or the Tulip Era. It was generally accepted that, because Ottoman diplomats visited Paris in 1720, and openly admired the French palaces in which they were received, the Sa'dabad palace begun soon after their return must have been inspired by French models.[63]

The published works of Can Erimtan, Shirine Hamadeh, and Sedad H Eldem reject this understanding. Erimtan suggested that the building of the Sa'dabad palace in Safavid style and its obviously Persian-inspired name demonstrated Ottoman preoccupation with the continuing military and cultural rivalry between the two empires. Erimtan and Hamadeh both raised the possibility of a domestic precedent for Sa'dabad in their respective publications, but did not elaborate.[64] Eldem, who in 1977 referred to Sa'dabad as 'the greatest and finest example of 18th-century domestic architecture', dismissed the possibility of 'French influence', stating that he was 'unable to find any part reminiscent of French art'. The only possible resemblance, he argued, was the shape and length of the canal at Sa'dabad, which was comparable with that at Fontainebleau, southeast of Paris. The water features at Sa'dabad, however, 'were built in complete conformity with Turkish architectural principles and decor'.[65] Eldem did not identify these architectural elements, but I maintain that they were 'principles and decor' known to Ahmet III during his upbringing in the imperial 'architecture of happiness' built along the riverbanks on the outskirts of Edirne in the 17th century.

The qualities of openness, transparency, and a general sense of being filled with light that Ahmet III's father introduced to the building program at the Edirne Palace are the same qualities that Shirine Hamadeh linked to the 'emblematic power of Safavid Persia'[66] and to the 'opening up' of Ottoman design and culture in the 18th century. Hamadeh describes this process as 'unique to Istanbul'.[67] Yet there is evidence that they were already a key component of the architecture of the Edirne Palace in the era of Mehmet IV. For Ahmet III, not only did the 18th-century process he had begun re-present the spatial and decorative qualities of his father's 17th-century additions at the Edirne complex, but also, in its new setting away from the Topkapı Palace near the upper waters of the Golden Horn, the 'Abode of Happiness' allowed him to continue a cherished way of life.

'ILM AND THE AESTHETIC OF HAPPINESS

According to the *Encyclopaedia of Islam* in its second edition, the term *'ilm al-jamāl* ('knowledge or science of beauty') describes the concept of aesthetics in modern Arabic usage, which is missing from historical Islamic civilisation.[68] Doris Behrens-Abouseif, amongst others, notes that architecture, for example, had pre-eminent status in the traditional Islamic world, yet there were no theoretical writings on architectural design or construction.[69] The aim instead was an interpretation of beauty revealed through order, proportion, and harmony. These were notions inherited from ancient Greece, yet free from formal concepts. The aesthetic ideal in Islam was underpinned both by a Hadith that states that 'God is beautiful and loves all beauty' and by the mystic teachings of influential theologians and Sufis, such as al-Ghazālī (d. 1111) and Ibn 'Arabī.[70] 'Aesthetic expression', continues the *Encyclopaedia of Islam*, was closely linked to certain artistic features, of which 'poetry is the outstanding genre', conveying ideals of beauty 'both in content and in structure'.[71]

In light of this, I argue that the literary culture of the Ottomans played a significant role in conceptualising and experiencing the imperial complex at Edirne. Following Shirine Hamadeh and Vildan Serdaroğlu, the Persian poetry revered by the Ottoman elite may be seen as a useful 'tool to probe Ottoman architectural consciousness'.[72] Poetry conveyed the social ideals and order of the Ottoman world view in classical Persian *ghazāl* form with mystical undercurrents and notions of universal beauty.[73] The 'poetics' of the architecture of the Edirne Palace may be compared to structures used by poets to 'build' and embellish their verse, skills usually acquired after long training and accumulation of knowledge (*ʿilm*) from a master.[74] Persian stories in verse have been likened to strings of precious pearls: carefully crafted, polished, and strung together in an ordered fashion. In this way, poetry created a sophisticated interplay of form and ornament that was greater than the sum of its parts.[75] Persian poets sometimes likened their work to the disciplined crafts of the weaver or the builder. Nasir-i Khusrau in the 11th century compared one of his poems to a palace complex complete with gardens and a view: 'A palace of my poem I'll make / in which from its verses I'll form / flowerbeds and verandas'.[76] One of the words for poetry in both Arabic and Persian is *naẓm*, 'ordering', whereas the word for prose is *nathr*, 'scattering'.[77]

Poets often implied order by describing opposites such as the beauty of spring contrasted with the desolation of winter, the enclosed palace gardens compared to the open spaces beyond, the magnificence of the sultan and the servitude of his subjects.[78] Palace architecture could thus be seen as 'rhetorical' in its ordering of individual structures into a harmonious and unified precinct unified by gardens, a scheme that reflected Ottoman and Islamic cultural concepts of outer and inner, periphery and centre, exposure and sanctuary. Walter Andrews has noted that Ottoman political ideology was concentric in nature. It was characterised by rings of hierarchy leading inwards to physical and emotional proximity to the sultan. The theoretical role of government was also conceived as a notion of layers of interdependence, the so-called Circle of Equity. One of the principles of this concept was that 'the world is a garden; its walls are the state'[79], a suggestion of the order, wellbeing, and happiness experienced in and provided by the palace precinct. Although beauty (*al-jamāl*) did not constitute a branch of knowledge (*ʿilm*) in itself, the term *ʿilm al-jamāl* suggests an appreciation of spiritual beauty. This was inherent in the meaning of *saʿāda* (happiness), when it was understood as being the ultimate objective of the virtuous soul, and as encompassing key attributes of an ideal ruler: wisdom, piety, and justice. The perception of the beauty and happiness of the key Ottoman palaces played a role in protecting and shielding the sultan and the Ottoman dynasty, which ruled uninterrupted for nearly 600 years.[80]

NOTES

1 Examples include Çiğdem Kafescioğlu, 2009, *Constantinopolis/Istanbul: Cultural Encounter, Imperial Vision and the Construction of the Ottoman Capital* (University Park, PA: The Pennsylvania State University Press); Leslie Peirce, 2004,'Changing Perceptions of the Ottoman Empire: The Early Centuries', *Mediterranean Historical Review* 49(1): 6-28; and Nurhan Atasoy and Lâle Uluç, 2012, *Impressions of Ottoman Culture in Europe: 1453-1699* (Istanbul: Armaggan Publications).

2 Peirce, 2004, 19, 21.

3 Research into the Edirne Palace was carried out during the course of an Australian Postgraduate Award in the history program of the School of Historical and European Studies, La Trobe University, Melbourne. The only monograph published on the palace is Rifat Osman, 1957, *Edirne Sarayı* (Ankara: Türk Tarih Kurumu Basımevi), who writes that the Ottoman sources refer to the complex as *Saray-ı Cedid-i Amire, 21.*

4 Halil İnalcık, 2004, 'Periods in Ottoman History: State, Society and Economy', in Halil İnalcık and Günsel Renda, eds., *Ottoman Civilization*, vol. 1 (Istanbul: Republic of Turkey, Ministry of Culture and Tourism), 78-80; Rhoads Murphey, 2008, *Exploring Ottoman Sovereignty: Tradition, Image and Practice in the Ottoman Imperial Household, 1400-1800* (London: Continuum Books), 3, 44; Kafescioğlu, 2009, 1-5, 130-1.

5 Sussan Babaie, 2008, *Isfahan and its Palaces: Statecraft, Shīʿism and the Early Architecture of Conviviality in Early Modern Iran* (Edinburgh: Edinburgh University Press), 100.

6 Fire destroyed most of the palace when local authorities exploded the palace armoury ahead of Russian military advances during the 1870s. Süheyl Ünver, n.d., Süleymaniye Kütüphanesine Hediye Ettiği, Defter 3; Tahsin Öz, 1993, 'Edirne Yeni Sarayında Kazı ve Araştırmalar', in *Edirne: Edirne'nin 600. Fethi Yildönümü Armağan Kitabi* (Ankara: Türk Tarih Kurumu Basımevi), 217-22.

7 Degree of orientation taken from Google Earth, 'Edirne Saray', <https://www.google.com/maps/@41.6912877,26.5557001,1120m/data=!3m1!1e3>, accessed 11 June 2018.

8 I am grateful to Satoshi Kawamoto for the reference to the orientation of the Edirne Old Palace. Evliya Çelebi, 1999, *Evliya Çelebi Seyahatnamesi*, ed. SA Kahraman and Y Dağli, vol. 3 (Istanbul: Yapi ve Kredi Bankasi), 255.

9 Gülru Necipoğlu, 1990, 'Review of Ca'fer Efendi, *Risāle-i Miʿmāriyye, An Early Seventeenth-Century Ottoman Treatise on Architecture*', *Journal of the Society of Architectural Historians* 49(2): 210-13.

10 Gülsüm Nalbantoğlu, 1998, 'The Birth of an Aesthetic Discourse in Ottoman Architecture', *Journal of Fine Arts (METU)* 8(2): 115-22.

11 Mohammad Gharipour, 2013, *Persian Gardens and Pavilions: Reflections in History, Poetry and the Arts* (London: IB Taurus), 23.

12 Quoted in Gharipour, 2013, 30-2.

13 Sheila Blair, 1993, 'The Ilkhanid Palace', *Ars Orientalis* 23: 241.

14 Stephen Frederic Dale, 2010, *The Muslim Empires of the Ottomans, Safavids and Mughals* (Cambridge: Cambridge University Press), 135-76; see also Stephen Frederic Dale, 2004, *The Garden of the Eight Paradises: Babur and the Culture of Empire in Central Asia, Afghanistan and India, 1483-1530* (Leiden: Brill), 18.

15 Ali Anooshahr, 2009, *The Ghazi Sultans and the Frontiers of Islam: A Comparative Study of the Late Medieval and Modern Periods* (London: Routledge), 153-4.

16 Blair, 1993, 241.

17 A Süheyl Ünver, 1953, *Edirnede Fatih'in Cihannüma Kasrı* (Istanbul: Ismail Akgün Matbaasi).

18 Sedad H Eldem, 1977, *Saʿdabad* (Istanbul: Milli Eğitim Basımevi).

19 D Fairchild Ruggles, 2008, *Islamic Gardens and Landscapes* (Philadelphia: University of Pennsylvania Press), 42.

20 Scott Redford, 2003, 'Thirteenth-Century Rum Seljuq Palaces and Palace Imagery', *Ars Orientalis* 23: 219.

21 Julian Raby and Zeren Tanındı, 1993, *Turkish Bookbinding in the Fifteenth Century: The Foundation of an Ottoman Court Style*, ed. Tim Stanley (London: Azimuth Editions), 29; Gönül Tekin, 2004, 'Turkish Literature: Thirteenth to Fifteenth Centuries', in Halil Inalcık and Günsel Renda, eds., *Ottoman Civilisation*, vol. 2 (Ankara: Republic of Turkey Ministry of Culture and Tourism), 497-520.

22 The manuscript is one of four extant Turkish language copies, all in the collection of the Topkapı Sarayı Kütüphanesi (TSK). Murat II's dated copy is TSK H116. Bağcı, 2000, 165,fn. 24, 175.

23 Tekin, 2004, 511.

24 Serpil Bağcı et al., 2006, *Osmanlı Resim Sanatı* (Istanbul: TC Kültür ve Turizm Bakanlığı Yayınları), 24.

25 Eleanor Sims, 2012, '"Bahram Gur Visits the Lady from Khwarazm in the Blue Pavilion on Wednesday" and Other Similar Representations from Illustrated Manuscripts by Nizami, Hatifi and Mir ʿAli Shir in the Bodleian Library', in Susan Scollay, ed., *Love and Devotion: From Persia and Beyond* (Melbourne: Macmillan Art Publishing), 49-53.

26 Samir Mahmoud, 2011, 'Color and the Mystics: Light, Beauty, and the Spiritual Quest', in Jonathan Bloom and Sheila Blair, eds., *'And Diverse Are Their Hues': Color in Islamic Art and Culture* (New Haven: Yale University Press): 112-17.

27 This is held in the Topkapı Sarayı Kütüphanesi, TSK R862. Julian Raby, 1980, '"El Gran Turco": Mehmed the Conqueror as a Patron of the Arts of Christendom', unpublished PhD thesis, University of Oxford, 151; Ernst J Grube, 1987, 'The Date of the Venice *Iskander-nama*', *Islamic Art* 2: 192.

28 Marble was recycled from local churches. Tayyib Gökbilgin, 1993, 'Edirne Hakkinda Yazilmiş Tarihler ve *Enis-ül Müsamirin*', in *Edirne'nin 600 Fetih Yildnumu Armağan Kitabi* (Ankara: Türk Tarih Kurumu Basımevi), 92.

29 Aziz Nazmi Şakir-Taş, 2009, *Adrianopol'den Edirne'ye: Edirne ve Civarında Osmanlı Kültür ve Bilim Muhitinin Oluşumu (XIV-XVI. Yüzyıl)* (Istanbul: Boğaziçi Üniversitesi Yayınevi), 134-5; Ünver, 1953, 13.

30 Sedad H Eldem, 1969, *Köşkler ve Kasırlar* (Istanbul: Devlet Güzel Sanatlar Akademisi Yüksek Mimarlık Bölümü Rölöve Kürsüsü, Kutulmuş Matbaası), vol. 1, 58.

31 Günkut Akın, 1995, 'The Muezzin Mahfili and Pool of the Selimiye Mosque in Edirne', *Muqarnas* 12: 76.

32 The early sultans were attended by dervishes at their accession ceremonies. Godfrey Goodwin, 1997, *The Janissaries* (London: Saqi Books), 56. Murat II was closely associated with the Mevlevi order. Ünver, n.d., Defter 42 and 59.

33 Julie Scott Meisami, 2001, 'Palaces and Paradises: Palace Description in Medieval Persian Poetry', in Oleg Grabar and Cynthia Robinson, eds., *Islamic Art and Literature* (Princeton: Markus Weiner Publishers), 21.

34 Quoted in Gonül Evyapan,1999, *Old Turkish Gardens* (Ankara: Middle Eastern Technical University), 13.

35 Gülru Necipoğlu, 1991, *Architecture, Ceremonial and Power: The Topkapı Palace in the Fifteenth and Sixteenth Centuries* (Cambridge, Mass.: MIT Press), 13, 108-9.

36 Gülru Necipoğlu, 1986, 'Plans and Models in Fifteenth and Sixteenth Century Architectural Practice', *Journal of the Society of Architectural Historians* 45(3): 236.

37 Doğan Kuban, 2011, *Sinan's Art and Selimiye* (Istanbul: Türkiye Iş Bankası Kültür Yayınları), 50-1.

38 Alain De Botton, 2006, *The Architecture of Happiness* (London: Penguin Books), 103.

39 Konstantin Mihailovic, 1975, *Memoirs of a Janissary*, trans. Benjamin Stolz (Ann Arbor: University of Michigan), 44, 69. Also see note 32 above.

40 Badi' al-Din Manuchihr al-Tajiri al-Tabrizi, *Dilsuznama*, dated AH 860/1455-56 CE, Edirne (Oxford: Bodleian Library, MS Ouseley), 133. See Yoltar-Yıldırım, 2012, 243.

41 Literally, 'Book of Heart Burnings' (in Persian *dil* means heart; *suz* means burning).

42 Ayşin Yoltar-Yıldırım, 2012, 'The 1455 Oxford *Dilsuznama* and its Literary Significance in the Ottoman Realm', in S Bağcı and Z Yasa Yaman, eds., *Tradition, Identity, Synthesis, Cultural Crossings and Art: Studies in Honour of Günsel Renda* (Ankara: Hacateppe University Press), 246.

43 Susan Scollay, 2012b, 'An Ottoman Garden of Love: The Oxford *Dilsuznama*, the "Book of Compassion"', in Susan Scollay, ed., *Love and Devotion: From Persia and Beyond* (Melbourne: Macmillan Art Publishing), 119-33.

44 Walter B Denny, 2004, *The Artistry of Ottoman Ceramics* (London: Thames and Hudson), 68-71.

45 For a discussion comparing the gaze in art of different cultures, see Hans Belting, 2011, *Florence and Baghdad: Renaissance Art and Arab Science* (Cambridge, Mass.: Harvard University Press), 262-6.

46 Süleyman Derin, 2012, 'Earthly and Spiritual Love in Sufism: Ibn 'Arabi and the Poetry of Rumi', in Susan Scollay, ed., *Love and Devotion: From Persia and Beyond* (Melbourne: Macmillan Art Publishing), 57.

47 Caroline Finkel, 2005, *Osman's Dream* (London: John Murray), 277-80; Leslie Peirce, 1993, *The Imperial Harem: Women and Sovereignty in the Ottoman Empire* (Oxford: Oxford University Press), 257.

48 Marc David Baer, 2008, *Honored by the Glory of Islam: Conversion and Conquest in Ottoman Europe* (Oxford: Oxford University Press), 134; Pal Fodor, 1986, 'State and Society, Crisis and Reform in Fifteenth and Seventeenth Century Ottoman Mirrors for Princes', *Acta Orientalia Academiae Scientarium Hungaricae* 40: 219.

49 Eldem, 1969, vol. 2, 115.

50 Eldem, 1969, vol. 2, 14.

51 Eldem, 1969, vol. 2, 111-23.

52 The term çatma was also used by the Ottomans to describe luxurious, voided and brocaded, silk velvet fabric. Amanda Phillips, 2012, 'The Historiography of Ottoman Velvets, 2011-1572: Scholars, Craftsmen, Consumers', *Journal of Art Historiography* 6: 3.

53 Mahvash Alemi, 2007, 'Princely Safavid Gardens: Stage for Rituals of Imperial Display and Political Legitimacy', in Michael Conan, ed., *Middle East Garden Traditions: Unity and Diversity* (Washington: Dumbarton Oaks), 113; Cristina D'Ancona, 2016, 'Greek Sources in Arabic and Islamic Philosophy', in Edward N Zalta (ed.), *The Stanford Encyclopedia of Philosophy*, <https://plato.stanford.edu/archives/spr2016/entries/arabic-islamic-greek/>, accessed 2 March 2017.

54 Gharipour, 2013, 128.

55 Manu P Sobti and Mohammad Gharipour, 2011, 'The Hues of Paradise: Examining Colour Design Layout in the Persian Garden', in Jonathon Bloom and Sheila Blair, eds., *'And Diverse Are Their Hues': Color in Islamic Art and Culture* (New Haven: Yale University Press), 316; Gharipour, 128; Alemi, 2007, 116-17.

56 Babaie, 2008, 50-3.

57 Babaie, 2008, 166-7.

58 Eldem, 1969, vol. 2, 115. The use of poetic couplets as decoration in palaces was a long-held tradition in Iran and its neighbours. Blair, 1993, 243.

59 Quoted in William Chittick, 2014, 'Ibn Arabi', in Edward N Zalta, ed., *The Stanford Encyclopaedia of Philosophy*, <https://plato.stanford.edu/archives/spr2014/entries/ibn-arabi/>, accessed 2 March 2017. See also Michael Barry, 2004, *Figurative Art in Medieval Islam* (Paris: Flammarion), 246; Mahmoud, 2011, 104, 107, 119; B Deniz Çaliş-Kural, 2014, Şehrengiz, Urban Rituals and Deviant Sufi Mysticism in Ottoman Istanbul (Surrey: Ashgate), 237.

60 Chronicle of Asık Ali Ağa, quoted in Eldem, 1969, vol. 2, 113. I am grateful to Alexander Dawe for his translation.

61 Shirine Hamadeh, 2008, 'Introduction', in *The City's Pleasures: Istanbul in the Eighteenth Century* (Seattle: University of Washington Press,) 4.

62 Eyewitness account by English traveller, Charles Perry (1698-1780), recounted in Charles Perry, 1743, *A View of the Levant: In Four Parts* (London: T Woodward), 24-5.

63 Can Erimtan, 2008, *Ottomans Looking West? The Origins of the Tulip Age and its Development in Modern Turkey* (London: IB Tauris), 74-7; Godfrey Goodwin, 1971, *A History of Ottoman Architecture* (London: Thames and Hudson), 373; Doğan Kuban, 2010, *Ottoman Architecture*, trans. Adair Mill (Woodbridge, Suffolk: Antique Collectors' Club), 507-8, 516; Çaliş-Kural, 2014, 193-7.

64 Can Erimtan, 1999, 'The Case of Saadabad: Westernization or Revivalism', in *Proceedings of the 10th International Congress of Turkish Art* (Geneva: Fondation Max Van Berchem), 289; Hamadeh, 2008, 71.

65 Eldem, 1977, 132.

66 Shirine Hamadeh, 2004, 'Ottoman Expressions of Early Modernity and the "Inevitable" Question of Westernization', *Journal of the Society of Architectural Historians* 63(1): 43.

67 Hamadeh, 2008, 11.

68 S. Khawaji, ʿIlm al-jamāl', in Bernard Lewis et al., eds., 1986, *Encyclopedia of Islam*, vol. 3 (Leiden: Brill), 1133-4.

69 Doris Behrens-Abouseif, 1999, 'Introduction', in *Beauty in Arabic Culture* (Princeton: Marcus Wiener Publishers), 3.

70 Samer Akkach, 2005, *Cosmology and Architecture in Premodern Islam: An Architectural Reading of Mystical Ideas* (Albany: SUNY), 3; Mahmoud, 2011, 105-10.

71 Khawaji, 1986, 1134.

72 Hamadeh, 2008, 14; Vildan Serdaroğlu, 2006, 'When Literature and Architecture Meet: Architectural Images of the Beloved and the Lover in Sixteenth-Century Ottoman Poetry', *Muqarnas* 23: 273-5.

73 Walter Andrews, Nejaat Black and Mehmet Kalpaklı, eds., 2006, *Ottoman Lyric Poetry: An Anthology* (Seattle: University of Washington Press), 4-8; Walter Andrews, 1985, *Poetry's Voice, Society's Song: Ottoman Lyric Poetry* (Seattle: University of Washington Press), 4-5.

74 Behrens-Abousief, 1999, 96; Parviz Morewedge, 2004, 'Knowledge', in Richard C Martin, ed., *Encyclopedia of Islam and the Muslim World*, vol. 1 (New York: Macmillan Reference USA), 400-1.

75 Meisami, 2001, 1, 15-16.

76 Meisami, 2001, 16. See also Akkach, 2005, 88.

77 Annemarie Schimmel, 1992, *A Two-Colored Brocade: The Imagery of Persian Poetry* (Chapel Hill: University of North Carolina Press), 2.

78 Çaliş-Kural, 2014, 157.

79 Andrews, 1985, 155-65, 207; Norman Itzkowitz, 1972, *The Ottoman Empire and Islamic Tradition* (New York: Alfred A Knopf), 88.

80 Jo Tonna, 1990, 'The Poetics of Arab-Islamic Architecture', *Muqarnas* 7: 182; Hamid Dabashi, 2001, 'Khwajah Nasir al-Din al Tusī', in Seyyed Hossein Nasr et al., eds., *History of Islamic Philosophy* (London: Routledge), 566-8.

CHAPTER 10

ʿ*ILM* OR FASHION? THE QUESTION OF IDENTITY IN THE BATIK DESIGNS OF JAVA

JAMES BENNETT

ABSTRACT

Southeast Asian scholars of Javanese textiles commonly interpret geometric batik motifs, generically known as *ceplokan*, as visual expressions of *ʿilm* specifically referencing the teaching of *tawḥīd*. This interpretation has been especially popular over recent decades among local Muslim commentators, as it emphasises the apparent religious orthodoxy of batik, which is prized as a national art form in Indonesia and Malaysia, and has been recognised for inclusion on the UNESCO Representative List of the Intangible Cultural Heritage of Humanity (2009). The chapter investigates the long history of *ceplokan*, which is among the most popular of the design categories, with origins dating back to the pre-Islamic Early Classic Period (c. 700-900 CE) in Java. It examines whether the geometric motifs developed as a conscious response to *ʿilm*, or rather whether they represent a process of cultural negotiation by which older Hindu-Buddhist textile designs were reinterpreted in the context of the new dress fashions that emerged following the ascendency of Islam in Java in the 16th century. *Ceplokan* patterns became particularly admired in the Javanese sultanates, which nurtured Islamic identity through the promotion of *ʿilm* and wider participation in the international world of Islamic culture. In this context, imported Indian textiles, featuring similar geometric designs, were a contributing factor to the development of the batik style now closely identified with Javanese aesthetics. The spiritual values that became associated with the court production of batik patterns, notably *ceplokan*, ensured that the textile art form acquired a unique significance, leading to its modern-day interpretation as an expression of *ʿilm*.

TAWḤĪD AND *CEPLOKAN*

In 2012, the Islamic Arts Museum of Malaysia presented an exhibition of the batik collection of the anthropologist Ann Dunham (d. 1995), mother of the former United States president Barack Obama. Dunham assembled the collection of around 32 textiles from the 20th century, mostly long wrap cloths (*kain panjang*) and tube skirts (*sarong*), while living in Java for several decades from 1967. Among the works exhibited in *Ann Dunham's Legacy: A Collection of Indonesian Batik* in Kuala Lumpur were examples of central Javanese and north-coast Javanese geometric *ceplokan* and related *kawung* patterns. The Malaysian scholar Sheila Yussof, in her subsequent 2014 review of the Dunham exhibition, notes that the collection includes 'geometric patterns (which tend to be the earlier designs) … such as the *parang* and *kawung* designs and the *shariʿa*-compliant design like *ceplok*'.[1] The popularity of the three categories of batik pattern, especially *ceplokan* and *kawung*, is evident in their widespread use for commercially printed textiles and decorative arts in Indonesia and Malaysia today. Her reference to *sharīʿa* acknowledges a common perception that their geometric formalism, almost invariably lacking naturalistic imagery, avoids the risks leading to the idolatry of representation and thus is 'strictly Islamic'.[2]

Yussof's observation is symptomatic of the tendency, over recent decades, among Malaysian and Indonesian scholars to seek to locate Southeast Asian Islamic art history within the perceived boundaries of orthodox doctrinal knowledge, often through specifically referencing *tawḥīd* (divine unity). The rise of religious nationalism in Malaysia and Indonesia has deeply influenced contemporary discourse surrounding the region's aesthetic identity, and especially the history of batik, which is claimed as a national art form by both Malaysia and Indonesia, and which finds its historical heartland in Java.[3] The First National Cultural Congress, held in Kuala Lumpur in 1971, sought to directly equate Malay art forms with Islam.[4] The Indonesian emphasis on the significance of knowledge of *tawḥīd* in art is highlighted in the 1995 curatorial manifesto of Jakarta's Islamic Arts Festival, *Istiqlal II*, which included contemporary batik. The manifesto states that art is intended as a 'service to God ... a realisation of the oneness, the unity, of God'.[5] The Malaysian art historians Raja Fuziah, Raja Yun Uda, and Abdul Rahma Al-Ahamdai define the evolution of the archipelago's Islamic art traditions as being guided by knowledge of specific principles whose 'core consciousness is Tawhid, or the unity of Allah'.[6] Their colleague Othman Yatim chose a *ceplokan* textile from the southern Philippines to illustrate his proposition that the choice of geometric motifs was a conscious decision by Muslim artists, in that it 'helps strengthen the teaching of Tawhid ... [as] they symbolise an eternal continuity depicting the characteristics of Allah which has no beginning or end'.[7] The Islamic Arts Museum of Malaysia's *The Message and the Monsoon: Islamic Art in Southeast Asia* (2004) exhibition catalogue further suggests that 'the discouragement of figural representation resulted in the highest level of artistic creativity'.[8] The exhibition's focus on non-figurative works of art, including various *ceplokan* textiles, implies that the heritage of Islamic art in the region was inextricably linked to knowledge of these doctrinal strictures.

The use of geometric patterns in the Indo-Malay world, however, predates the arrival of Islam. There is evidence of *ceplokan* motifs already being present in Javanese art of the early Hindu-Buddhist period between the 7th and 10th centuries. This suggests that knowledge of doctrines like *sharīʿa* and *tawḥīd* had little direct influence on their formative development.[9] The retrospective application of theological terms to historical styles avoids the vexing issue of establishing precise dates for the evolution of geometric styles in batik. Ironically, such an approach detracts from understanding the seminal role of *ceplokan* in defining Southeast Asian Islamic aesthetics, the heritage of which the Anne Dunham collection demonstrates. An examination of the history of *ceplokan* batik reveals that this heritage is not so much inspired by a conscious desire to articulate orthodox theological knowledge, but was rather a manifestation of a complex and nuanced cultural dialogue during the 16th- to 18th-century Islamic period in Java as well as in its cultural diaspora throughout the Indo-Malay archipelago.[10] Central to this dynamic was the influential role of commercially imported Indian textiles, commonly displaying *ceplokan*, so prized by the sultanate courts for wear and exchange as trade goods.

DEFINITIONS OF *CEPLOKAN*

The Indonesian batik scholar Judi Achjadi defines *ceplokan* in its simplest form as 'the effect created by dropping the contents of an egg in a frying pan or motifs that assume a similarly round shape ... constantly repeated ... [and] often set within squares'.[11] The Javanese word is intended to be onomatopoeic, imitating the sound of something being dropped or plunked down.[12] The repeated round shapes in *ceplokan* typically assume the appearance of flowers drawn from above in a star or rosette configuration with four or eight points.[13] An elegant *kain panjang*, depicting two classic variants of *ceplokan*, from the Javanese north-coast batik centre of Indramayu, features in the Dunham collection (Figure 10.1).

Ceplokan encompass a diverse array of pattern-types whose boundaries often defy precise categorisation. The batik designer Iwan Tirta, also known as Nusjirwan Tirtaamidjaja, observed that the interlocking quatrefoil *kawung* pattern may be considered a type of *ceplokan* but 'because of its great antiquity and striking severity ... has become regarded as a separate type of batik design'.[14] Another important related family are the *ganggong* motifs, named for their resemblance to a certain species of freshwater marsh plant and featuring a star or cross 'with its points drawn out into long coils like the stamens of a flower'.[15] There is also the western Indian double-ikat woven *patola* recreated in batik *cinde* designs where the batik imitation of the weave is known as *nitik*. A magnificent Yogyakarta *cinde* cloth in the Dunham collection incorporates around 26 different versions of *ceplokan* and *kawung* in *nitik* style.[16] The Dutch East Indies scholars, JE Jasper and Mas Pirngadie, in their pioneer 1916 study of batik, also categorise *tambalan*, a batik motif imitating patchwork cloth stitched in triangular patterns, as *ceplokan*.[17]

Despite contemporary readings of the geometric patterns, such as those proposed by Yussof and Yatim, it is telling that there are only two references to Islam in the 139 *ceplokan* motif names recorded by Jasper and Pirngadie. The motif *Goerit wesi latar ireng* (Gurit wesi on a black background) is described as gaining its title from the name of one of the heroes in the Javanese romance *Serat Menak* (Story of the Noble Man). The story-cycle recounts the adventures of Amīr Ḥamza, uncle of the Prophet Muhammad; it was once popularly performed in the Javanese rod-puppet theatre. The second example, *Cinde kenanga latar ireng* (ylang-ylang flowers on a black background), is entitled 'Allah's nine *wali* of the blessed island of Java, one in the centre and the other eight radiating

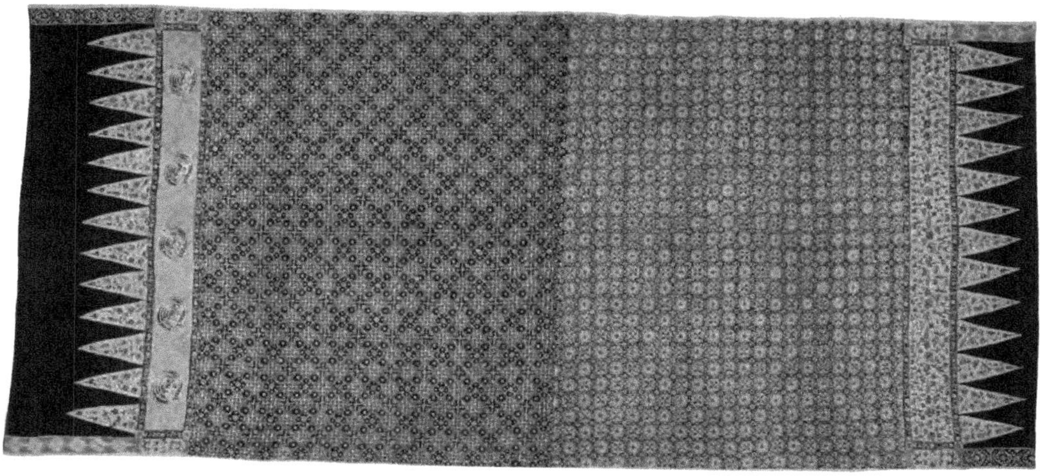

Figure 10.1 *Kain panjang* (long hip cloth), printed on cotton. White and blue with *pagi-sore* and *ceplok* patterning, 104 x 250 cm. Indramayu, North Coast Java, 20th century AD/14th century AH. Reproduced from Anne Dunham Collection, © Islamic Arts Museum Malaysia.

around him'.[18] Other additional titles listed for this *ceplokan* version of an Indian woven *patolu* motif include the 'Wheel of faith with eight spokes' (an apparent allusion to the Buddhist *dharmacakra*) and 'Vishnu's *cakra* with eight rays'.

The alternative names for the ylang-ylang flowers design testify to the extent to which Islam and earlier Hindu-Buddhist identity shared the same tradition in the popular imagination of batik makers and wearers until the 20th century. The distinct four-pointed configuration that is a definitive element of *ceplokan* motifs led many 20th-century batik scholars to adopt the pre-Islamic Javanese term *mancapat* (outer four) to describe them.[19] The scholar of Southeast Asian textiles Robyn Maxwell, encapsulating the views of much Dutch scholarship, proposes that the star/rosette motifs of such *ceplokan* reflect an ancient preoccupation with the Hindu-Buddhist ritual orientation of *mandala* aligned to the four cardinal points.[20] Scholars of Malay-Indonesia archipelago art since the 19th century have evoked the 'layer cake' model to describe the cumulative processes by which different foreign influences, including Islam, overlaid a unique indigenous artistic identity.[21] The evocation of *sharīʿa* compliance and of *tawḥīd* by Yussof and previously cited scholars may be understood as seeking to counter this history of depreciating the significance of Islam in the cultural heritage of Malaysia and Indonesia.

The Javanese poet Yasadipura II, author of *Sasana Sunu* (1819), was certainly aware of the popularity of *ceplokan* among the Arab communities in Java, such as Kampong Kauman located near the Great Mosque and *kraton* (palace) in Surakarta where he lived. The communities consisted largely of Hadrami immigrants who were widely respected for the religious authority derived from their *sayyid* (descendants of the Prophet) ancestry. They were also successful merchants and were actively involved in batik manufacture. Geometric patterns, often imitating imported Indian *patola*, were produced and worn by Indo-Arabian *kauman* wives and devout local women in accordance with Islamic precepts.[22] The popularity of the patterns extended beyond textiles to the use of European-manufactured tiles to create *ceplokan* floor mosaics in the early-20th-century mansions of wealthy merchants in *kauman* centres, such as Kota Gede, Yogyakarta. The batik scholar Fiona Kerlogue, commenting on a cloth imitating a *patolu* pattern created by batik makers of Arab descent in Pekalongan, notes that its appearance is evocative of ceramic tiles decorating Middle East mosques.[23]

When *Sasana Sunu* advises the reader to wear batik *ceplokan* and imported Indian *patola*, Yasadipura does not specifically cite *tawḥīd* but differentiates these designs from batik 'made in the present era' in the Indonesian translation of the text.[24] The time-honoured use of *ceplokan* imbued the designs with an inherent superiority over the fashionable trends of batik made in the degenerate era when the author lived under the *kāfir* (infidel) Dutch occupation of Java. The implicit suggestion is that the prestige of *ceplokan* derived foremost from their antiquity. Yasadipur , familiar with the genealogies of the Central Javanese royal houses, which extended back to the Hindu-Buddhist Majapahit dynasty that ended around 1500, would have understood antiquity as contiguous with the pre-Islamic ancestral past.

CEPLOKAN IN THE HINDU-BUDDHIST PERIOD AND THE ARRIVAL OF ISLAM

The oldest known depictions of *ceplokan* motifs in Indonesia are decorative reliefs found at the Buddhist temple of Candi Sewu, erected around 782 CE, in Central Java (Figure 10.2). The reliefs appear to replicate textile hangings, and the art historian Hiram Woodward proposes that

Figure 10.2 Carved stone panels based on textile patterns, found at Candi Sewu temple, Central Java, erected c. 782 CE, documented in 1865 photograph (1403-3792-25). © Museum Volkenkunde.

the designs may be based on imported Chinese woven silks.[25] As well as two basic geometric configurations, a third *ceplokan* design consists of a striking three-dimensional representation of square compartments, each containing a flower. This evokes the stone *peripih* boxes, whose consecrated offerings included gold foil flowers, interred beneath the sanctuary foundations of Javanese Hindu and Buddhist temples. The probability that *ceplokan* possessed spiritual significance during the early Hindu-Buddhist period has been supported by the art historian Mary-Louise Totton in her analysis of decorative imagery on the Loro Jonggrang temple, adjacent to Sewu at Candi Prambanan, the construction of which commenced less than a century later in 850. Here, carved representations of *ceplokan* textiles appear on the walls of the Siva *garbhagriha* (womb chamber) sanctuary and in the spiritually potent threshold space of the vestibule.[26] The continuing ritual significance of the geometric motifs is demonstrated by their frequent appearance in Hindu-Buddhist sculpture in subsequent centuries. Images of deities dated c. 1300 from Candi Singosari in Malang, East Java, include Durga, wearing *ceplokan*, slaying the demon Mahisha and the temple guardians, Nandisvara and Mahakala, dressed in *kawung* wrap cloths.

The lasting presence of *ceplokan,* following the gradual ascendancy of Islam in the 16th century, is a reminder that the use of notional terms, like 'Hinduism', 'Buddhism', and 'Islam', to define art forms is 'problematic because each of these terms implies a wide disparity ... in practices and beliefs'.[27] The continuity of the motifs may be understood through examining the complex, sometimes contradictory, processes by which Javanese society negotiated the arrival of the new religion at a time of expanding international trade. The initial spread of Islam into Southeast Asia was largely peaceful, and the phenomenon of gradual conversion resulted in the host societies fostering a 'Muslim progeny with strong pre-Islamic cultural and religious roots'.[28] The Portuguese observer Tomé Pires in 1515 recorded the important role that Muslim foreigners, often from merchant backgrounds, played in establishing the Javanese sultanates, whose multicultural populations further nurtured the dynamic of syncretism. The historian Merle Ricklefs suggests that the dynamic surrounding the establishment of their Islamic identity included 'both Islamisation of the Javanese and Javanisation of foreign Muslims'.[29] This process is typically seen in the utilisation of Hindu-Buddhist architectural elements in early Javanese mosques and the tombs of saints who were also often of foreign birth or descent.[30]

The conversion to Islam was not always a process of seamless syncretism. In his survey of the history of batik in Indonesia, the great Javanese batik artist and connoisseur KRT Hardjonogoro observes that 16th-century Java experienced a 'spiritual and cultural revolution of great intensity'.[31] In some circumstances this required the abrupt abandonment of pre-existing art traditions that did not resonate with the new beliefs. *Serat Dermangandul*, a satiric polemic written around 1879, possibly by a Christian Javanese, speaks of the early burning of non-Islamic texts, positing that otherwise the Javanese would have remained 'infidels for a thousand years'.[32] This revisionist account of the spread of Islam in Java is nevertheless supported by the almost complete disappearance of Majapahit literature on the island by the end of the 16th century. The changing cultural landscape is evident in the widespread destruction of pre-Islamic places of worship with their associated iconography. Renovations of the 16th-century Mantingan Mosque in Jepara, Central Java, in 1978-81 revealed the recycling of stone reliefs, depicting the *Ramayana* epic, apparently from a Hindu temple.[33] The *Ramayana* figures had been deliberately defaced and their reverse sides finely carved with the non-figurative decoration for which the mosque is justly famous today.

The continuity of indigenous elements of material culture, including textiles, was ensured through their reconceptualisation within narratives of Islamic piety, while maintaining selected references to the pre-Islamic ancestral past.[34] For example, the 18th-century compilation *Babad Tanah Jawi* (Chronicle of the Land of Java) lists the rice goddess Dewi Sri, whose Sanskrit name testifies to her Hindu-Buddhist origins, as an eighth-generation descendant from the Quranic Adam.[35] 19th-century Javanese sculptures of Dewi Sri, the tutelary consort of the Mataram sultans, and her incestuous brother, Mas Sadono, depict them clothed in the attire of the Mataram sultanate (1587-1755). Their dress testifies to a shift in Javanese clothing fashion that accompanied increasing religious and economic links with the wider Muslim world of the Middle East and south Asia.[36] *Ceplokan* appear as patterns, usually batik, on long wrap cloths worn by Dewi Sri and Mas Sadono, who are known as *loro blonyo* (the inseparable couple). *Ceplokan*, such as the *jelamprang* motif, also feature as an Indian woven *patola* silk wrap worn by Dewi Sri.

The paired sculptures were customarily installed in the ceremonial wedding chamber, known as *petanen*, literally meaning 'the place of the farmer', in an aristocratic Javanese house. The decoration of the ritual space typically included imported *patola* draped from pillars and wooden screens painted in imitation of stacked *patola* textiles, featuring a diverse variety of *ceplokan*.[37] The prominent display of *ceplokan* in the *petanen*, venerated for its association with fecundity and spiritual potency, evokes the use of *ceplokan* decoration at the Hindu and Buddhist sanctuaries of Loro Jonggrang and Sewu temples around 1000 years earlier in Central Java. The ritual significance of the woven *patola* with their geometric patterns reflects the wider status of foreign textiles traded into the Malay-Indonesian archipelago. The Indian cloths are inextricably interwoven with the history of *ceplokan* in the Javanese and Malay batik of South Sumatra, and exerted a profound contribution in the development of an Islamic aesthetic in Southeast Asia.

CEPLOKAN IN INDIAN TRADE TEXTILES

Until the late 18th century, brilliantly dyed Indian cloths were the most sophisticated textile manufacture known, and their international popularity ensured their currency as a major product of exchange in Indian Ocean maritime commerce, specifically in the Southeast Asian spice trade. The importation of the textiles into the archipelago achieved its zenith during the 16th to 18th centuries, a period marking the ascendancy of powerful Islamic sultanates, such as Demak and Banten. Unlike the naturalistic flowers-and-foliage chintz sent to Europe, geometrically patterned configurations feature prominently in the cloth cargoes destined for Southeast Asia. Their definitive role in the historical development of Indonesian batik practice can be seen by comparing a trade textile produced in the 17th century in Gujarat, the first region in India to embrace Islam, with a batik cloth from Jambi, South Sumatra, dated around two centuries later (Figures 10.3 and 10.4).

Ceplokan patterns appear in Gujarat trade textiles during the mediaeval period and were widely traded across the Islamic world, as testified by cloth fragments found at Fustat, Egypt.[38] The patterns display close similarities with Gujarati Islamic architectural ornament, notably the magnificent *jali* window screens at the mosque of Sayyid 'Alam, erected in 1412 in Ahmedabad. These may have intentionally referenced textiles rather than being the source of their inspiration. The mosque's combination of Islamic and Hindu architectural elements is a reminder that some of the earliest examples of *jali* screens in the form of *ceplokan* appear at 11th-century Hindu temples in Karnataka. The Indian architectural historian MA Dhaky documents *ceplokan* stone screens that flank the doorway to the *garbhagriha* chamber, a ritually potent location like that which occurs at Candi Prambanan, Central Java, at the Galagesvara temple at Heggere, Tumkur.[39] The continuing imitation of draped cloth in stonework features at the 1442 tomb of Ahmad Shah, Ahmedabad, which may also have been carved by Hindu craftsmen. The decorative reliefs imitate the geometric designs of the woven *patola* and their dye-printed copies, for which the region is renowned.[40]

Figures wearing garments featuring *ceplokan* and *kawung* appear around the same time on a group of textiles exported from the Gujarati workshops to the archipelago market.[41] The figures are sometimes referred to as Jain women due to their stylistic similarity to contemporaneous Jain

Figure 10.3 Length of cloth, ceremonial textile and sacred heirloom, c. 1690, Gujarat, India; found in Tanah Toraja, South Sulawesi. Cotton, natural mordant dyes, batik and block print, 420.0 x 77.0 cm. Gift of Michael and Mary Abbott 1996. Gift of Michael and Mary Abbott 1996 to the Art Gallery of South Australia, Adelaide. Courtesy of the Art Gallery of South Australia, Adelaide.

Figure 10.4 Shoulder cloth or wrap garment, with rhombic design. Late 19th century, Jambi, Sumatra. Cotton, natural dyes, hand batik. 104.0 x 240.0 cm. Gift of Michael and Mary Abbott through the Art Gallery of South Australia Foundation. Courtesy of the Art Gallery of South Australia, Adelaide, 2003.

illuminated manuscripts from western India. The exceptionally long cloths, often measuring over 5 metres in length, possibly were intended as hangings in the style of the modern-day Balinese *ider-ider* valances that decorate temple pavilions during Hindu festivals. The Gujarati figurative textiles completely disappeared from fashion in the early 17th century. The stylised portrayals of the women in the last phase of production could reflect changing attitudes to figurative realism in the archipelago market, which was increasingly conscious of its Islamic identity. It may be more than coincidence that Javanese performance tradition attributes changes to the design of *wayang kulit* (shadow puppets), at this same time, as resulting from the adoption of Islam. The saintly Sunan Giri (d. 1506) is said to have ordered the creation of less naturalistic puppets in order to circumvent Islamic proscriptions against figurative realism.[42]

By the 17th century, there was a major shift in Indian export production to the Coromandel Coast (modern-day Tamil Nadu and Andhra Pradesh) within the cultural and political sphere of the Deccan sultanates, notably Golconda. The people of the Deccan sultanates shared many similarities in dress with the northern Indo-Persian Mughal courts but with a preference for locally manufactured mordant- and resist-dyed textiles.[43] The Indian block-printing expert Eiluned Edwards observes how the extravagant patronage of textile production in the milieu of the courts was matched by the courtiers' equally prodigious consumption for purposes of wear, decoration of architectural spaces and royal encampments, ceremonial gift giving, and payment of tribute taxes.[44] Nevertheless, the patterns of surviving Deccan fabrics document little evidence of the styles, most notably the geometric designs, exported into the Malay-Indonesia archipelago. An exception is the miniature portrait, dated c. 1675, of Sultan Abu'l Ḥasan Quṭb Shāh, last ruler of the Qutb Shahi dynasty (Figure 10.5). The Golconda sultan is painted wearing a floral rhombic pattern remarkably similar to a cloth length of the same period found in Indonesia (Figure 10.6).

The Indian names of the numerous geometric designs in the trade textiles appear to be unrecorded, and it is unlikely that contemporaneous observers regarded them as representing a single collective category of patterns. Ruurdja Laarhoven, in her definitive study of Indian trade textiles, lists 79 varieties of Indian textiles, exported by the Dutch Vereenigde Oost-Indische Compagnie (United East Indies Company, hitherto referred to as the VOC) during the 17th to early 18th centuries, with several names implying the presence of geometrical patterns.[45] Double-ikat silk *patola* from Gujarat are among the most numerous Indian trade cloths featuring *ceplokan* to survive in Indonesia, both as double-ikat lengths and mordant dye-printed cotton copies. The woven *patola* continued to be exported until the 1930s to the Dutch East Indies, where Central Javanese palaces valued their use in court dance costumes, ceremonial trousers, and drapes.

Laarhoven notes that VOC records list *sarasa*, chintz, and *tapi* as displaying floral patterns, such as specified in a 1682 Dutch order from Batavia (Jakarta) to Coromandel Coast factors.[46] However, the references to floral patterns do not necessarily always imply the chintz manufactured for the European market. Both schematic and naturalistic depictions of flowers feature in a wide variety of textiles. It is probable that the obviously recognisable subject of flowers prompted the naming of designs rather than their geometric structure, which may have appeared of secondary significance to the viewer. The art historian and curator John Guy classifies the *jelamprang* batik motif, found in Indian *patola* and their dye-printed imitations traded by the VOC, as geometric, although the common Javanese name for the motif refers to the blossom of a magnolia species.[47]

VOC records most clearly referencing geometric patterns are the *telpocan* produced on the Coromandel Coast. Laarhoven describes it as 'a *chintz* cloth with a special pattern embellished

Figure 10.5 Portrait of Sultan Abu'l Ḥasan Quṭb Shāh wearing a skirt cloth featuring a Coromandel coast design, c. 1675, Golkonda, Telangana, India, opaque watercolour and gold on paper, 22.1 x 14.2 cm; San Diego Museum of Art, Edwin Binney 3rd Collection, San Diego (1990.491) © San Diego Museum of Art.

Figure 10.6 Ceremonial cloth and sacred heirloom early 18th century. Handspun cotton, natural dyes, mordants, 405 x 115 cm. Gift of Michael and Mary Abbott 1988, conserved with the assistance of Brian O'Keeffe AO and Bridget O'Keeffe AM. © National Gallery of Australia.

with gold leaf' and *tapi telpocan* featuring a 'circular or cruciform patterned gold leaf, the ground red or black'.[48] *Telpocan* is also written *tjeplok*, as in the Javanese and Indonesian *ceplokan* in VOC sources, and most certainly refers to a Javanese batik design. The earliest reference to *tjeplok* is a Dutch textile trade report from 1603 describing the pattern as like 'round thalers or other crosses'.[49] Jasper and Pirngadie record a Javanese batik *kawung* motif under the *ceplokan* category, with the remarkably similar name of *kawoeng pitjis latar poetih* (small coins on a white background *kawung*). The authors describe its distinguishing feature to be 'small crosses'.[50]

The presence of Javanese nomenclature in VOC commercial orders suggests the close relationship between the Indian and Javanese textiles, even to the application of gold leaf to *kawung* in the style of Javanese *prada* and Malay *telepok* gilding practices. There is ample evidence that Indian producers were directly replicating examples of cloths shipped for that purpose from Indonesia during the 17th and 18th centuries. The present writer has documented several Indian textiles, copied from Indonesian prototypes, in the collection of the Art Gallery of South Australia.[51] These include a Coromandel Coast imitation of a batik *dodot* wrap garment displaying a *parang* pattern in the Cirebon style. As Maxwell declares, there were 'many and varied ... creative responses that the interplay between Indian and Indonesian textiles evoked'.[52] Such was the resulting hybrid style that modern-day Indian observers are often unable, or surprised, to identify the Indian origins of trade cloths produced for the Southeast Asian markets. Their response indicates the extent to which firsthand knowledge of Javanese and other Southeast Asian textile fashions influenced the Indian workshops.

INDIAN *CEPLOKAN* IN THE JAVANESE COURTS

The Indian textiles traded to Indonesia survive today because they were preserved as ancestral heirlooms (*pusaka*), most commonly in non-Islamic contexts. The treasured fabrics were only exposed for public display during ceremonies associated with rites of passage. Yet many of the same styles of imported textiles were the garments of choice for both daily and ceremonial wear among the aristocrats and *orang kaya* (wealthy merchants) in the archipelago's Islamic courts during the 16th to 18th centuries. In 1705 the VOC councillor, Cornelis Chastelein, reported that numerous members of the Javanese nobility wore Indian cloth while commoners wore cotton 'painted in their own style and called Batex'.[53] The niche market value placed on the imported textiles is documented in the lavish gold leaf decoration that was locally applied to numerous *sembagi* garments, featuring *ceplokan*, preserved in Malay heirloom collections.[54]

Indian copies of the voluminous Javanese court garment known as *dodot* or *kampuh* were produced in a variety of dimensions, often extraordinarily large.[55] The garments, with their distinctive rhombic or circular centre fields, commonly display geometric *ceplokan*, unlike Central Javanese batik versions from later in the 19th century, which typically utilise borders with foliage designs known as *semen* or *lung-lungan*.[56] The wear of these garments was not restricted exclusively to Javanese ethnicity but was once widespread among the archipelago's Islamic societies. Indian *dodot* with geometric motifs have been preserved in Lampung, a southern Sumatran region formerly under the suzerainty of the powerful Sundanese emporium sultanate of Banten (1526-1813).[57] Javanese dress was donned in the Malay courts of Palembang and Jambi, while 19th-century historical annals from Lombok describe Sasak 'chiefs and princes' wearing *dodot* in the presence of the ruler.[58] The Javanese *Babad Sengkala* (c. 1632) even records a Dutch delegation wearing *adodottan batik* (batiked dodot) at the Mataram court of Sultan Agung.[59]

The 17th- to 18th-century period marked the growth of sophisticated indigenous batik-making traditions in Java, as well as South Sumatra, which eventually replaced the imported cloth. It is often tellingly impossible to differentiate between the Indian or local origin of textiles depicted in Javanese figurative art of the 18th to 19th centuries, so symbiotic was their stylistic relationship. Cornets de Groot, a Dutch official posted in Gresik, documented 36 designs in his 1822 account of Javanese batik production, and the majority represent *ceplokan* found also in Indian examples.[60] The batik historian Itie Van Hout notes the resemblance of these designs to garments depicted on *wayang* figures in an unusual c. 1850 batik *sarung* in the Tropenmuseum collection. Geometric patterns are predominantly worn amongst characters of upper-class status and their retainers.[61] This relationship between *ceplokan* and social rank also appears in the British Museum's collection of 90 rod-puppets, assembled by Sir Thomas Stamford Raffles during his time in Java (1811-16).[62] The depiction of a Javanese bridal couple, apparently of aristocratic status and both wearing *ceplokan*, in Raffles's *History of Java* (1817) further underscores the connection. The bride's garment is the *jelamprang* pattern often associated with the dress of the *loro blonyo* rice goddess Dewi Sri and the decoration of the ritual wedding chamber, evoking notions of fertility related to the goddess and to nuptial ceremonies.

CEPLOKAN AS AESTHETIC SENSIBILITY

To understand the extent to which *ceplokan* batik may have nurtured an Islamic art style, as understood by Indonesian and Malaysian commentators, it is necessary to examine the religious environment in which batik developed within the context of Islamic court culture. *Hikayat Isma Yatim* (Story of Isma Yatim), a Malay text dating from the middle of the 17th century, was likely written to instruct the pious well-born reader in appropriate behaviour, where the knowledge of courtly arts was considered an essential ingredient.[63] The unknown author describes the refined hero as being an accomplished poet, musician, and textile artist.[64] The aristocratic connection between batik making and religious devotion is documented in Cirebon, West Java. Panembahan Trusmi (Ki Kedeng), a princely student of the 16th-century Sufi heretic martyr Siti Jenar and follower of the saintly Sunan Gunung Jati, is attributed as being the founder of a mystical guild of batik artists.[65] The Panembahan's grave in Cirebon continues today to be a destination for pilgrimages by batik artists.[66]

Hikayat Isma Yatim may be describing an idealised situation because women were the chief producers of fabric, with Cirebon a marked exception. A member of a Dutch East Indies Company mission in 1656 reported observing thousands of women engaged in batik production in the Mataram *kraton*.[67] The report, while certainly somewhat exaggerated, may reflect an outsider's impression of the very important practical and symbolic roles of women in Central Java, where only females surrounded the ruler in his inner court.[68] As in later practice, aristocratic women likely engaged only in the key activity of drawing the designs with hot wax on cloth, a task requiring refined skills and critically determining the quality and status of the cloth. Young girls first learnt designs through the elementary tasks of waxing the reverse side of patterned cloths (*nerusi*) or applying the wax in-fills (*tembok*) to blank areas of the designs drawn by skilled senior women. On completion of the batik work, the cloth was subsequently sent to low-class male artisans outside the palaces for the laborious specialist work of dyeing and removing wax.

The court women may have sung devotional lyrics as they communally created batik together, similar to a recent custom in Central Java.[69] Their expression of faith certainly extended to recitations of the Quran. The emphasis on textual knowledge in Islam inspired the patronage of religious scholarship, regarded as an act of piety. The most notable personage in this field is Ratu Pakubuwana (d. 1732), who was the wife, mother, and grandmother of three successive Mataram rulers. The queen was responsible for the composition and/or recension of three major texts that were regarded as possessing talismanic power for the wellbeing of the kingdom.[70] Ratu Pakubuwana was almost certainly schooled in the art of batik making from a young age, yet Jasper and Pirngadie's 1916 inventory of *ceplokan* titles suggests that it was unlikely that even such an accomplished believer interpreted textiles designs in the context of mainstream theological teachings. An important feature of Javanese and Malay court culture is the notion of hidden knowledge. *Hikayat Isma Yatim* enumerates the qualities of a perfect woman as including the six perfections of faith in Allah; nevertheless, the text declares, 'As concerns the last two perfections (*ma'rifat* and *tawḥīd*), I must keep silence about them, because they are secret ones'.[71]

Justine Boow, in her seminal *Symbol and Status in Javanese Batik* (1988), records that late-20th-century Central Javanese batik makers emphasise the character, or *sifat*, of a design rather than its meaning (*arti*). The use of the Arabic loan word *sifat* 'placed the interpretation of batik designs within an Islamic aesthetic and religious tradition'.[72] Boow observes that many patterns are seen as mystically powerful, and their creation may even be surrounded by certain taboos. Nevertheless, individual Javanese interpretations of the patterns are highly idiosyncratic and personal, often intended to reflect the commentator's own cultural expertise and refinement through familiarity with courtly values, rather than to be read as a means to 'communicate, or express, the nature of an external reality'.[73]

The cloistered religious environment in which court women produced batik before the 20th century may inevitably have influenced the choice of designs, although there is a general lack of primary textual evidence as to how batik makers read their creations in early times. The batik scholar Rens Heringa, noting that this absence may be a result of Javanese social dynamics, proposes that 'knowledge regarding the deeper meaning of art is attributed to men ... [T]he manufacture of textiles, a female task, was considered unworthy of description in written texts'.[74] This was compounded by a remarkable sense of the power of historical continuity. Neither arbitrary innovation nor its extensive verbalisation in aesthetic practice was privileged over the faithful act of transmitting ancestral traditions, such as time-honoured *ceplokan*, which were believed to be supernaturally or ritually significant.[75] The internalisation of complex free-hand drawn motifs like the time-honoured *ceplokan* through repetitive practice ensured the unity of the *ẓāhir* (external) and *bāṭin* (internal) aspects of existence, as understood by Javanese textile artists and connoisseurs. The dual aspects, represented by intuitive knowledge and perfected technique, were considered essential to creating the ceremonially potent cloths such as *ceplokan*.

Knowledge of Islam was especially meaningful within the environments of Javanese palaces, which were imbued with the practice of Sufi mysticism. Spiritual power was focused around the presence of the ruler, who represented the tangible manifestation of the *wahyu* (blessing) of Allah on earth. In the late 18th century, the Surakarta and Yogyakarta courts issued a series of edicts listing certain batik as restricted motifs only permitted for wear by the sultan and surrounding kin. The lists cite *ceplokan* alongside other designs, such as the winged *Garuda ageng* and vegetal *semen* with their naturalistic references, suggesting that the geometric patterns, while revered, did not occupy a uniquely exclusive status at that time in Central Java. On 2 April 1769, the Surakarta court forbade non-royal persons from wearing the *jelamprang* pattern.[76] An undated Yogyakarta decree likewise forbade the wearing of both *kawung* and *sembagen huk*, whose name suggests a pattern associated with imported Indian *sembagi* cloths. The edicts were not addressing material issues of sumptuary excess but the inappropriate use of patterns that were recognised as embodying unseen mystical forces. The contemporary Yogyakarta batik artist Agus Ismoyo, speaking from an informed familiarity with the philosophy of Yogyakarta court batik traditions and Javanese mysticism, interprets *kawung* as symbolising pockets of hidden knowledge.[77]

CEPLOKAN AS SPIRITUAL EXPRESSION

The intricate and time-demanding practice of making batik has always been associated with qualities of patience and perseverance, virtues repeatedly praised in the Quran and Hadiths. Present-day Yogyakarta batik makers often repeat the admonition *Harus hati tenang* (The heart must be calm). Heringa cites an early Islamic treatise that presents batik making as 'a metaphor for the spiritual maturation of a woman'.[78] The circumstances attributed to the invention of *truntum*, one of the most classic and simple variants of *ceplokan*, testify to the close link drawn between women's batik making and pious religious virtues (Figure 10.7).[79]

The story is recounted in a unique anonymous Javanese manuscript entitled *Mula bukane ana jarik truntum* (The Origin of the *truntum* Pattern), preserved in the archives of Museum Radya Pustaka, Surakarta. Kanjeng Ratu Beruk (c. 1703-63), consort of the Susuhunan of Surokarta, Pakubuwono III, was so upset at neglect by the ruler that she spent her days patiently making batik while nightly contemplating the stars in the heavens as her only companions. The Radya Pustaka manuscript observes: 'Perhaps her exercise was meditational, because the lady's pain was great: her husband Sri Sunan had rejected her'.[80]

One day the Susuhunan passed the queen at work and was so moved by the beauty of her new batik design, worked with such patience in the face of hardship — a quality deeply valued in Islam — that love was renewed. The queen subsequently named the design *truntum*, which means 'to grow'. Hardjonogoro interprets it to mean 'the budding of love' and notes that 'in contemplative practice of batik, Kanjeng Ratu Beruk found a certain mercy, felt contact with the life force, mover closer to her Creator, and obviously this vitality shook the soul of Sri Sunan'.[81]

There are various readings of the origin of the name *truntum*. One version attributes the name to the Javanese phrase *teruntum-tuntum*, meaning to 'grow again', while another version says it derives from the word *tumaruntum*, meaning 'guiding', and a third interpretation relates the name to *tentrem*, meaning 'peaceful'.[82] While the account clearly draws a connection between the appearance of the stars in the night sky and Ratu Beruk's design, the same motif is often equated with flowers. The antiquity of *truntum*-like motifs is documented in Gujarati resist-dyed fragments retrieved from mediaeval sites in Fustat, Egypt, the designs of which Ruth Barnes, historian of Indian trade textiles, describes as eight-petal rosettes.[83] The religious associations of the rosette design have continued until today in the Muslim world. Kerlogue records that in modern-day batik-making traditions in Jambi, flower motifs are called 'stars' because they are a reminder of the Garden of Paradise in the heavens above.[84]

The seminal influence of early local and imported geometric designs on Javanese Islamic aesthetic tradition is conclusively documented in a 20th-century *kain panjang* pattern, the antecedent of which is the rhombic *ceplokan* configuration first seen at the 8th-century Buddhist temple of Candi Sewu. The wrap cloth displays the Yogyakarta court pattern known as *ciptoning* (creating tranquillity) (Figure 10.8).[85] Set within the repeated diamond-shaped lozenges is a *wayang* couple,

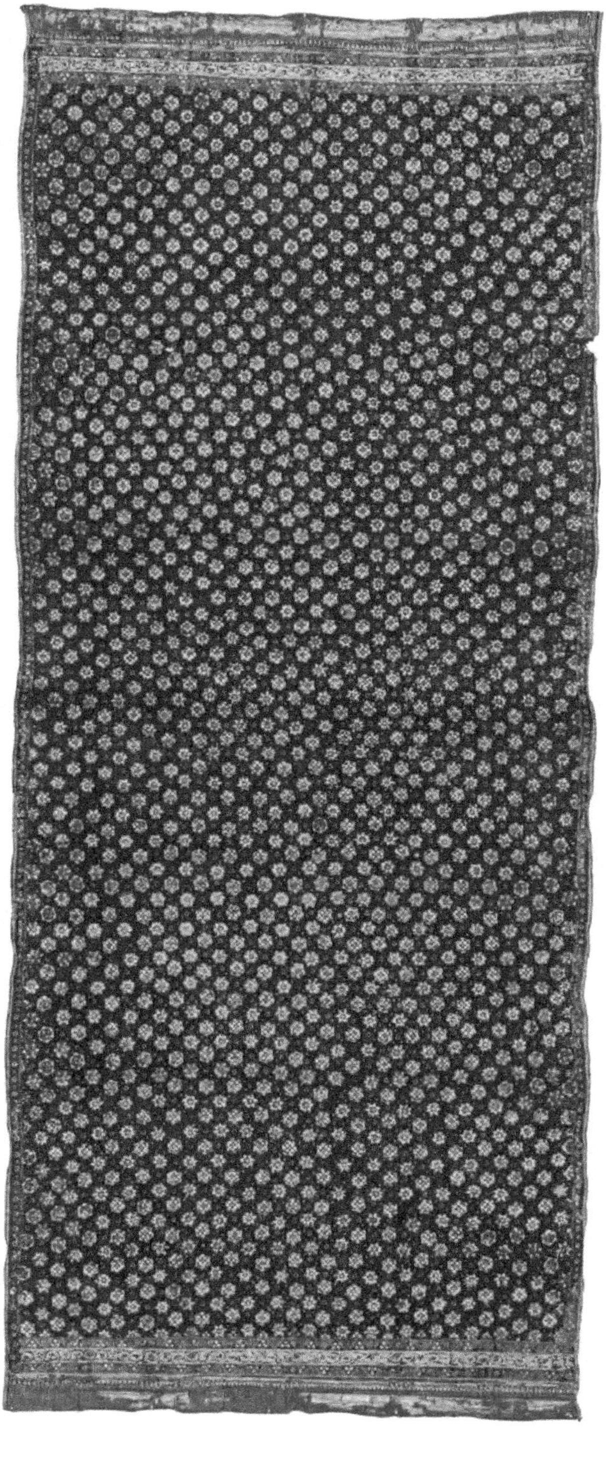

Figure 10.7 Ceremonial cloth with gold leaf (kain prada), with 'truntum' motif. Late 19th century, probably north coast of Java, gold applied in Bali. Cotton, hand cap batik, indigo dye, gold. 80.0 x 191.0 cm. Gift of Michael Abbott AO QC through the Art Gallery of South Australia Foundation, 2013. Donated through the Australian Government's Cultural Gifts Program. Courtesy of the Art Gallery of South Australia, Adelaide.

Figure 10.8 Wrap cloth (*kain panjang*), with 'creating tranquillity' (*ciptoning*) design detail. Late 20th century, Yogyakarta, Central Java. Cotton, dyes, hand batik. 122.0 x 206.0 cm. The Abbott Gift Year 2000. Courtesy of the Art Gallery of South Australia, Adelaide.

representing the ideal lovers Arjuna and Sembhadra, whose experience of romantic perfection presents a poetic analogy to the blossoming flowers featured in Javanese rhombic *ceplokan* of the early Hindu-Buddhist era and the 17th-century cloth pattern worn by Sultan Abu'l Hasan Qutb Shah. The rhombic borders consist of the *parang* design that the much-revered Sultan Agung (r. 1613-45) of Mataram is said to have conceived while practising religious austerities on Java's south coast. Achjadi interprets *ciptoning* as expressing the hope that 'the wearer will become a person able to guide others on attaining nobility of character and to point out the right road' to Allah.[86]

CONCLUSION

The batik *ceplokan* known today, with their immense diversity, derived their fundamental origins from basic geometric elements found in textile motifs dating to the Hindu-Buddhist period on Java. The spread of knowledge of Islam, from around the 16th century onwards, resulted in makers and wearers seeing the old designs with new eyes. Their fashionable appeal was enhanced by the replication of geometric designs in popular imported Indian textile. This continuing diversification of *ceplokan* in the new religious context ensured a close association with Islamic identity. Both the Museum Radya Pustaka manuscript 'The Origin of the *truntum* Pattern' and the symbolism of *ciptoning* testify to *ceplokan*'s association with Muslim religious values. This association arose through the special circumstances attributed to their original creation or the perceived talismanic powers of patterns that ensured that the wearer possessed the inner moral qualities necessary for the wellbeing of others. There is little evidence from the past that *ceplokan* textiles were created as a conscious expression of *sharīʿa* compliance or knowledge of *tawḥīd*. Nevertheless, the blessed qualities of inner growth, calm, and submission to guidance, to which patterns like the *truntum* and *ciptoning* allude, are all attributes of spiritual maturity still valued today in Java's Muslim culture.

ACKNOWLEDGMENTS

My thanks to Professor Samer Akkach, Emeritus Professor Virginia Hooker, and Michael Abbott AO QC for all their advice and assistance to me in writing this chapter.

NOTES

1 Sheila Ainon Yussof, 2014, 'The Politics, Art and Science of Batik', *IAIS Malaysia Bulletin on Islam and Contemporary Issues* 20: 14.

2 Rens Heringa, 1996, 'The Historical Background of Batik in Java', in Rens Heringa and Harmen C Veldhuisen, eds., *Fabric of Enchantment: Batik from the North Coast of Java from the Inger McCabe Elliot Collection at the Los Angeles County Museum of Art* (Los Angeles: Los Angeles Country Museum of Art). JE Jasper and Mas Pirngadie record only one *ceplokan* figurative motif that is *Tjeplok grameh latar ireng* (Gourami fish on a black background): 1916, *De Inlandsche Kunstnijverheid in Nederlandsch Indië III: De batikunst* (Netherlands: Van Regeeringswege Gedrukt en Uitgegevan Te 'S-Gravenhage Door De Broek & Kunstdrukkerij, Mouton & Co), 132. They note the popularity of this motif in Indian and Persian Islamic art.

3 There have been distinct differences in the unfolding dynamics of religious nationalism in Malaysia and Indonesia. In Malaysia, this commenced as a politically driven movement, whereas in Indonesia it was neither state-directed nor identified with one particular ethnic group but was a growing response to the global resurgence of Islam from the mid- to late 1970s. For an overview of batik in this religious-political context, see Marshall Clark, 2013, 'Cultural Politics: Batik and Wayang in Indonesia and Malaysia', *The Asian Arts Society of Australia Review* 22(2): 13-15.

4 Nirajan Rajah, 2001, 'Insyirah Al-Sadr: The Art of Sulaiman Esa' in Petronas Gallery', in *Insyirah: Lukisan Sulaiman Esa dari 1980 hingga 2000* (Kuala Lumpur: Petronas Gallery), 33.

5 WM Abdul Hadi et al., 1995, 'Pengantar Tim Curator (Curators' Comment)', in *Seni Rupa Kontemporer Istiqlal: Istiqlal Contemporary Art* (Jakarta: Yayasan Festival Istiqlal), 12: 'Dalam tradisi Islam, seni adalah sarana ibadah. Semua bentuk ibadah adalah realisasi tauhid, penyaksian dan pembuktian bahwa Tuhan itu adalah satu'.

6 Raja Fuziah Raja Yun Uda and Abdul Rahma Al-Ahamdai, 2000, 'Malay Arts and Crafts: Islamic Inspiration in Creativity,' in Mohd Taib Osman, ed., *Islamic Civilization in the Malay World* (Kuala Lumpur: Dewan Bahasa dan Pustaka & The Research Centre for Islamic History, Art and Culture), 285.

7 Several scholars have thoroughly analysed how *tawḥīd* came to occupy a 'central position' in the interpretation of geometrical designs; see in particular Othman Yatim, 1995, *Islamic Arts* (Kuala Lumpur: Dewan Bahasa dan Pustaka), 5; and Gülru Necipoğlu, 1995, *The Topkapi Scroll: Geometry and Ornament in Islamic Architecture: Topkapi Palace Museum Library MS H.1956/Gülru Necipoğlu; with an Essay on the Geometry of the Muqarnas by Mohammad al-Asad* (Santa Monica, CA: Centre for the History of Art and Architecture). This commenced in late-19th-century European Orientalism and was later widely promoted in publications associated with the World of Islam Festival, launched in 1976, greatly influencing the scholarship of Southeast Asian art historians and contemporary artists, such as Sulaiman Esa (Malaysia) and AD Pirous (Indonesia).

8 Dzul Haimi Mhd Zain, 2004, 'The Art of Nusantara: The Southeast Frontier of Islam', in Islamic Arts Museum Malaysia, *The Message and the Monsoon: Islamic Art in Southeast Asia* (Kuala Lumpur: Islamic Arts Museum of Malaysia), 17.

9 The general history of *ceplokan* and *kawung*, which are among the earliest and most widely distributed patterns known to artists, is outside the scope of this chapter. A Harappan storage jar, dated 2700-2000 BCE, in the National Museum of India collection, is probably the oldest surviving representation of *kawung*. *Ceplokan*-like geometric patterns appear in diverse media all over the Muslim world, most notably in 15th- to 16th century Anatolian-style carpets.

10 Refer James Bennett, 2005, *Crescent Moon: Islamic Art and Civilisation of Southeast Asia* (Adelaide: Art Gallery of South Australia), 32, for a discussion of the widespread vogue among Muslim elite circles throughout the Indo-Malay archipelago for adopting the Javanese court fashions in the visual and performing arts.

11 Judi Achjadi, 2011, *The Glory of Batik: The Danar Hadi Collection* (Jakarta: Bab Publishing House), 34.

12 My appreciation is expressed to Emeritus Professor Virginia Hooker for sharing her email correspondence (11 April 2016) on the subject with Professor George Quinn, Australia National University. Professor Quinn cites the onomatopoeic use of the Javanese word in *endhog ceplok* (fried egg) and *keplok-keplok* (clap hands or applaud).

13 A Steinmann, 1947, 'Batik Designs', *CIBA Review* 58: 2114.

14 N Tirtaamidjaja, 1966, *Batik: Pola dan Tjorak* (Jakarta: Penerbit Djambatan), 25. Among Javanese batik makers the *kawung* design is often described as being inspired by the shape of a split *areca* palm nut, which was once commonly chewed with betel leaf as a mild stimulant. Jan Wisseman Christie notes a Central Javanese inscription, dated 877, listing a *luir mayang* textile pattern and this may refer to the *areca* blossom: 1993, 'Ikat to Batik? Epigraphic Data on Textiles in Java from the Ninth to the Fifteenth Centuries', in Marie-Louise Nabholz-Karaschoff et al., eds., *Weaving Patterns of Life: Indonesian Textile Symposium 1991* (Basel: Museum of Ethnography), 20. This suggests the possibility that the pattern's name alludes to a very early version of *kawung* or *ceplokan*.

15 Tirtaamidjaja, 1966, 25.

16 Islamic Arts Museum of Malaysia, 2012, *Ann Dunham's Legacy: A Collection of Indonesian Batik* (Kuala Lumpur: Islamic Arts Museum of Malaysia), 94-5. The textile is published upside down.

17 Ruth Barnes and Mary Hunt Kahlenberg, eds., illustrate the earliest surviving *tambalan* batik cloth, which is radiocarbon-dated to the 17th century: 2010, *Five Centuries of Indonesian Textiles* (Munich: Delmonico Books Prestel), 124. James Bennett and Russell Kelty, eds., illustrate an 18th-century Indian trade-textile version of the design: 2015, *Treasure Ships: Art in the Age of Spices* (Adelaide: Art Gallery of South Australia), 224. According to one Javanese tradition, the magical patchwork jacket, named Antakusama, miraculously fell down from heaven through the roof of the Great Mosque of Demak.

18 Jasper and Pirngadie, 1916, 144.

19 Early 20th-century Dutch structuralist anthropologists, including JP de Josselin de Jong and WH Rassers, first appropriated the term in an attempt to rationalise diverse Javanese classificatory systems. It originally referred to the territorial stratification of villages.

20 Robyn Maxwell, 2003b, *Textiles of Southeast Asia: Tradition, Trade and Transformation* (Hong Kong: Periplus Editions), 203; Véronique Degroot (2012), in 'Temples and Landscapes in South Central Java', in Alexandra Haendel, ed., *Old Myths and New Approaches: Interpreting Ancient Religious Sites in Southeast Asia* (Clayton: Monash University Publishing), 131-2, proposes a more complex picture, as epigraphical evidence suggests that 'two perceptions of space were challenging one another' in early Javanese Hindu-Buddhist society. One was the imported Indian perception of the east/south/west/north cardinal directions and the other was an indigenous Javanese dualistic viewpoint emphasising east/west and north/south. Moreover, John Miksic warily notes that the actual meaning of the word *mandala* changed greatly from the early Javanese Hindu-Buddhist period to the later Majapahit era: 2012, 'Life Among the Ruins: Habitation Sites of Trowulan', in Alexandra Haendel, ed., *Old Myths and New Approaches: Interpreting Ancient Religious Sites in Southeast Asia* (Clayton: Monash University Publishing), 159.

21 James Bennett analyses the evolution of the 'layer cake' model and doctrinal approaches, here typified by Yussof and Yatim, in Indonesian and Malaysian art scholarship: 2010, 'Islamic Art in Southeast Asia', in Jan Van Alphen, ed., *A Passage to Asia* (Brussels: Bozar, Centre for Fine Arts), 149-68. The historical foundations for the 'layer cake' can be found in Thomas Stanfford Raffles's *The History of Java*, the theme of which was the lost greatness of Java's pre-Islamic past: 1988 (Singapore: Oxford University Press).

22 Rens Heringa, 1996, 'The Historical Background of Batik in Java', in Rens Heringa and Harmen C Veldhuisen, eds., *Fabric of Enchantment: Batik from the North Coast of Java from the Inger McCabe Elliot Collection at the Los Angeles County Museum of Art* (Los Angeles: Los Angeles Country Museum of Art), 62; my appreciation is expressed to Jahfar Shareef for pointing out in a personal communication to me (November 2016) that the same *patola* motifs occur as mosque decoration in the Malabar communities of Kerala, India, many of which also comprised Arab traders married to local women. The textile motifs are also documented appearing in Hindu temple frescoes of the same period in south India.

23 Fiona Kerlogue, 2004, *The Book of Batik: Featuring Selections from the Rudolf G. Smend Collection* (Singapore: Archipelago Press), 45.

24 Andhika Utama, 2011, 'Terjemahan Teks Serat Sana Sunu', *Jawa Ampuh Blog*, <http://jawaampuh.blogspot.com.au/2011/01/terhemahan-teks-serat.sana.sunu>, accessed 22 June 2016.

25 Hiram W Woodward, 1977, 'A Chinese Silk Depicted at Candi Sewu', in KL Hutterer, ed., *Economic Exchange and Social Interaction in Southeast Asia* (Ann Arbor: University of Michigan), 233-43.

26 Mary-Louise Totton, 2005, 'Cosmopolitan Tastes and Indigenous Designs — Virtual Cloth in a Javanese *candi*', in Ruth Barnes, ed., *Textiles in Indian Ocean Societies* (London: Routledge), 119.

27 Angelo Andrea Di Castro, 2012, 'Graves, Trees and Powerful Spirits as Archaeological Indicators of Sacred Spaces', in A Haendel, ed., *Old Myths and New Approaches: Interpreting Ancient Religious Sites in Southeast Asia* (Clayton: Monash University Press), 239.

28 Peter Riddell, 2003, *Islam and the Malay-Indonesian world: Transmission and Response* (Singapore: Horizon Books), 2.

29 Merle Calvin Rickleffs, 2001, *A History of Modern Indonesia since c.1200* (Stanford: Stanford University Press), 16.

30 See Uka Tjandrasasmita, 1984, *Islamic Antiquities of Sendang Duwur* (Jakarta: Pusat Penelitian Arkeologi Nasional); Moehamad Habib Mustopo, 2001, *Kebudayaan Islam di Jawa Timur: Kajian Beberapa Unsur Budaya Masa Peralihan* (Yogyakarta: Penerbit Jendela); and Made Wijaya, 2014, *Majapahit Style* (Sanur: Yayasan Beringin Berapi).

31 See KRT Hardjonogoro, 1980, 'The Place of Batik in the History and Philosophy of Javanese Textiles: A Personal View', in Mattiebelle Gittinger, ed., *Indonesian Textiles: Irene Emery Roundtable on Museum Textiles 1979 Proceedings* (Washington: The Textile Museum), 232-42.

32 Quoted in S Supomo, 1997, 'From Sakti to Shahadah: The Quest for New Meanings in a Changing World Order', in PG Riddell et al. eds., *Islam: Essays on Scripture, Thought and Society* (Leiden: Brill), 224; Ricklefs describes the anonymous author referring to the destroyed Majapahit books as 'the honoured *Buda*

heirlooms'. MC Ricklefs, 2007, *Polarising Javanese Society: Islamic and Other Visions (c. 1830-1930)* (Singapore: NUS Press), 204.

33 Replicas of the carved stones depicting the *Ramayana* epic were cast in fibreglass during the restoration project and are now stored in the Ronggowarsito Provincial Museum, Semarang, Central Java.

34 The reconceptualisation of pre-Islamic sacred sites as locations for the veneration of Muslim saints is comprehensively discussed in Henri Chambert-Loir, 2002, 'Saints and Ancestors: The Cult of Muslim Saints in Java', in Henri Chambert-Loir et al., eds., *The Potent Dead: Ancestors, Saints and Heroes in Contemporary Indonesia* (Honolulu: University of Hawai'i Press), 132-40.

35 James J Fox, 1997, 'Sunan Kalijaga and the Rise of Mataram', in PG Ridell et al., eds., *Islam: Essays on Scripture, Thought and Society* (Leiden: Brill), 189.

36 James Bennett, ed., 2011, *Beneath the Winds: Masterpieces of Southeast Asian Art from the Art Gallery of South Australia* (Adelaide: Art Gallery of South Australia), 34-5, plate 10. For other typical examples of *loro blonyo,* see Helen Ibbitson Jessup, 1990, *Court Arts of Indonesia* (New York: The Asia Society Galleries in Association with Harry N Abrams, Inc), 29, Figure 3/No. 146, and 58, Figure 38. The new Muslim elements of dress include the *kuluk*, derived from the Ottoman fez, worn by Sadono.

37 Bennett, ed., 2011, 34, fn 6; Bruce W Carpenter illustrates a painted screen that he describes as representing stacked *patola* cushions: 2009, *Javanese Antique Furniture and Folk Art: The David B Smith and James Tirtoprodjo Collections* (Singapore: Editions Didier Millet), 45.

38 John Guy, 1998, *Woven Cargoes: Indian Textiles in the East* (London: Thames and Hudson), 42-3.

39 Madhusudan Amilai Dhaky, 2005, *The Indian Temple Traceries* (Gurgaon: American Institute of Indian Studies Centre for Art and Archaeology), 195, pl. 336. The author also illustrates another example at the contemporaneous Candramaulīśvara temple at Unkal, Karnataka.

40 Illustrated in Guy, 1998, 44, Figure 49.

41 Maxwell, 2003a, 130; James Bennett, 2013, ed., *Realms of Wonder: Jain, Hindu and Islamic Art of India* (Adelaide: Art Gallery of South Australia), 28, Figure 12; Ruth Barnes, 2006, 'Indian Textiles for Island Taste: The Trade to Eastern Indonesia', in Rosemary Crill, ed., *Textiles from India: The Global Trade* (Oxford: Seagull Books), 107, suggests that the figurative cloths were primarily produced for the Indian market, although their surviving presence in eastern Indonesian collections suggests that the cloths likely were also used in Java, where they were commonly traded.

42 James R Brandon, 1970, *On Thrones of Gold: Three Javanese Shadow Plays* (Cambridge, Mass.: Harvard University Press), 6.

43 Rosemary Crill, ed., 2015, *The Fabric of India* (London: V&A Publishing), 123.

44 Eiluned Edwards, 2016, *Imprints of Culture: Block Printed Textiles of India* (New Delhi: Niyogi Books), 65.

45 Ruurdje Laarhoven, 1994, 'The Power of Cloth: The Textile Trade of the Dutch East India Company (VOC) 1600-1780', unpublished PhD thesis, Australian National University, Appendix A.

46 Laarhoven, 1994, 19.

47 Guy, 1998, 91. The design is also known in Java as *cakar ayam*, literally 'hen's claw', due to its perceived resemblance to the marks made by a hen scratching in the dirt.

48 Laarhoven, 1994, 65-6.

49 Quoted in Itie Van Hout, ed., 2001, *Batik: Drawn in Wax* (Amsterdam: Royal Tropical Institute), 143.

50 Jasper and Pirngadie, 1916, 153.

51 Bennett, ed., 2011, 116-17, pl. 51, 124-3, pl. 55.

52 Maxwell, 2003a, 143.

53 Quoted in Harmen C Veldhuisen, 1993, *Batik Belanda 1840-1940: Dutch Influence in Batik from Java: History and Stories* (Jakarta: Gaya Favorit Press), 22. The possible exception is Mataram, during the 17th century, which was locked in a deadly economic and political struggle with the VOC who were the major vendors of Indian textiles.

54 Illustrated in Bennett and Kelty, eds., 2015, 162-3, also 318, cat. no. 230.

55 According to the formal/informal levels of language, *Dodot* is *ngoko* in informal Javanese, and *kampuh* is *krama inggil* in the formal language (AN Suyanto, 2002, *Sejarah Batik Yogyakarta*, Yogyakarta: Rumah Penerbitan

Merapi, 33); Indian *dodot* in the collection of the Art Gallery of South Australia include one typical textile measuring 199.0 cm by 303.0 cm.

56 An example of an Indian *dodot*, with a *ceplokan* pattern, made for the Indonesian market, is illustrated in Bennett and Kelty, eds., 2015, p. 157, cat. no. 212.

57 Robert J Holmgren and Anita E Spertus record that present-day Lampung informants have no memory of the heirloom cloths ever being worn, although 19th-century *tampan*, known also as 'ship cloths', depict figures wearing the voluminous garment: 1991, 'Is *geringsing* Really Balinese?', in Gisela Völger and Karin v. Weck, eds., *Indonesian Textiles: Symposium 1985* (Cologne: Ethnologica), 59.

58 Bennett, ed., 2011, 116.

59 GP Rouffaer and HH Juynbool, 1914, *De batik-kunst in Nederlandsch-Indië*, 1, 427-8, cited in Homgren and Spertus, 1991, 74, fn 6. The authors propose that the Javanese likely referred to Indian, as well as local, wax-resist cloths as 'batik'.

60 Veldhuisen, 1993, 29.

61 Van Hout, ed., 2001, 136-45.

62 Anthony Forge, 1989, 'Batik Patterns in the Early Nineteenth Century', in M Gittinger, ed., *To Speak with Cloth* (Los Angeles: Museum of Cultural History), 100, 104.

63 Vladimir Braginsky, 2004, *The Heritage of Traditional Malay Literature: A Historical Survey of Genres, Writings and Literary Views* (Leiden: KITLV Press), 401.

64 PP Roorda van Eysinga, ed., 1821, *Hikayat Isma Jatiem*, Batavia, Lands Drukkerij (in Jawi), 2-11, cited in Braginsky, 2004, 401. Tirtaamidjaja (1966, 19) observes that the courtly association of music and batik in the Javanese world is apparent in some of the oldest Mataram gamelan melodies that bear the titles of batik patterns, including *kawung*.

65 *Tempo* magazine (25 June 2005). The memory of Panembahan Trusmi is annually celebrated by local batik artists in the Ganti Welit ceremony held at his grave site.

66 According to Kraton Kasepuhan accounts, another Cirebon aristocrat, Panembahan Ki Dalem Sepuh, designed the extraordinary state carriage known as *Singabarwang* in the mid-16th century. The carriage's carved ornament testifies to the designer/maker's close familiarity with the cloud-like *wadasan* rock pattern of Cirebon batik, or perhaps the batik pattern is derived from carved ornament.

67 Cited in Fiona Kerlogue, 1997, 'Batik Cloths from Jambi, Sumatra', unpublished PhD thesis, University of Hull, 19.

68 Sarah Weiss, 2006, *Listening to an Earlier Java: Aesthetics, Gender and the Music of Wayang in Central Java* (Leiden: KITLV), 60. The mystical significance of the presence of female energy at the kingdom's heart of power almost certainly imbued the core female activity of making batik with deep meaning.

69 Justine Boow, 1988, in *Symbol and Status in Javanese Batik* (Perth: Asian Studies Centre, University of Western Australia, 19), observes that 'singing *macapat* [when making batik] was considered a suitable educational and morally uplifting activity for the women of the house while the men attended the mosque'.

70 Merle Ricklefs, 1998, *The Seen and Unseen Worlds in Java, 1726-1749: History, Literature and Islam in the Court of Pakubuwana II* (St Leonards, NSW: Allen & Unwin) is a comprehensive study of the life and times of the Ratu at the Mataram court and the three texts, *Carita Iskandar* (Story of Alexander the Great), *Carita Yusuf* (Story of Joseph) and *Kitab Usulbiyah*, all produced in 1729.

71 Quoted in Braginsky, 2004, 403.

72 Boow, 1988, 91.

73 Boow, 1988, 88. For an extensive discussion of issues related to the question of meaning in Central Javanese batik in the late 20th century, see this author's monograph.

74 Heringa, 1996, 33.

75 The observations by Ricklefs, 1998, 34, regarding spiritual values in the Mataram court during the 17th to 18th century are particularly relevant for understanding probable attitudes to batik practice.

76 Jasper and Pirngadie, 1916, 144; the forbidden (*larangan*) motifs were subsequently adopted by batik makers who were working outside the palace environment and whose clientele were non-aristocrats. This kind of batik became known as 'merchant batik' (*batik sudagaran*) as opposed to 'palace batik' (*batik keraton*).

77 Agus Ismoyo and Nia Fliam, personal communication with the author, May, 2011.

78 Heringa, 1980, 33. Clifford Geertz records the East Javanese metaphor of 'drawing a batik design on the heart' (*mbatik manah*) as a mystical experience: 1960, *The Religion of Java* (Chicago: The University of Chicago Press), 287.

79 Figure 10.7 illustrates an example of *truntum* motif not unlike the background configuration in Hardjonogoro's own *truntum* motif known as 'Butterflies' (*Kupu-kupu*), illustrated in nwww Rupii, 2015, <http:// rupipitruntum. blogspot.com.au>, 31 March 2016. The classic version of *truntum* usually displays radial lines connecting the flower/star motifs.

80 Quoted in Hardjonogoro, 1980, 229-30. Hardjonogoro appears to identify Kanjeng Ratu Beruk as the wife of Sunan Paku Buwono III.

81 Hardjonogoro, 1980, 33.

82 'K. Ratu Kencana', 2015, *Geni*, available at: <www.geni.com/people/K-Ratu-Kencana/60000000 14559561542>, accessed 3 April 2016; Rupii, 2015; Kusuma Dewangga, 2013, 'Behind Batik's *Truntum* Motif', *TNOL Asia*, <http://www.tnol.asia/arts-culture/19374-behind-batiks-truntum-motif.html>, accessed 25 June 2016.

83 Ruth Barnes, 1997, 'Indian Block-Printed Textiles in Egypt: The Newberry Collection in the Ashmolean Museum, Oxford; Catalogue: Blue and White Textiles', *Jameel Online Centre*, <jameelcentre.ashmolean.org/ collection/7/10236/ 10323>, accessed 14 April 2016.

84 See Kerlogue, 1997.

85 *Ciptoning* may be considered one of a generic group of motifs, often associated with wedding rituals, known as *sido mukti*, meaning 'continuously prospering'. The writer's experience speaking with Central Javanese batik connoisseurs suggests that there is considerable debate whether *sido mukti* are *ceplokan* or not. Boow, 1988, 122, describes a similar Yogyakarta batik and documents four different names for the same design.

86 Judi Achjadi, 2014, *The Jakarta Textile Museum* (Jakarta: Indonesian Heritage Society), 128.

CHAPTER 11

CURATING *ʿILM*: CHAPTER OR BRIDGE?

SAM BOWKER

ABSTRACT

As a versatile and distinctive approach to the concept of 'knowledge', *ʿilm* can influence the curation of art exhibitions. The act of curatorship is an act of explicit knowledge production, with intentions that are distinct from the haptic knowledge of the makers or the tacit knowledge of the visitors and/or the previous owners of the objects displayed. The curation of exhibitions acknowledges that those forms of knowledge can be balanced, which is a core component of museum and gallery education. The concept of *ʿilm* provides a means to conceptualise this need to frame 'knowledge' holistically. This study is based on the observation that audiences responded differently to Egyptian Tentmaker Applique exhibitions (*khiyāmiyya*, appropriated as *khayamiya*) held in regional Australia and the Islamic Art Museum Malaysia (IAMM) in Kuala Lumpur. From an immersive setting within Islamic visual culture, these textiles formed a new 'chapter' in a much larger story. Within Australia, these spectacular textiles were admired for their affinities to quilting and were appreciated by visitors as cultural 'bridges'. Each exhibition enabled the creation and transmission of haptic, tacit, and explicit knowledge — forms of knowledge that can all be considered under the conceptual structures of *ʿilm*. Yet each model — chapter and bridge — featured limitations that shaped the goals of each exhibition. This study identifies the implications of these forms of knowledge when situating 'Islamic' art in the context of exhibitions, and what *ʿilm* may offer curators and educators as a conceptual framework.

HOW MIGHT WE INTERPRET *ʿILM* WITHIN ART?

This study engages theoretically with the notion of *ʿilm* at three levels: explicit, tacit, and haptic knowledge. In broad terms, the decisions and actions of art curatorship constitute a form of knowledge production that takes two basic forms: chapters (explicit knowledge) and bridges (tacit knowledge). These forms of knowledge are distinct from the haptic knowledge (dexterity) of specialist practitioners, including artists and artisans, because they are not intrinsic to the production and cultural context of the items exhibited. All three of these forms of knowledge inform the explicit knowledge of exhibition visitors, just as they are in turn informed by the context of the exhibition.

For this study, the word 'chapter' stands as a definable and communicable form of explicit knowledge. By contrast, tacit knowledge constitutes 'bridges'. These 'bridges' are diverse and potentially unpredictable points of engagement, but they are one of the most profound means available for curators to communicate with audiences. If knowledge (*ʿilm*) is taken to have two forms — information and observation, as opposed to conjecture (*zaan*) — then *'ilm* might be regarded as variations on explicit and/or haptic knowledge, resulting in chapters. By contrast, conjecture forms a bridge. This is because both conjecture and bridges are a means, not an end, towards knowledge. The proposed curatorial models of 'chapter' and 'bridge' provide ways of considering knowledge by its potential to enable change. This includes consideration of what is being changed, and the means by which that change is initiated. In the words of the curator Michael Belcher:

> An exhibition exists to communicate with the visitor in order to bring about change. This can be an increase in knowledge, greater awareness and understanding of concepts or facts previously unknown. Or it can also be an emotional change — elation, enjoyment or sadness — brought through an aesthetic experience.[1]

The change enabled by a new 'chapter' is a revision or extension of explicit knowledge — it is defined, and measurable in relation to context. The change enabled by a bridge is far more abstract and ambiguous. It is individually specific, tacit (relatively incommunicable), and open-ended. These distinct forms of knowledge, which are offered as interpretations of *'ilm*, can be seen echoed in the responses of visitors to art exhibitions. To consider this hypothesis, this study considers one case study through several iterations — exhibitions of Egyptian Tentmaker Applique, *khiyāmiyya*, curated between 2007 and 2016 — to consider how new knowledge was represented in visitor responses to these artworks and artisans. The differentiation between 'chapters' and 'bridges' is not mutually exclusive, but is intended to provide a model for further consideration.[2]

It should also be emphasised that this proposed model is only one means of conceptualising *'ilm* in the interpretation of art. Mohammed Hamdouni Alami adapted the concept of *bayān* (exposition, or making things clear) from the work of the 9th-century Muʿtazilī literary scholar al-Jāḥiẓ, *al-Bayān wa-l-tabyīn*. His unorthodox interpretations of al-Jāḥiẓ's work, particularly his *Kitāb al-ḥayawān* (Book of Animals), led to Alami's proposal of a series of concepts to articulate 'meaning' within Islamic art and architecture.[3] This essentially semiotic approach could potentially inform approaches to art criticism. Specifically, Alami claims that al-Jāḥiẓ's *bayān* was structured by five elements: *lafẓ* (speech), *khaṭṭ* (writing), *'aqd* (calculation), and *ishāra* (sign or gesture), followed by ḥāl (state or condition).[4] Al-Jāḥiẓ probably did not intend the concept of *bayān* to inform art curation, but of Alami's five elements, the latter two are especially pertinent to the curation of art. *Ḥāl* (state) offers a mode of object-centred meaning or visual analysis. *Ishāra* (gesture) offers an assessment of the movements of the human body for their communicative potential. More than body language, *ishāra* includes eliciting meaning from actions, including the movements of an artist as they create a new work. Alami also establishes a basis for 'the craftsman's great secret', *tasṭīr* (writing and drawing). This term designates the knowledge of hidden lines that underpin geometric design, formative but rendered invisible once the work is completed.[5] Alami's study of pre-19th-century Arab aesthetics is continued in his second book. In this he examines texts by Ibn al-Haytham and the *Ikhwān al-Ṣafā'* (the Brethren of Purity, a group of authors and editors responsible for a collaborative 10th-century encyclopaedia) to find aesthetic commentaries applicable to the experiences of Fatimid Egyptian artisans, notably 'painting and its effects on the soul'.[6]

Beyond Alami's contested interpretation of al-Jāḥiẓ, the work of Adam Mestyan on the etymology of the Arabic term *fann* is pertinent to this discussion.[7] Today, *fann* is usually translated as 'art'. Mestyan's analysis considers the origin of this term in relation to comparable terms like *ṣinā'a*. Like the Greek term *techne*, this is 'craft, practical knowledge, or skill', potentially 'haptic' knowledge (which in Ottoman Turkish was *ṣan'at*). Mestyan noted that '*ṣināʿa* and *ʿilm* were used in opposition to one another in the debate about whether medicine was an art/craft (*techne/ṣināʿa*), or a science (*episteme/ʿilm*)'.[8] In 19th-century Ottoman Turkish

> *ṣanʿa(t)* already carried the meaning of an independent sphere of human activity, based on its close association with architecture, book illustrations, and all kinds of creative and beautiful crafts, as well as the creative genius behind them. Yet it is even more curious why this word was not chosen to translate 'art'.[9]

Mestyan's study into *fann* was prompted by observations regarding the 19th-century translation of Western European discourses on art into Arabic. Hence, such recent use of *fann* was shaped by broader Arabic discourses within modern art, echoing mediaeval uses of *fann* as a term of differentiation, like 'field of knowledge', then in relation to poetry as a variation on *adab* (elegant behaviour). Amongst other sources, Mestyan attributes the current interplay between *ṣināʿa, fann*, and *ʿilm* to the 1828 *Dictionnaire francais-arabe* compiled by Ellious Bochtor and 'enriched' by Arman Caussin de Perceval.[10] This text appears to have influenced many subsequent dictionaries, concurrent with colloquial use of these three terms as documented in late-19th-century Egyptian-Arabic, and it informed Rifāʿa al-Ṭahṭāwī's text of his trip to Paris (*Takhlīṣ al-ibrīz fī talkhīṣ Bārīz*), published in 1834. Mestyan noted that al-Ṭahṭāwī's account is the 'first time, to the best of my knowledge, that the new European concept of (intellectual/fine) art as an independent category is explained in Arabic'.[11] Specifically, al-Ṭahṭāwī claimed:

> Science [*al-ʿilm*] consists of empirical knowledge, achieved by evidence, while art [*al-fann*] is the knowledge of making [*ṣināʿa*] something by specific rules ... This is the classification of the French scholars. But in our use, sciences and arts are one thing. There is a difference only in the being of art [*kawn al-fann*] as independent knowledge [*ʿilm*] in itself and as a tool for others.[12]

Between Alami and Mestyan, we can see how multiple models may be drawn upon for the interpretation of 'art' from Arabic literature, both lexigraphically and semiotically. As such, the challenge of holistically translating *ʿilm* is beyond the ambition of this study.[13] Rather, this is a reflection on the experiences of curating one particular form of Egyptian textile art, and the implications of the forms of knowledge drawn from those exhibitions.

CURATING 'CHAPTERS' — DEFINED CONTRIBUTIONS TO EXPLICIT KNOWLEDGE

Explicit knowledge is developed through communicated learning. It is possible to explain an explicit concept, unlike a tacit concept, which can be understood but not so readily explained. For the purposes of this study, a 'chapter' is a concrete field of new and explicit knowledge within the scholarship and curation of art or material culture. Unlike 'bridges', chapters are academic outputs. They seek to provide and define new contributions to a field of knowledge, for the benefit of those who are already familiar with the field. The outcomes of chapters are easy to trace: one simply follows the citations. This is where conferences, symposia, and research projects are most comfortably situated. Exhibitions dedicated to under-represented artists or very specific forms of art and material culture lend themselves to the 'chapter' model. Explicit knowledge is versatile, accessible, challenging, and verifiable.

Yet chapters are not invented to serve as prisoners of the ivory tower. The collective fields of Islamic art have been displayed and studied with a renewed urgency in recent years. The immediate social purpose of these exhibitions frames any claim to detached scholarly discourse, even when dealing with the sparse remnants of long-deceased dynasties in distant empires. This is not unique to our situation today, as the 1950s, 1970s, and 2000s also saw proliferations of new scholarship and revised curatorship within Islamic art. These can be linked to popular and academic interests sparked by the Gulf Oil Crisis and the Iranian Revolution in the 1970s, as well as the establishment of Israel in 1948, amongst other major international events.

The chapter of explicit knowledge is one form of *'ilm*. This leaves us with the bridge of tacit knowledge, through which what is 'known' becomes 'meaningful'. As Seif el Rashidi noted in his observations on engagement in museums of Islamic art, a balance needs to be sought between academic specialists and diverse general audiences, noting the limitations of potential understanding.[14] The best we can generate is a spark, or perhaps a bridge, which leads to ignition and exploration.

CURATING 'BRIDGES' — AMBIGUOUS CONTRIBUTIONS TO TACIT KNOWLEDGE

Academic initiatives emphasising the potential role of art as a 'cultural bridge' can echo calls for harmonious or empathic relations between gallery audiences and art producers.[15] These are often situated in terms of transregional, linguistic, or geographic bridging (such as the representation of the Silk Road or Mediterranean as a cultural bridge).[16] As an example of this trend, the authors and editors of the influential text *Islamic Art and the Museum* make no direct reference to the curatorial objective of forging cultural bridges through art exhibitions.[17] Nor does this phrase appear in the papers of any author associated with the Islamic Art edition of the *Journal of Art Historiography* (Issue 6, June 2012). Similarly, the synopses of the biannual conferences and other activities of the Historians of Islamic Art Association (HIAA) to date have rarely made use of the term 'cultural bridge'. This suggests that the term 'cultural bridge' is more likely to be favoured in the context of journalism over scholarship, being ostensibly a good thing but also ambiguous and problematic as a measurable form of knowledge.

However, the application of 'bridges' in relation to Islamic art can be overt. The social and political desire to forge 'bridges' appears as a driving factor in the funding of extensive renovations, expansions, and new constructions for galleries of Islamic art worldwide. The 'Building Bridges Program' of the Doris Duke Charitable Foundation supports the development of 'experiences that advance relationships and understanding' through Islamic arts and culture in the USA.[18] The 'cultural bridge' model is also appealing as a form of diplomacy, as noted by Cynthia Schneider and others.[19] Frederick Winship and other recent commentators have also featured the term 'cultural bridge' prominently in their reviews of exhibitions of Islamic art.[20] In Australia, where Islamic art has been under-represented, similar use of this term appears in statements by the Council for Australian-Arab Relations, supported by the Australian government, through initiatives like the Arab Film Festival.[21]

The desire to form 'cultural bridges' is not unique to Islamic art. Similar desires can be traced through the ambitions of projects linked to Indigenous Australian art, contemporary Asian art, Pacific art, and art forms representative of marginalised communities or misunderstood interests.

Beyond the material value of art collections, they provide opportunities for understanding, empathy, and knowledge through exposure to some of the most beautiful objects humanity has to offer. The assumption in these endeavours is that bridges can be formed through the sharing of knowledge. This is not inconceivable, but the problem for curators is that they can only build half a bridge — specifically, the first half or the starting point. The rest of this bridge is obscured by fog, as it is challenging to determine the ongoing impact of a visitor's experience or their changed knowledge after visiting an exhibition.

In 2010, the Australian curator Djon Mundine proposed three rules of curatorship. Above all, an exhibition should 'make the artist look good', and it should 'leave a legacy'.[22] The institution, whenever possible, should also try to acquire a work from that exhibition. Comparable proposals are often encountered in manuals and treatises on curatorship, such as de Salvo and Kuoni's three principal tasks: '[a]dvocating for artists and their art; communicating to an interested public; and confronting the reality of institutions we work with'.[23] Within such objectives, we find agendas for both artists and art institutions. The legacy of a cultural bridge is challenging to assess, so it remains an optimistic but ambiguous contribution to knowledge. The most concrete 'outcomes' tend to be described in reference to subsequent changes that can be seen in the work of visiting artists or historians — for example, Henri Matisse, Vassily Kandinksy, Carl Becker, and Max van Berchem owed debts to the 1910 exhibition of Islamic Art in Munich.[24]

An alternative measurement of connectivity or engagement with an exhibition can be situated through empathic or emotional responses. As previously mentioned by Michael Belcher, and many others, emotional change can be brought on by an aesthetic experience. The challenge in assessing this form of knowledge is once again the problem of obscurity. Tears, for example, represent a complex emotional response that resists translation into communicable knowledge. A visitor expressing tears has been profoundly moved, but moved how? In what way, or why, was that experience transformative for them?

Understanding knowledge as a 'bridge' relies on empathic communication and dialogue between the visitor and the thing exhibited. If the 'bridge' is more physically defined, through interaction between regions or aspects of material culture, then the metaphor of a 'chapter' within knowledge becomes more accurate.

CURATING *KHIYĀMIYYA* — HAPTIC KNOWLEDGE AND AWE

A further challenge facing curators is the attempt to convey haptic knowledge. Haptic knowledge is essentially knowledge developed by hand, resulting in nuanced manual skills. This is the knowledge gained by those who have invented or mastered a physical process, such as dancing, playing sport, playing a musical instrument, or sewing needle-turned applique. In other words, tacit knowledge includes a contextual understanding of an art practice, but haptic knowledge is the skill of making artworks.

Oleg Grabar noted that we have no evidence to believe that viewers and artisans interpreted complex geometric designs in the same way. The knowledge of the artisan is distinct from that brought to the artwork by the viewer; it is usually in-depth for technical understanding, but not necessarily for symbolism.[25] Such specialised haptic knowledge does not lend itself easily to communication through exhibitions: what is known is not easily shown. Rather than trying to develop a visitor's skills to those of a master artisan, curatorial approaches to haptic knowledge are more likely to give the visitor an initial understanding of particular skills through the use of demonstrations, be they recorded or performed live. It can be sufficient to instil respect for the subject by promoting an appreciation of the skills involved — the spinning of a wheel, the layering of wire, the blowing of molten glass, the threading of a needle.

In the most engaging scenario, the appreciation of a challenging skill can also be manifested in terms of respect or even awe. People who have attained admirable knowledge can constitute a spectacle, especially when that knowledge is displayed. This is the basic market principle underpinning a performer's appeal. It is also the reason why the Egyptian tentmakers, like the practitioners of many other skilled manual professions in the Darb al-Amar region of Cairo, showcase the sewing of applique panels along the Street of the Tentmakers, even though the majority of sewing is performed in offsite workshops. It reinforces the fact that all their work is handmade, that the retailer is an authority on the subject. It is impressive to watch the skilled tentmakers confidently sewing by hand at considerable speed, flipping and folding fabrics with dexterity, and bringing complex, colourful forms into their final shape. There is a considerable history of the display of these skills in international exhibitions. Skilled Egyptian craftsmen demonstrated their skills in weaving, copper-smithing, and woodcarving at various international exhibitions, such as the Exposition Internationale of Vienna in 1878. The question of the expressive agency retained by those 'performers' is debatable, though it remains a crucial feature of Tentmaker Applique exhibitions today.

Egyptian Tentmaker Applique

Egyptian Tentmaker Appliques, or *khiyāmiyya*, are decorative textiles that once served as embellished tents. These textiles are formed through a layering of cotton cut by hand with large scissors, then sewn to a canvas backing with needle-turned applique. The art form possesses remarkable continuity despite radical changes facing the work of tentmakers of Cairo.[26] Their work now consists of decorative wall hangings, but once formed monumental textile pavilions called *surādiq*. These street-sized tents were used to host weddings, funerals, graduations, feasts, and festivals throughout Egypt. These tents are still used across Egypt today, but they now consist of machine-printed fabrics that imitate their original patterns and vibrant colours.

The apprenticeship of a tentmaker can take up to a decade; it is recognised at various stages through a hierarchy of achievements. A young tentmaker starts by sharing scissors with their mentor, until they have earned the right to their own pair. They also earn the right to sit on a cushion in the workshop once they have earned their place on the team. Though there were more than 300 tentmakers in the 1970s, there are around 100 working today. This is a critically endangered Egyptian profession, invested with unique tacit, haptic, and explicit knowledge. The holistic scope of this knowledge may be regarded as the *'ilm* of *khiyāmiyya*. Prior to 2003, no scholarly publications had attempted to describe the work of the tentmakers of Cairo.[27] Until 2012, *khiyāmiyya* was not named in any broad reviews of Middle Eastern textiles or Islamic art, though it had been infrequently mentioned in books dedicated to Egyptian or African art of the 20th century. Few museums or galleries worldwide were known to possess examples of this art form. When they did, they were rarely aware of comparable examples. As a result of this sparse scholarly terrain, each exhibition of Egyptian Tentmaker Applique presented an opportunity to create new chapters.

Quilt exhibitions: 'Stitch like an Egyptian'

In 2007, the Australian quiltmaker Jenny Bowker (the author's mother) brought an exhibition of contemporary Egyptian applique and two tentmakers to the Australian Quilt Convention in Melbourne.[28] This event, *Stitch Like an Egyptian*, could be seen as a chapter, given that it allowed for the display of an unfamiliar form of quilting in Australia; but the outcomes of this exhibition were primarily described as bridges (ambiguous tacit knowledge). The quilters were keen to meet master craftsmen, and the tentmakers were received as 'rock stars' simply for doing something they did in Cairo every day. The haptic knowledge of the tentmakers was readily understood by quilt exhibition audiences. The explicit knowledge of new approaches to applique, the Egyptian context of *khiyāmiyya*, and the appearance of the work were also readily understood within the framework of quilting. This is unusual, and such insights cannot be taken for granted.

This exhibition, just like subsequent exhibitions, was a moving experience for the tentmakers as well as their audiences. Some of the quilters found that meeting Muslim men from Egypt, who knew how to create extraordinary artwork in applique, caused them to reconsider their perceptions of the people of the Middle East. In terms of *ʿilm*, this encounter situated observation against conjecture. The tentmakers, particularly Ahmed Naguib, felt appreciated for their knowledge.[29] He was applauded for finishing a small lotus flower, a standing ovation for an everyday action. This understanding and appreciation formed tacit knowledge, bridges rather than chapters, because the summarisation of what became known was distinct from the experience of learning that knowledge.

As noted by observation and visitor's books during the exhibitions in Wagga, Albury and Kuala Lumpur, the recorded responses to the work of the tentmakers (that is, the actual objects on display) ranged from interest to awe, tending towards the latter.[30] The objects were described with relation to their technical sophistication, composition, colour, and content — all explicit knowledge, but the interaction, as tacit knowledge, was much more challenging to describe. The *Stitch Like an Egyptian* exhibitions were designed to commercially benefit the tentmakers, so the appliques on display were for sale. The sale of an artwork indicates its appeal, but cannot make any claims regarding knowledge. Instead, the most consistently revealing encounter in these exhibitions was the interaction between audience and performer, a skilled tentmaker observed by those who recognised the knowledge being shared.

GALLERY EXHIBITIONS — *KHEDIVAL TO CONTEMPORARY*

The exhibitions curated by the author for Charles Sturt University (CSU) in 2013, 2015, and 2016 differed in several ways from the quilt exhibitions curated by Jenny Bowker and the American Quilt Society (AQS). They were intended to serve as chapters, situating new knowledge as a result of primary research into the history of Egyptian Tentmaker Applique. Beyond contemporary textiles, historic examples from the Khedival period (1867-1914) and touristic panels from the early 20th century were displayed as a survey of changes in this Egyptian art form. None of the exhibits were for sale, and no tentmakers were present in person. The aim was for the objects themselves to speak on behalf of their history. As the poet al-Thaʿālibī (d. 1038) claimed: 'Our monuments bear witness to ourselves, therefore, after we are gone, look at our works'.[31]

Given the demonstrated significance of participation by a tentmaker at quilt exhibitions, the CSU exhibitions included a three-minute video by Kim Beamish. *My Name is Hossam* (2013) was developed as a trailer for the feature-length documentary film *The Tentmakers of Cairo* (2015), which was also produced and directed by Kim Beamish.[32] It features the tentmaker Hossam Farouk sewing in his shop along the Street of the Tentmakers, at prayer in an old mosque, cooking with his family, and reading the newspaper in his home. During this montage he speaks in colloquial Egyptian Arabic about what his work means to him, how his knowledge of the art form developed, and what he values in his life beyond his work. This short film introduces the Egyptian context for the tentmakers today, showing how their hand-sewn textiles juxtapose colour and tactility against the crowds, concrete, and dust of Cairo.

A second short film was also screened in the *Khedival to Contemporary* exhibitions. This was a montage of archival photographs depicting Egyptian Tentmaker Applique in historical and contemporary use. It was designed to solve the problems of contextualising the art as it appears in Egypt, as well as of displaying small photographs without claiming excessive space or exposing the originals to light. This montage was set to instrumental Egyptian *'ūd* music to create a nuanced ambience in the exhibition space, commensurate with the soft-spoken narration and street sounds of *My Name is Hossam*. The objective of music in exhibition spaces can be explicit knowledge — this sound has meaning — but in this case it was tacit, setting an acoustic context that accompanied the textiles without direct symbolic meaning.[33]

The CSU exhibitions were held in the HR Gallop Gallery in Wagga Wagga and the Albury Library Museum. These are small cities in regional New South Wales, Australia. They were selected because they host CSU campuses and because they suited the scale of the textiles being displayed. For example, the *Rhode Island Panel* was suspended from the ceiling in Albury as a reference to the architectural use of these textiles as *surādiq* pavilions, forming an awning and a dramatic entrance to the exhibition. This also overlapped with the *Arabian Nights*' trope of a flying carpet, assisted by the coincidental exhibition of a video in a neighbouring room depicting aerial drone footage flying over local wheat fields.

The third space was much larger, the Islamic Art Museum Malaysia (IAMM) in Kuala Lumpur. In that context, the exhibition was centred around the Egyptian tent from their collection, which formed the basis for Heba Barakat's book *Beyond Boundaries: Tents of the Islamic World* (2003). When shown at large scale in the IAMM, this exhibition presented the opportunity to situate Egyptian Tentmaker Applique within the broader canon of Islamic art history, including references to parallels found elsewhere in the IAMM's collection. The tentmaker Mohammed Mahmoud also led workshops in Tentmaker Applique at the beginning of the exhibition, but did not demonstrate the sewing techniques inside the exhibition itself.

To connect the knowledge of the tentmakers to the experiences of Australian audiences, the exhibitions in Wagga Wagga and Albury emphasised the importance of touristic *khiyāmiyya*. These smaller figurative compositions, featuring scenes from ancient Egyptian art or daily life in Egypt, were frequently collected as souvenirs by soldiers and nurses during World War I and World War II. This was a gesture towards the establishment of cultural bridges, as these textiles had been inherited by regional Australian audiences, and were thus more familiar than the grand Khedival appliques. However, this genre was excluded from the Islamic Art Museum Malaysia, possibly because these appliques were seen as relatively kitsch.

The legacies of these gallery exhibitions could be measured as chapters. Concurrent with the Australian projects, a team at the University of Durham in the UK led by Professor James Piscatori curated an atmospheric exhibition in the Norman Chapel and commissioned oral histories from the tentmakers. Tentmaker exhibitions were also curated by John and Joan Fisher in the UK, Germany, and Holland, as well as by the American Quilt Society (AQS) in the USA. This was a lively period in the generation and distribution of new knowledge about the Egyptian tentmakers.

Visitor responses

Responses to each gallery exhibition were noted in visitor's books, in daysheets by gallery staff, and during post-exhibition feedback interviews. At the IAMM, the majority of visitor responses came from international visitors to Malaysia, and written comments in at least eight languages filled four books. The Australian exhibitions contained many comments from interstate Australian and unspecified (presumably local) visitors, filling two books. As noted by Lorenz Korn, nationalism and orientalism have shaped understanding and scholarship of Islamic art.[34] These records broadly demonstrated some of these inclinations. Very few visitors apparently knew of *khiyāmiyya* prior to their visit. Visitors who identified as Egyptian left remarks such as 'This has made me proud to be Egyptian', and were often surprised to see these familiar textiles celebrated on this scale. At the IAMM, 'I am proud to be Muslim' was very frequently noted. Australians usually commented on the intricacy of the 'amazing' and 'beautiful' designs. Many hoped to visit Egypt one day.

Though no actual tentmakers were present within the actual exhibition spaces, visitors to each of the exhibitions reported that this was a surprisingly emotional experience. They expressed tears in response to these historic textiles. Crying in art exhibitions, as well as in response to architecture, cinema, and music, is not uncommon. It has been described through the Spanish idiom *duende*, or variations on Stendhal or Florentine syndrome, in which one is overwhelmed by an aesthetic experience. This state could be compared to *ʿilm ḥuḍūrī*, an innate understanding developed through unmediated, direct experience, possibly mystical, as opposed to *ʿilm ʿaqlī* (rational and calculated knowledge).

The reasons given for this unexpected response were often vague, evidently drawn from the visitors' own tacit understanding of these textiles and their context. It was informed by their understanding that this art form was endangered, that it rarely appeared in surveys of Islamic arts, that it was made by hand on such a grand scale. That it came unexpectedly from the Middle East, often seen by audiences in the context of contemporary conflict, also played a role. Yet the claim that a 'brilliant' artwork can bring an audience to tears is also based on the intensity of meaning generated by the audience's interpretation. This is *ʿilm* — the connection of knowledge to socio-political and moral context, as well as the pursuit of that knowledge.

In 2010, a Tumblr feed hosted by the Museum of Modern Art in New York (MOMA) was dedicated to visitors crying during individual intimate audiences with Marina Abramovic. It appeared to be a form of joke at first, but there is an intangible power within relational aesthetics that can cause an intense and indescribable emotional response. If this tacit knowledge can be achieved through firsthand encounters with the tentmakers of Cairo, then this is a bridge worth pursuing.

The 99 Names: Individual ʿilm

Emotive knowledge is a profound form of tacit understanding. An alternative manifestation of knowledge is the tentmaker's own perceptions of their work. On the whole, the tentmakers make their work so that it can be sold. In rare instances, a personal drive to create something entirely new, or with specific symbolic meaning, results in textiles bearing exceptional knowledge.

The last masterpiece by the tentmaker Mohammed Dendon was a complex calligraphic rendition of the 99 Names of Allah, *al-Asmāʾ al-Ḥusnā*. This series of divine attributes is believed to grant entry to Paradise to the person who memorises and recounts them. Dendon started sewing this panel shortly after being diagnosed with a serious illness in 2009. He completed the piece, which for him could be described as neither a chapter nor a bridge, but a passport to Paradise. *The 99 Names* by Mohammed Dendon was displayed as the final work of the IAMM exhibition, and upon its own wall in Wagga Wagga, and in the Art Gallery of South Australia. It was excluded from the Albury exhibition because it provided an obvious target for Islamophobic vandalism. This decision was informed by the experience of the artist Fatima Killeen at the Canberra Islamic Centre, whose works had been damaged by vandals who broke into the mosque in April 2014. To her credit, Killeen let the damaged works remain in their 'altered' state, reminiscent of Marcel Duchamps' *Large Glass*, as statements regarding Islamic identity in Australia in the early 21st century. In this case, the lack of knowledge about Islamic arts, or a skewed perception of that knowledge, influenced the curation of the Albury exhibition.

CONCLUSION

We might divide the objectives of art exhibitions into forms of knowledge informed by *ʿilm*. These could include the explicit chapter, the tacit bridge, and the haptic understanding of the artist (which might also be called *ṣanʿa* or *ḥurfa*, 'craft' in Arabic, or perhaps *fann*). Each can be defined by their objective as a contribution or use of knowledge. Though the 'chapter' advances claims for the application and definition of new knowledge, the 'bridge' sets up knowledge as a foundation for future interactions, a comparatively undisciplined and open-ended outcome. There is a place for both in art curation, and they are not mutually exclusive. For curators, a knowledgeable performer's creation can be displayed in a manner that is potentially awe-inspiring or emotionally transformative. The Egyptian tentmakers are conscious of the appeal of tacit knowledge as a form of performance. These exhibitions shared the objective of raising knowledge as both 'chapter' and 'bridge'. The measure of all exhibitions can be assessed by their ability to leave a legacy through the knowledge they have developed. Considering the limitations and potential of the 'chapter' and the 'bridge' provides curators with a methodological tool informed by the concept of *ʿilm*.

NOTES

1 Michael Belcher, 1992, 'Communicating through Museum Exhibitions', in M Thompson, ed., *Manual of Curatorship: A Guide to Museum Practice*, 2nd ed. (Oxford: Butterworth Heinemann), 649.

2 The name of the exhibition used the term 'khayamiya', derived from the Arabic term for tentmakers, *khiyāmiyya*. This spelling was an approximation developed for English-speaking audiences, who previously called these textiles 'Egyptian Quilts'. As noted by Samer Akkach in email correspondence with me, the term *khiyāmiyya* derives from the Arabic *khiyam* or *khiyām*, the plural of *khayma*, 'tent', the verb of which, *khayyama*, means 'to camp'. Accordingly, *khiyāmiyya* (with stress on the last *y*), refers to the makers of tents, for whom the Street of the Tentmakers, *Shāriʿ al-Khiyāmiyya*, near Bab Zweiyla in Cairo, was named.

3 Mohammed Hambouni Alami, 2014, *Art and Architecture in the Islamic Tradition: Aesthetics, Politics and Desire in Early Islam* (London: IB Tauris).

4 Alami, 2014, 40.

5 Alami, 2014, 200-1.

6 Mohammed Hambouni Alami, 2015, *The Origins of Visual Culture in the Islamic World: Aesthetics, Art, Architecture and Early Islam* (London: IB Tauris).

7 Adam Mestyan, 2011, 'Arabic Lexicography and European Aesthetics: The Origin of *Fann*', *Muqarnas* 28(1): 69-100.

8 Mestyan, 2011, 75.

9 Mestyan, 2011, 77.

10 Mestyan, 2011, 84.

11 Mestyan, 2011, 88.

12 Al-Ṭahṭāwī, 2003, 23, quoted in Mestyan, 2011, 88.

13 For an example of this attempt resulting in controversy, read the account of Edwin Lewis's 1882 speech in Beirut on 'knowledge, science, and wisdom', subsequently reprint by *al-Mutataf*. See Marwa S Elshakry, 2008, 'Knowledge in Motion: The Cultural Politics of Modern Science Translations in Arabic', *Isis* 99(4): 701-30.

14 Seif El Rashidi, 2012, 'Museums of Islamic Art and Public Engagement', in Benoît Junod et al., eds., *Islamic Art and the Museum: Approaches to Art and Archaeology of the Muslim World in the Twenty-First Century* (London: Saqi), 209-14.

15 For example, consider the 2008 forum 'The Islamic Spectrum in Australia — Building Cultural Bridges through Understanding', held at the University of South Australia in Adelaide and hosted by the Bob Hawke Prime Ministerial centre and the NEXUS Multicultural Arts Centre through the funding of the Australia Council for the Arts and participation by the Australian Federation of Islamic Councils. This type of event implies that the 'bridges' formed are between public agencies as much as between individuals. See University of South Australia, 2008, 'The Islamic Spectrum in Australia — Building Cultural Bridges through Understanding', *University of South Australia News and Events*, media release, 30 April, <http://w3.unisa.edu.au/news/2008/300408.asp>, accessed 21 April 2017.

16 An example is the 'Art as Cultural Bridge' seminar by the Asian Studies Development Program in the University of Hawaii — 'Thinking through Diversity: Bridging Cultural Differences in Asian Traditions' — co-ordinated by Paul Lavy in July 2012.

17 Benoît Junod et al., eds, 2012, *Islamic Art and the Museum: Approaches to Art and Archaeology of the Muslim World in the Twenty-First Century* (London: Saqi Books).

18 Doris Duke Charitable Foundation, 2016, 'Building Bridges Program', *DDCF*, <http://www.ddcf.org/what-we-fund/building-bridges/>, accessed 5 April 2017.

19 Cynthia P Schneider, 2007, 'Building Cultural Bridges between the US and the Islamic World: Challenges and Possibilities', *Qatar Conferences*, <http://www.qatarconferences.org/usislamic2007/doc/building.pdf Qatar>, accessed 21 April 2017.

20 Frederick M Winship, 2004, 'Islamic Art Emerges as Cultural Bridge', *United Press Internaitonal Inc. (UPI)*, <http://www.upi.com/Islamic-art-emerges-as-cultural-bridge/11311083505680/>, accessed 21 April 2017. As an indicative sample see also: Robert McMahon, 2002, 'In Nervous Times, Islamic Art in Museums Seen as Cultural Bridge', *Radio Free Europe/Radio Liberty (RFE/RL)*, <http://www.rferl.org/a/1099888.html>, accessed 21 April 2017; John Tagliabue, 2005, 'Saudi Vows Millions for a New Wing at the Louvre', *Chicago Tribune*, 28 July, <http://articles.chicagotribune.com/2005-07-28/news/0507280188_1_islamic-art-islamic-world-cultures>, accessed 1 March 2018; and Simon Rettig, 2016, Press briefing for the exhibition *The Art of the Qur'an*, Freer and Sackler Museum, Washington DC, October 2016-February 2017, <http://www.asia.si.edu/press/2016/art-of-the-quran.asp>, accessed 21 April 2017.

21 Sam Bowker, 2015a, 'The Invisibility of Islamic Art in Australia', *The Conversation*, 28 July, <https://theconversation.com/the-invisibility-of-islamic-art-in-australia-44714>, accessed 5 May 2016.

22 Djon Mundine, quoted by Shane Wolff, 2010, 'Three Rules of Curating', *The Art Life*, 15 October, <http://theartlife.com.au/2010/three-rules-of-curatorship/>, accessed 21 April 2017.

23 Donna De Salvo and C Kuoni, eds., 2001, *Words of Wisdom: A Curator's Vade Mecum on Contemporary Art* (New York: Independent Curators International), 48.

24 Oleg Grabar, 2013, 'The Role of the Museum in the Study and Knowledge of Islamic Art', in Benoit Junod et al., eds., *Islamic Art and the Museum: Approaches to Art and Archaeology of the Muslim world in the Twenty-First Century* (London: Saqi Books), 23.

25 Oleg Grabar, 1992, *The Meditation of Ornament* (Princeton: Princeton University Press), 151.

26 For more information on Khayamiya, consult John Feeney, 1986, 'The Tentmakers of Cairo', *Saudi Aramco World* 37(6): 16-25; and Sam Bowker, 2014a, 'The Urban Fabric of Cairo: Khayamiya and the Suradeq', *International Journal of Islamic Architecture* 3(2): 475-501, reprinted in Christiane Gruber, ed., 2016, *Islamic Architecture on the Move: Motion and Modernity* (Chicago: University of Chicago Press); Sam Bowker 2014b, 'Pavilions of Splendour', *Hali* 179: 71-7; and Sam Bowker, 2015b, 'Matisse and the Khayamiya', *The Burlington Magazine* 157(1353): 843-5.

27 In 2003, two important and independent overviews were published in one year: Heba Barakat, 2003, *Beyond Boundaries* (Kuala Lumpur: Islamic Art Museum Malaysia); and Blaire Gagnon, 2003, 'Egyptian Appliques', *Uncoverings* 24 (Lincoln: American Quilt Study Group).

28 Sam Bowker, 2014c, 'The Symmetry of Khayamiya and Quilting: International Relations of the Egyptian Tentmakers', *Craft + Design Enquiry* 6: 29-60. A tentmaker exhibition was also held at the Egyptian Embassy in Canberra in October 2013 as part of the 'Windows on the World' centenary of Canberra celebration.

29 Bowker, 2014c.

30 Bowker, 2014c.

31 Quoted in Alami, 2014, 203.

32 Kim Beamish, 2015, *The Tentmakers of Cairo*, 94-minute documentary film (Cairo: Non d'script), http://www.tentmakersofcairo.com, accessed 26 October 2018.

33 Future research to investigate the links between music and Egyptian art remains to be carried out, though it is possible that Khedival tentmaker epigrams could be fragments of song lyrics from the vernacular (*baladi*) *mawaal* genre.

34 Lorenz Korn, 2012, 'Intrinsic Goals and External Influence: On Some Factors Affecting Research and Presentation of Islamic Art', in Benoit Junod et al., eds., *Islamic Art and the Museum: Approaches to Art and Archaeology of the Muslim world in the Twenty-First Century* (London: Saqi Books), 84-8.

BIBLIOGRAPHY

Abbas, Saiyed Anwer. 2010. *Incredible Lucknow: A Selection of 51 Published Articles on Lucknow's Monuments, History and Culture*. Lucknow: Saiyed Anwer Abbas.

Abdel-Kader, Ali Hassan. 2013. *The Life, Personality and Writings of Al-Junayd: A Study of a Ninth Century Mystic with an Edition and Translation of his Writings*. Selangor: Islamic Book Trust.

'Abduh, Muhammad. n.d. *Al-islam wa-l-naṣrāniyya maʿ al-ʿilm wa-l-madaniyya*. Alexandria: al-Manār.

Abdul Hadi, WM et al. 1995. 'Pengantar Tim Curator (Curators' Comment).' In *Seni Rupa Kontemporer Istiqlal: Istiqlal Contemporary Art* (12-15). Jakarta: Yayasan Festival Istiqlal.

Abou-El-Haj, Rifa'at Ali. 1992. *Formation of the Modern State: Ottoman Empire from the 16th to 18th century*. Albany: SUNY.

Aboebakar Atjeh, Haji. 1948. *Sedjarah al-Qoeran*. Jogjakarta: Kementerian Agama.

Abū'l Fazl. 2010. *Āʾīn-i Akbarī*. 3 vols. Vol. I translated by H Blochmann and edited by DC Phillott; vols. 2 and 3 translated by HS Jarrett, revised by Jadunath Sarkar. Calcutta: The Asiatic Society (1st ed., 1866-94, revised ed., 1927-49).

_______. 2000. *Akbarnāma*. Translated by H Beveridge. 3 vols. Calcutta: The Asiatic Society (1st ed. 1897-1921).

_______. 1998. 'Akbar's *Dasturu'l-'amal* (A Circular Enumerating the Duties of Officers) Addressed to the 'Ummāl and Mutasaddīs of the Empire (21 March 1594).' In Mansura Haidar, trans., *Mukātabāt-i-ʿAllāmī (Inshā'i Abu'l Fazl)* (79-88). New Delhi: Munshiram Manoharlal.

Achjadi, Judi. 2014. *The Jakarta Textile Museum*. Jakarta: Indonesian Heritage Society.

_______. 2011. *The Glory of Batik: The Danar Hadi Collection*. Jakarta: Bab Publishing House.

Adamson, Peter. 2014. *Classical Philosophy: A History of Philosophy without any Gaps*, vol. 1. Oxford: Oxford University Press.

Adıvar, Adnan. 2000. *Osmanlı Türk'lerinde İlim*. Istanbul: Remzi.

Ahmad, Raja Ali Haji. 1982. *The Precious Gift* (Tuhfat al-Nafis). Translated and edited by Virginia Matheson and Barbara Watson Andaya. Kuala Lumpur: Oxford University Press.

Akbar, Ali. 2013. *Manuskrip Al-Qur'an di Pulau Penyengat*. Jakarta: Lajnah Pentashihan Mushaf Al-Qur'an.

Akın, Günkut. 1995. 'The Muezzin Mahfili and Pool of the Selimiye Mosque in Edirne.' *Muqarnas* 12: 63-83. https://doi.org/10.2307/1523224.

Akkach, Samer. 2017. *Marṣad Istanbul: hadm al-raṣd wa raṣd al-hadm. Taṭawwr thaqāfat al-ʿulūm fī al-Islām baʿd Copernicus*. Doha: Arab Centre for Research and Policy Studies.

_______. 2015. 'Beautiful Names of God.' *The Encyclopaedia of Islam Three* (54-7). Leiden: Brill.

_______. 2005. *Cosmology and Architecture in Premodern Islam: An Architectural Reading of Mystical Ideas*. Albany: SUNY.

Aksan, Virginia H and Daniel Goffman. 2007. 'Introduction: Situating the Early Modern Ottoman World.' In Virginia Aksan and Daniel Goffman, eds., *The Early Modern Ottomans: Remapping The Empire* (1-12). Cambridge: Cambridge University Press.

Alam, Muzaffar. 2004. *The Languages of Political Islam, India 1200-1800*. Chicago: University of Chicago Press.

_______. 2000. 'Akhlaqi Norms and Mughal Governance.' In Muzzafar Alam et al., eds., *The Making of Indo-Persian Culture — Indian and French Studies* (67-95). New Delhi: Manohar Publishers.

Alami, Mohammed Hambouni. 2015. *The Origins of Visual Culture in the Islamic World: Aesthetics, Art, Architecture and Early Islam*. London: IB Tauris.

_______. 2014. *Art and Architecture in the Islamic Tradition: Aesthetics, Politics and Desire in Early Islam*. London: IB Tauris.

Alemi, Mahvash. 2007. 'Princely Safavid Gardens: Stage for Rituals of Imperial Display and Political Legitimacy.' In Michael Conan, ed., *Middle East Garden Traditions: Unity and Diversity* (113-37). Washington: Dumbarton Oaks.

Ali Haji, Raja. 1982. *The Precious Gift (Tuhfat al-Nafis) An Annotated Translation by V Matheson and BW Andaya*. Kuala Lumpur: Oxford University Press.

Ali, Salim. 1968. 'Dodo.' In MA Alvi and A Rahman, *Jahangir — the Naturalist* (15-17). New Delhi: Indian National Science Academy.

_______. 1927. 'The Moghul Emperors of India as Naturalists and Sportsmen.' *Journal of the Bombay Natural History Society*. Part I 31(4): 833-61; Part II 32(1): 34-63; Part III 32(2): 264-73.

Alvi, MA. 1999. 'Jahangir's Passion for Exotic Animals.' In Som Prakash Verma, ed., *Flora and Fauna in Mughal Art* (83-93). Mumbai: Marg Publications.

Alvi, MA and A Rahman. 1968. *Jahangir — the Naturalist*. New Delhi: Indian National Science Academy.

_______. 1940. *Fathulllah Shirazi, a Sixteenth Century Indian Scientist*. Delhi: National Institute of Sciences of India.

Andrews, Walter. 1985. *Poetry's Voice, Society's Song: Ottoman Lyric Poetry*. Seattle: University of Washington Press.

Andrews, Walter, Nejaat Black and Mehmet Kalpaklı. 2006. *Ottoman Lyric Poetry: An Anthology*. Seattle: University of Washington Press.

Andrews, Walter G and Irene Markoff. 1987. 'Poetry, the Arts, and Group Ethos in the Ideology of the Ottoman Empire.' *Edebiyat* 1(1): 28-70.

Anooshahr, Ali. 2009. *The Ghazi Sultans and the Frontiers of Islam: A Comparative Study of the Late Medieval and Modern Periods*. London: Routledge.

Ansari, SM Razaullah. 2016a. 'Astronomy in Medieval India.' In Helaine Selin, ed., *Encyclopaedia of the History of Science, Technology, and Medicine in Non-Western Cultures* (716-26). Dordrecht: Springer. https://doi.org/10.1007/978-94-007-7747-7_10114.

_______. 2016b. 'Raja Ratan Singh.' In Helaine Selin, ed., *Encyclopaedia of the History of Science, Technology, and Medicine in Non-Western Cultures* (3690-4). Dordrecht: Springer.

_______. 2014. 'Transmission of the Modern Exact Science to the Muslim World.' In Ibrahim Kalin, ed., *The Oxford Encyclopedia of Philosophy, Science, and Technology in Islam*, vol. 1 (376-85). Oxford: Oxford University Press.

_______. 2011. 'Early Modern Observatories in India, 1792-1900.' In Debi Prasad Chattopadhyaya, ed., *History of Science, Philosophy and Culture in Indian Civilization* (349-80). New Delhi: Pearson Education.

_______. 2005. 'Hindu's Scientific Contributions in Indo Persian.' *Indian Journal of History of Science* 40(2): 205-21.

_______. 1985. 'The Observatories Movement in India during the 17th to 18th Centuries.' *Vistas in Astronomy* 28: 379-85. https://doi.org/10.1016/0083-6656(85)90054-6.

_______. 1978. 'The Establishment of Observatories and the Socio-Economic Conditions of Scientific Work in Nineteenth Century India.' *Indian Journal of History of Science* 13(1): 62-71.

_______. 1976. 'The Early Development of Western Astronomy in India.' *Vistas in Astronomy* 20: 195. https://doi.org/10.1016/0083-6656(76)90033-7.

Anṭūn, Faraḥ. 1903. *Ibn Rush wa falsafatuhu*. Alexandria: al-Jāmiʿa.

Aristotle. 2009. *Politics*. Translated by E Barker. Oxford: Oxford University Press.

Arnaldez, R. 2012. 'Hayʾa.' In P Bearman et al., eds. *Encyclopaedia of Islam, Second Edition*. Available at: <http://dx.doi.org.proxy.library.adelaide.edu.au/10.1163/1573-3912_islam_SIM_2823>. Accessed 6 March 2017.

Arnold, David. 2000. *Science, Technology and Medicine in Colonial India*. Cambridge, Mass.: Cambridge University Press. https://doi.org/10.1017/CHOL9780521563192.

Atasoy, Nurhan and Lâle Uluç. 2012. *Impressions of Ottoman Culture in Europe: 1453-1699*. Istanbul: Armaggan Publications.

Avicenna. 2005. *The Metaphysics of The Healing (Al-Shifāʾ): A Parallel English-Arabic text*. Translated by M Marmura. Utah: Brigham Young University Press.

Azra, Azyumardi. 2004. *The Origins of Islamic Reformism in Southeast Asia: Networks of Malay-Indonesian and Middle Eastern Ulama in the Seventeenth and Eighteenth Centuries*. Crows Nest, NSW: Asian Studies Association of Australia.

al-Baba, Kamil. 1992. *Dinamika Kaligrafi Islam* (The Dynamics of Islamic Calligraphy). Translated by Didin Sirojuddin AR. Jakarta: Darul Ulum Press.

Babaie, Sussan. 2008. *Isfahan and its Palaces: Statecraft, Shiʿism and the Early Architecture of Conviviality in Early Modern Iran*. Edinburgh: Edinburgh University Press.

Bābur, Zahiru'd-din Muhammad Pādshah Ghāzī. 1990. *Bābur-Nāma, The Memoirs of Babur*. Translated by Annette Susannah Beveridge. New Delhi: Munshiram Manoharlal (1st ed. 1921).

Bacon, Roger. 1996. *Perspectiva*. Translated and edited by C David Lindberg. Oxford: Clarendon Press.

_______. 1983. *De Speculis Comburentibus* (Philosophy of Nature). Translated and edited by C David Lindberg. New York: Oxford University Press.

Bacqué-Grammont, Jean-Louis. 1997. 'La description de Chypre dans le Cihān-nümā de Kātib Çelebi.' *Epetērida tou Kentrou Epistēmonikon Erevnōn* 23: 189-214.

_______. 1996. 'Les routes d'Asie centrale d'après le Cihān-Numā de Kātib Çelebi.' *Cahier d'Asie Centrale* 1(2): 311-22.

Baer, Marc David. 2008. *Honored by the Glory of Islam: Conversion and Conquest in Ottoman Europe*. Oxford: Oxford University Press. https://doi.org/10.1093/acprof:oso/9780195331752.001.0001.

Bağcı, Serpil. 2000. 'From Translated Word to Translated Image: The Illustrated *Şehname-i Turki* Copies.' *Muqarnas* 17: 162-76.

Bağci, Serpil et al. 2006. *Osmanlı Resim Sanatı*. Istanbul: TC Kültür ve Turizm Bakanlığı Yayınları.

Barakat, Heba. 2003. *Beyond Boundaries*. Kuala Lumpur: Islamic Art Museum Malaysia.

Barkey, Karen. 1994. *Bandits and Bureaucrats: The Ottoman Route to State Centralisation*. New York: Cornell University Press.

Barnes, Ruth. 2006. 'Indian Textiles for Island Taste: The Trade to Eastern Indonesia.' In Rosemary Crill, ed., *Textiles from India: The Global Trade* (99-116). Oxford: Seagull Books.

_______. 1997. 'Indian Block-Printed Textiles in Egypt: The Newberry Collection in the Ashmolean Museum, Oxford; Catalogue: Blue and White Textiles.' *Jameel Online Centre*. Available at: <jameelcentre.ashmolean.org/collection/7/10236/ 10323>. Accessed 18 November 2014.

Barnes, Ruth and Mary Hunt Kahlenberg, eds. 2010. *Five Centuries of Indonesian Textiles*. Munich: Delmonico Books Prestel.

Barry, Michael. 2004. *Figurative Art in Medieval Islam*. Paris: Flammarion.

Bartsch, Katharine and Elise Kamleh. 2014. 'Karbala in Lucknow: An Itinerary of Architectural Mobility.' *International Journal of Islamic Architecture* 3(2): 267-302. https://doi.org/10.1386/ijia.3.2.267_1.

Bayly, A. 1994. 'Colonial Star Wars: The Politics of the Heavens in India c. 1780-1880.' Unpublished manuscript. Cited in Matthew Edney, *Mapping an Empire: The Geographical Construction of British India, 1765-1843* (316-17). Chicago: University of Chicago Press.

_______. 1989. *Imperial Meridian: The British Empire and the World, 1780-1830*. London: Longman.

Bayrak, Tosun. 2000. *The Name and the Named*. Kentucky: Fons Vitae.

Beach, Milo Cleveland and Ebba Koch. 1997. *King of the World: The Padshahnama, An Imperial Mughal Manuscript from the Royal Library, Windsor Castle*. London: Azimuth Editions.

Beamish, Kim. 2015. *The Tentmakers of Cairo*. 94-minute documentary film. Cairo: Non d'script. Available at: <http://www.tentmakersofcairo.com>. Accessed 25 October 2018.

Behrens-Abouseif, Doris. 1999. *Beauty in Arabic Culture*. Princeton: Marcus Wiener Publishers.

Belcher, Michael. 1992. 'Communicating through Museum Exhibitions.' In M Thompson, ed., *Manual of Curatorship: A Guide to Museum Practice*. 2nd ed. Oxford: Butterworth Heinemann, 649-59.

Belting, Hans. 2011. *Florence and Baghdad: Renaissance Art and Arab Science*. Cambridge, Mass.: Harvard University Press.

Bennett, Clinton. 2005. *Muslims and Modernity*. London: Continuum.

Bennett, James, ed. 2013. *Realms of Wonder: Jain, Hindu and Islamic Art of India*. Adelaide: Art Gallery of South Australia.

_______. 2011. *Beneath the Winds: Masterpieces of Southeast Asian Art from the Art Gallery of South Australia*. Adelaide: Art Gallery of South Australia.

_______. 2010. 'Islamic Art in Southeast Asia.' In Jan Van Alphen, ed., *A Passage to Asia* (149-68). Brussels: Bozar, Centre for Fine Arts.

_______. 2005. *Crescent Moon: Islamic Art and Civilization of Southeast Asia*. Adelaide: Art Gallery of South Australia.

Bennett, James and Russell Kelty, eds. 2015. *Treasure Ships: Art in the Age of Spices*. Adelaide: Art Gallery of South Australia.

Berlian, Ilham. 2011. 'Peran Lembaga Kaligrafi al-Qur'an (LEMKA) dalam dakwa melalui seni Kaligrafi Islam' (The role of the Institute of Qur'anic Kaligrafi [LEMKA] in spreading Islam through Islamic Calligraphy). Unpublished Honours thesis, Universitas Islam Negeri Syarif Hidayatullah, Jakarta.

Bernier, Francois. 1983. *Travels in the Mogul Empire AD 1656-1668*. Translated by Archibald Constable. New Delhi: Oriental Books (1st ed. 1934).
Bhatt, Ravi. 2006. *The Life and Times of the Nawabs of Lucknow*. New Delhi: Rupa and Co.
Birūnī, al-. 1879. *The Chronology of Ancient Nations (Athārul Bākiya)*. Translated by CE Sachau. Pall Mall: William H Allen and Co.
Blair, Sheila. 2006. *Islamic Calligraphy*. Edinburgh: Edinburgh University Press.
_______. 1993. 'The Ilkhanid Palace.' *Ars Orientalis* 23: 239-48.
Boow, Justine. 1988. *Symbol and Status in Javanese Batik*. Perth: Asian Studies Centre, University of Western Australia.
Boullata, Issa J. 1990. *Trends and Issues in Contemporary Arab Thought*. Albany: SUNY.
Bowker, Sam. 2015a. 'The Invisibility of Islamic Art in Australia.' *The Conversation*, 28 July. Available at: <https://theconversation.com/the-invisibility-of-islamic-art-in-australia-44714>. Accessed 5 May 2016.
_______. 2015b. 'Matisse and the Khayamiya.' *The Burlington Magazine* 157(1353): 843-5.
_______. 2014a. 'The Urban Fabric of Cairo: Khayamiya and the Suradeq.' *International Journal of Islamic Architecture* 3(2): 475-501. Reprinted in Christiane Gruber, ed., 2016. *Islamic Architecture on the Move: Motion and Modernity*. Chicago: University of Chicago Press.
_______. 2014b. 'Pavilions of Splendour.' *Hali* 179: 71-7.
_______. 2014c. 'The Symmetry of Khayamiya and Quilting: International Relations of the Egyptian Tentmakers.' *Craft + Design Enquiry* 6: 29-60.
Braginsky, Vladimir. 2004. *The Heritage of Traditional Malay Literature: A Historical Survey of Genres, Writings and Literary Views*. Leiden: KITLV Press.
Brandon, James R. 1970. *On Thrones of Gold: Three Javanese Shadow Plays*. Cambridge, Mass.: Harvard University Press. https://doi.org/10.4159/harvard.9780674734043.
Brown, Malcolm. 2001. 'A "Complimentary Mission" from Nawab Nasir-Ud-Din Haider to King William IV.' *Asian Affairs* 32(3): 279-86. https://doi.org/10.1080/714041447.
Bruinessen, Martin van. 1990. 'Kitab Kuning: Books in Arabic Script Used in the Pesantren Milieu.' *Bijdragen tot de Taal-, Land- en Volkenkunde* 146: 226-69. https://doi.org/10.1163/22134379-90003218.
Bucaille, Maurice. 1978. *The Bible, The Quran and Science*. Paris: Sehers.
Çaliş-Kural, B Deniz. 2014. *Şehrengiz, Urban Rituals and Deviant Sufi Mysticism in Ottoman Istanbul*. Surrey: Ashgate.
Carboni, Stefano. 2015. *The Wonders of Creation and the Singularities of Painting: A Study of the Ilkhanid London Qazvini*. Edinburgh: Edinburgh University Press.
Carpenter, Bruce W. 2009. *Javanese Antique Furniture and Folk Art: The David B Smith and James Tirtoprodjo Collections*. Singapore: Editions Didier Millet.
Castles, Lance. 1966. 'Notes on the Islamic School at Gontor.' *Indonesia* 1: 30-45. https://doi.org/10.2307/3350783.
Çelebi, Evliya. 1999. *Evliya Çelebi Seyahatnamesi*, vol. 3. Edited by SA Kahraman and Y Dağli. Istanbul: Yapi ve Kredi Bankasi.
Çelebi, Kātip. 2013. *Kitāb-ı Cihannüma* (Displaying the World). Edited by Fuat Sezgin. Istanbul: Boyut Yayınları.
_______. 2010. *Sullam al-Wuṣūl ilā Ṭabaqāt al-Fuḥūl*. Edited by Ekmeleddin Ehsanoğlu. Istanbul: Research Centre for Islamic History, Art and Culture.
_______. 2007. *Mizānü'l-Hakk fi İhtiyari'l-Ehakk*. Translated by Orhan Şaik Gökyay and Süleyman Uludağ. Istanbul: Kabalci.
_______. 1835. *Kashf al-ẓunūn 'an asāmī al-kutub wa-l-funūn*, vol. 1. Beirut: Dār Ṣadir, rep. London: Bentley ed.
Chambert-Loir, Henri. 2002. 'Saints and Ancestors: The Cult of Muslim Saints in Java.' In Henri Chambert-Loir et al., eds., *The Potent Dead: Ancestors, Saints and Heroes in Contemporary Indonesia* (132-40). Honolulu: University of Hawai'i Press.
_______. 1996. 'Keeping the Faith: A Qur'an School Library.' In Ann Kumar and John H McGlynn, eds., *Illuminations: The Writing Traditions of Indonesia* (38-9). Jakarta: The Lontar Foundation.
Chambert-Loir, Henri and Anthony Reid. 2002. *The Potent Dead: Ancestors, Saints and Heroes in Contemporary Indonesia*. Honolulu: University of Hawai'i Press.
Chittick, William. 2014. 'Ibn Arabi.' In Edward N Zalta, ed., *The Stanford Encyclopaedia of Philosophy*. Available at: <https://plato.stanford.edu/archives/spr2014/entries/ibn-arabi/>. Accessed 2 March 2017.

Christie, Jan Wisseman. 1993. 'Ikat to Batik? Epigraphic Data on Textiles in Java from the Ninth to the Fifteenth Centuries.' In Marie-Louise Nabholz-Karaschoff et al., eds., *Weaving Patterns of Life: Indonesian Textile Symposium 1991* (11-29). Basel: Museum of Ethnography.

Clark, Marshall. 2013. 'Cultural Politics: Batik and Wayang in Indonesia and Malaysia.' *The Asian Arts Society of Australia Review* 22(2): 13-15.

Cole, Juan. 1989. *Roots of North Indian Shi'ism in Iran and Iraq: Religion and State in Awadh, 1722-1859*. Berkeley: University of California Press.

Converse, Emma, trans. 1875. 'The English Observatories.' *Popular Science Monthly* 6: 530-41.

Corbin, Henry. 2013. *Temple and Contemplation*. London: Routledge.

______. 1994. *The Man of Light in Iranian Sufism*. Translated by N Pearson. New York: Omega Publications.

Correia-Afonso, John. 1980. *Letters from the Mughal Court, The First Jesuit Mission to Akbar (1580-1583)*. Anand: Gujarat Sahitya Prakash.

Crill, Rosemary, ed. 2015. *The Fabric of India*. London: V&A Publishing.

______. 2006. *Textiles from India: The Global Trade*. Calcutta: Seagull Books.

Dabashi, Hamid. 2001. 'Khwajah Nasir al-Din al Tusī.' In Seyyed Hossein Nasr et al., eds., *History of Islamic Philosophy* (527-84). London: Routledge.

Dale, Stephen Frederic. 2010. *The Muslim Empires of the Ottomans, Safavids and Mughals*. Cambridge: Cambridge University Press.

______. 2004. *The Garden of the Eight Paradises: Babur and the Culture of Empire in Central Asia, Afghanistan and India, 1483-1530*. Leiden: Brill.

Damisch, Hubert. 2016. *Noah's Ark: Essays on Architecture*. Translated by J Rose. Cambridge, Mass.: MIT Press.

D'Ancona, Cristina. 2016. 'Greek Sources in Arabic and Islamic Philosophy.' In Edward N Zalta (ed.), *The Stanford Encyclopedia of Philosophy*. Available at: <https://plato.stanford.edu/archives/spr2016/entries/arabic-islamic-greek/>. Accessed 2 March 2017.

Darrigol, Olivier. 2012. *A History of Optics from Greek Antiquity to the Nineteenth Century*. Oxford: Oxford University Press.

Davidson, Herbert. 1992. *Al-Fārābī, Avicenna and Averroes on Intellect: Their Cosmologies, Theories of Active Intellect, and Theories of Human Intellect*. New York: Oxford University Press.

Dawani, Jalal al-Din Muhammad Asad. 1895. *(Akhlaq-i Jalali) The Akhlak-i-Jalaly, Practical Philosophy of the Muhammadan People*. Translated by WF Thompson. Lahore: Caxton Printing Works.

De Botton, Alain. 2006. *The Architecture of Happiness*. London: Penguin Books.

Degroot, Véronique. 2012. 'Temples and landscapes in South Central Java.' In Alexandra Haendel, ed., *Old Myths and New Approaches: Interpreting Ancient Religious Sites in Southeast Asia* (121-33). Clayton: Monash University Publishing.

Deleuze, Gilles. 1995. *Negotiations*. New York: Columbia University Press.

______. 1995. 'Postscript on the Societies of Control.' In Giles Deleuze, *Negotiations*. New York: Columbia University Press.

Deleuze, Gilles and Felix Guattari. 2005. *Anti Oedipus*. India: Viva Books Private Limited.

Denny, Walter B. 2004. *The Artistry of Ottoman Ceramics*. London: Thames and Hudson.

Derin, Süleyman. 2012. 'Earthly and Spiritual Love in Sufism: Ibn 'Arabi and the Poetry of Rumi.' In Susan Scollay, ed., *Love and Devotion: From Persia and Beyond* (55-70). Melbourne: Macmillan Art Publishing.

De Salvo, Donna and C Kuoni, eds. 2001. *Words of Wisdom: A Curator's Vade Mecum on Contemporary Art*. New York: Independent Curators International.

Descartes, René. 1664. *L'Homme, et un Traitté de la Formation du Foetus*. Edited by Claude Clerselier. Paris: Charles Angot.

Dewangga, Kusuma. 2013. 'Behind Batik's *Truntum* Motif.' *TNOL Asia*. Available at: <http://www.tnol.asia/arts-culture/19374-behind-batiks-truntum-motif.html>. Accessed 25 June 2016.

Dhaky, Madhusudan Amilai. 2005. *The Indian Temple Traceries*. Gurgaon: American Institute of Indian Studies Centre for Art and Archaeology.

Di Castro, Angelo Andrea. 2012. 'Graves, Trees and Powerful Spirits as Archaeological Indicators of Sacred Spaces.' In A Haendel, ed., *Old Myths and New Approaches: Interpreting Ancient Religious Sites in Southeast Asia* (237-51). Clayton: Monash University Press.

Diner, Dan. 2009. *Lost in the Sacred: Why the Muslim World Stood Still.* Translated by Steven Rendall. Princeton: Princeton University Press.
Diskalker, DB. 1937. 'Foundation of an Observatory at Lucknow.' *Journal of the United Provinces Historical Society* 10(1): 10-11.
Divyabhanusinh. 1999. 'Hunting in Mughal Painting.' In Som Prakash Verma, ed., *Flora and Fauna in Mughal Art* (94-108). Mumbai: Marg Publications.
Doris Duke Charitable Foundation. 2016. 'Building Bridges Program.' *DDCF.* Available at: <http://www.ddcf.org/what-we-fund/building-bridges/>. Accessed 5 April 2017.
Douglass, Bruce. 1980. 'The Common Good and the Public Interest.' *Political Theory* 8(1): 103-17. https://doi.org/10.1177/009059178000800108.
Draper, John William. 1875. *History of the Conflict between Religion and Science.* New York: D. Appleton and Company.
Edney, Mathew. 1997. *Mapping an Empire: The Geographical Construction of British India, 1765-1843.* Chicago: University of Chicago Press. https://doi.org/10.7208/chicago/9780226184869.001.0001.
Edwards, Eiluned. 2016. *Imprints of Culture: Block Printed Textiles of India.* New Delhi: Niyogi Books.
Eldem, Sedad H. 1977. *Sa'dabad.* Istanbul: Milli Eğitim Basımevi.
_______. 1969. *Köşkler ve Kasırlar.* Istanbul: Devlet Güzel Sanatlar Akademisi Yüksek Mimarlık Bölümü Rölöve Kürsüsü, Kutulmuş Matbaası.
El Rashidi, Seif. 2012. 'Museums of Islamic Art and Public Engagement.' In Benoît Junod et al., eds., *Islamic Art and the Museum: Approaches to Art and Archaeology of the Muslim World in the Twenty-First Century* (209-14). London: Saqi.
El-Rouayheb, Khaled. 2015. *Islamic Intellectual History in the Seventeenth Century: Scholarly Currents in the Ottoman Empire and the Maghreb.* Cambridge: Cambridge University Press. https://doi.org/10.1017/CBO9781107337657.
_______. 2008. 'The Myth of "The Triumph of Fanaticism" in the Seventeenth-Century Ottoman Empire.' *Die Welt des Islams* 48(2): 196-221. https://doi.org/10.1163/157006008X335930.
Elshakry, Marwa S. 2008. 'Knowledge in Motion: The Cultural Politics of Modern Science Translations in Arabic.' *Isis* 99(4): 701-30. https://doi.org/10.1086/595767.
Erimtan, Can. 2008. *Ottomans Looking West? The Origins of the Tulip Age and its Development in Modern Turkey.* London: IB Tauris.
_______. 2007. 'The Perception of Saadabad: The "Tulip Age" and Ottoman Safavid Rivalry.' In Dana Sajdi, ed., *Ottoman Tulips, Ottoman Coffee: Leisure and Lifestyle in the Eighteenth Century* (41-62). London: Tauris Academic Studies.
_______. 1999. 'The Case of Saadabad: Westernization or Revivalism.' In *Proceedings of the 10th International Congress of Turkish Art* (287-90). Geneva: Fondation Max Van Berchem.
Esposito, John L. 1984. *Islam and Politics.* Syracuse: Syracuse University Press.
Evyapan, Gonül. 1999. *Old Turkish Gardens.* Ankara: Middle Eastern Technical University.
Fārābī, al-. 1998. *On the Perfect State* (Ārā' ahl al-Madīna al Fāḍila). Translated by R Walzer. Chicago: Kazi Publications.
Fārisī, Kamāl al-Dīn al-. 2009. *Kitāb al-baṣā'ir fī 'ilm al-manāẓir.* Edited by Muṣṭafā Mawālidī. Kuwait: Mu'assasat al-Kuwait li-l-Taqaddum al-'Ilmī.
_______. 1929. 'Kitāb tinqīḥ al-manāẓir li-zawī al-abṣār wa al-baṣā'ir'. Ḥaydar Ābād al-Dakan: Dā'irat al-Ma'ārif al-'Uthmāniyya
_______. n.d. 'Kitāb Tanqīḥ al-Manāẓir'. Istanbul: Topkapi Palace Museum, Ahmed III Library, MS 3340.
Fealy, Greg and Sally White, eds. 2008. *Expressing Islam: Religious Life and Politics in Indonesia.* Singapore: Institute of Southeast Asian Studies.
Fealy, Greg and Virginia Hooker, eds. 2006. *Voices of Islam in Southeast Asia: A Contemporary Sourcebook.* Singapore: Institute of Southeast Asian Studies.
Feeney, John. 1986. 'The Tentmakers of Cairo.' *Saudi Aramco World* 37(6): 16-25.
Fergusson, James. 1899. *History of Indian and Eastern Architecture.* London: John Murray. Originally published 1876.
Ferngren, Gary, ed. 2002. *Science and Religion: A Historical Introduction.* Baltimore: Johns Hopkins University Press).

Fikrī, Abdullah. 1876. *Risala fī muqārant ba'ḍ mabāhith al-hay'a bi-l-wārid fī al-nuṣūs al-shar'iyya.* Cairo: Maṭba'at al-Madāris al-Malakiyya.

Finkel, Caroline. 2005. *Osman's Dream.* London: John Murray.

Fisher, Michael. 1987. *A Clash of Cultures: Awadh, the British and the Mughals.* Riverdale, Md: Riverdale Company.

Fleischer, Cornell. 1983. 'Royal Authority, Dynastic Cyclism and "Ibn Khaldunism" in Sixteenth-Century Ottoman Letters.' *Journal of Asian and African Studies* 18: 198-220. https://doi.org/10.1177/002190968301800306.

Fodor, Pal. 1986. 'State and Society, Crisis and Reform in Fifteenth and Seventeenth Century Ottoman Mirrors for Princes.' *Acta Orientalia Academiae Scientarium Hungaricae* 40: 217-40.

Forge, Anthony. 1989. 'Batik Patterns in the Early Nineteenth Century.' In M. Gittinger, ed., *To Speak with Cloth* (91-106). Los Angeles: Museum of Cultural History.

Fox, James J. 1997. 'Sunan Kalijaga and the Rise of Mataram.' In PG Ridell et al., eds., *Islam: Essays on Scripture, Thought and Society* (187-218). Leiden: Brill.

Furlow, Christopher A. 1996. 'The Islamization of Knowledge: Philosophy, legitimation, and politics.' *Social Epistemology* 10(3/4): 259-71. https://doi.org/10.1080/02691729608578818.

Gade, Anna M. 2004. *Perfection Makes Practice: Learning, Emotion, and the Recited Qur'an in Indonesia.* Honolulu: University of Hawai'i Press.

Gagnon, Blaire. 2003. 'Egyptian Appliques.' *Uncoverings* 24 (131-62). Lincoln: American Quilt Study Group.

Gallop, Annabel Teh. 2015. 'A Jawi Sourcebook for the Study of Malay Palaeography and Orthography.' *Indonesia and the Malay World* 43(125): 13-171. https://doi.org/10.1080/13639811.2015.1008253.

Gallop, Annabel Teh and Ali Akbar. 2006. 'The Art of the Qur'an in Banten: Calligraphy and Illumination.' *Archipel* 72: 57-194. https://doi.org/10.3406/arch.2006.4028.

Geertz, Clifford. 1960. *The Religion of Java.* Chicago: The University of Chicago Press.

George, Kenneth M. 2010. *Picturing Islam: Art and Ethics in a Muslim Lifeworld.* London: Wiley-Blackwell. https://doi.org/10.1002/9781444318265.

Gharipour, Mohammad. 2013. *Persian Gardens and Pavilions: Reflections in History, Poetry and the Arts.* London: IB Taurus.

Ghazālī, al-. 2010. *Kitāb Sharh 'Ajā'ib al-Qalb* (The Marvels of the Heart). Translated by Walter James Skellie. Louisville: Vons Vitae.

_______. 1998. *The Niche of Lights* (Mishkāt al Anwār). Translated by D Buchman. Utah: Brigham Young University Press.

_______.1992, 1995. *The Ninety-Nine Beautiful Names of God, al-Maqsad al-asnā fi sharh asmā' Allāh al-husnā.* Translated with notes by David B Burrell and Nazih Daher. Cambridge: The Islamic Texts Society.

_______. 1980. *Deliverance from Error* (al-Munqidh min al Dalāl). Translated by RJ McCarthy. Kentucky: Fons Vitae.

_______. 1964. *Naṣīḥat al-Muluk of al-Ghazālī* (Counsel for Kings). Translated by FRC Bagley and edited by Huma'i Jalal. London: Oxford University Press.

Gibb, HAR and JH Kramers, eds. 1991. *Shorter Encyclopaedia of Islam.* Leiden: Brill.

Gökbilgin, Tayyib. 1993. 'Edirne Hakkinda Yazilmiş Tarihler ve *Enis-ül Müsamirin.*' In *Edirne'nin 600 Fetih Yildnumu Armağan Kitabi* (77-118). Ankara: Türk Tarih Kurumu Basımevi.

Goodwin, Godfrey. 1997. *The Janissaries.* London: Saqi Books.

_______. 1971. *A History of Ottoman Architecture.* London: Thames and Hudson.

Grabar, Oleg. 2013. 'The Role of the Museum in the Study and Knowledge of Islamic Art.' In Benoit Junod et al., eds., *Islamic Art and the Museum: Approaches to Art and Archaeology of the Muslim world in the Twenty-First Century* (17-27). London: Saqi Books.

_______. 1992. *The Meditation of Ornament.* Princeton: Princeton University Press.

Grosseteste, Robert. 1982. *Hexaëmeron.* Edited by Richard C Dales and Servus Gieben. London: Published for the British Academy by Oxford University Press.

_______. 1942. *On Light* (De Luce). Translated by Clare C Riedl. Milwaukee: Marquette University Press.

Grube, Ernst J. 1987. 'The Date of the Venice *Iskander-nama.*' *Islamic Art* 2: 187-95.

Guessoum, Nidhal. 2015. *Islam's Quantum Question.* London: IB Tauris.

Gunn, JAW. 1969. *Politics and the Public Interest in the Seventeenth Century*. London: Routledge & K Paul.

Guy, John. 1998. *Woven Cargoes: Indian Textiles in the East*. London: Thames and Hudson.

Habermas, Jurgen. 1989. *The Structural Transformation of the Public Sphere*. Translated by Thomas Burger. Cambridge, Mass.: The MIT Press.

Habib, Irfan. 1997. 'Akbar and Technology.' In Irfan Habib, ed., *Akbar and his India* (129-48). New Delhi: Oxford University Press.

_______. 1996. 'Reason and Science in Medieval India.' In JN Jha, ed., *Society and Ideology in India, Essays in Honour of Professor RS Sharma* (163-74). New Delhi: Munshiram Manoharlal Publishers.

_______. 1980. 'The Technology and Economy of Mughal India.' *Indian Economic and Social History Review* 17(1): 1-34. https://doi.org/10.1177/001946468001700101.

Hagen, Gottfried. 2007. 'Kātip Çelebi: Mustafa b. Abdullāh, Hācı Halīfe (b.1609; d. 1657).' *Historians of the Ottoman Empire*. Available at: <https://ottomanhistorians.uchicago.edu/en/historian/katib-celebi>. Accessed 25 January 2017.

_______. 2004. 'Afterword: Ottoman Understandings of the World in the Seventeenth Century.' In Robert Dankoff, ed., *An Ottoman Mentality: The World of Evliya Çelebi* (215-56). Leiden: Brill.

Hagen, Gottfried and Ethan L Menchinger. 2014. 'Ottoman Historical Thought.' In Prasenjit Duara et al., eds., *A Companion to Global Historical Thought* (92-106). New Jersey: John Wiley & Sons, Ltd. https://doi.org/10.1002/9781118525395.ch6.

Haleem, MAS Abdel. 2004. *The Quran: A New Translation*. Oxford: Oxford University Press.

Hallaq, Wael B. 1998. *A History of Islamic Legal Theories*. United Kingdom: Cambridge University Press.

Hamadeh, Shirine. 2008. *The City's Pleasures: Istanbul in the Eighteenth Century*. Seattle: University of Washington Press.

_______. 2004. 'Ottoman Expressions of Early Modernity and the "Inevitable" Question of Westernization.' *Journal of the Society of Architectural Historians* 63(1): 32-51. https://doi.org/10.2307/4127991.

Ḥamawī, Salīm Ilyās al-. 1875. *al-Barāhīn al-qaṭ'iyya 'alā 'adam dawarān al-kurā al-arḍiyya*. Alexandria: Maṭba'at al-Kawkab al-Sharqī.

Hammer, Joseph von. 1812. *Rumeli und Bosna Geographisch Beschrieben von Mustafa Ben Abdalla Hadschi Chalfa*. Vienna: Kunst- und Industrie-Comptoirs.

Hardjonogoro, KRT. 1980. 'The Place of Batik in the History and Philosophy of Javanese Textiles: A Personal View.' In Mattiebelle Gittinger, ed., *Indonesian Textiles: Irene Emery Roundtable on Museum Textiles 1979 Proceedings* (232-42). Washington: The Textile Museum.

Hardt, Michael. 1998. 'The Global Society of Control.' *Discourse* 20(3, Fall): 139-52.

Hardt, Michael and Antonio Negri. 2000. *Empire*. Cambridge M.A: Harvard University Press.

Harkness, Peter. 2003. *The Rose: An Illustrated History*. London: The Royal Horticultural Society.

Harrison, Peter. 2015. *The Territories of Science and Religion*. Chicago: Chicago University Press. https://doi.org/10.7208/chicago/9780226184517.001.0001.

_______. 2007. *The Fall of Man and the Foundations of Science*. Cambridge: Cambridge University Press. https://doi.org/10.1017/CBO9780511487750.

Harrison, Peter, ed. 2010. *The Cambridge Companion to Science and Religion*. Cambridge: Cambridge University Press. https://doi.org/10.1017/CCOL9780521885386.

Held, Virginia. 1970. *The Public Interest and Individual Interests*. New York: Basic Books.

Heringa, Rens. 1996. 'The Historical Background of Batik in Java.' In Rens Heringa and Harmen C Veldhuisen, eds., *Fabric of Enchantment: Batik from the North Coast of Java from the Inger McCabe Elliot Collection at the Los Angeles County Museum of Art* (31-8). Los Angeles: Los Angeles Country Museum of Art.

Holmgren, Robert J and Anita E Spertus. 1991. 'Is *geringsing* Really Balinese?' In Gisela Völger and Karin v. Weck, eds., *Indonesian Textiles: Symposium 1985* (59-80). Cologne: Ethnologica.

Hooker, Virginia. 2011. 'Lines of Meaning: Three Calligraphic Paintings by Didin Sirojuddin.' *Suhuf: Jurnal Kajian Al-Qur'an dan Kebudayaan* 4(2): 315-39.

Hourani, Albert. 2013. *Arabic Thought in the Liberal Age*. Cambridge, UK: Cambridge University Press.

Huff, Toby E. 2011. *Intellectual Curiosity and the Scientific Revolution: A Global Perspective*. Cambridge, NY: Cambridge University Press.

———. 2003. *The Rise of Early Modern Science: Islam, China and the West.* 2nd ed. Cambridge, UK: Cambridge University Press.

Huygens, Christiaan. 1728. *Opera Reliqua.* Amsterdam: Apud Janssonio-Waesbergios.

———. 1920. *Traité de la Lumiere.* Paris: Gauthier-Villars et cie.

Ibn al-Haytham. 1083. *Kitab al-Manazir.* Istanbul: Topkapi Palace Museum, MS Fatih 3212.

Ibn 'Arabī. 1911. *al-Futûhât.* Cairo edition, 3: 276-7.

Ibn Kathīr. 2014. *From the Beginning to the End* (al-Bidāyah wa al Nihāyah): *The Story of Creation, Ummahs of the Past, The Life of Muhammad up to 9 AH*, vol. 1. Translated by RA Rahman. Karachi: Darul Ishaat.

Ihsanoğlu, Ekmeleddin. 1992. 'Introduction of Western Science to the Ottoman World: A Case Study of Modern Astronomy (1660-1860).' In Ekmeleddin Ihsanoğlu. ed., *The Transfer of Modern Science and Technology to the Muslim World: Proceedings of the International Symposium on 'Modern Science and the Muslim World'* (67-120). Istanbul: Research Centre for Islamic History, Art, and Culture.

Inalcık, Halil. 2004. 'Periods in Ottoman History: State, Society and Economy.' In Halil İnalcık and Günsel Renda, eds., *Ottoman Civilization*, vol. 1 (230-5). Istanbul: Republic of Turkey, Ministry of Culture and Tourism.

———. 1973. *The Ottoman Empire: The Classical Age 1300-1600.* Translated by Norman Itzkowitz and Colin Imber. London: Weidenfeld and Nicholson.

Institute of Qur'anic Kaligrafi. 2011. 'Dinamika Perkembangan Seni Kaligrafi' (The Development of Indonesian Calligraphy). *LEMKA.* Available at: <http://lemkaonline.blogspot.com/>. Accessed 22 May 2013.

Irama, Rhoma. 2011. 'Music as a Medium for Communication, Unity, Education and *dakwah*.' In Andrew N Weintraub, ed., *Islam and Popular Culture in Indonesia and Malaysia.* London: Routledge, 235-56.

Isa, Shaykh 'Abd Al-Qadir. 2009. *Realities of Sufism.* Translated by SA Aziz. Netherlands: Sunni Publications.

Islamic Arts Museum of Malaysia. 2012. *Ann Dunham's Legacy: A Collection of Indonesian Batik.* Kuala Lumpur: Islamic Arts Museum of Malaysia.

Itzkowitz, Norman. 1972. *The Ottoman Empire and Islamic Tradition.* New York: Alfred A Knopf.

Jafri, Saiyid Zaheer Husain. 2016. *Awadh: From Mughal to Colonial Rule. Studies in the Anatomy of a Transformation.* New Delhi: Gyan.

Jahāngīr. 1999. *Jahāngīrnāma, Memoirs of Jahangir, Emperor of India.* Translated by Wheeler Thackston. New York: Oxford University Press.

———. 2003. *Tūzuk-i Jahāngīrī, The Memoirs of Jahāngīr.* Translated by Alexander Rogers and edited by Henry Beveridge. 2 vols. New Delhi: Munshiram Manoharlal (1st ed. 1909).

Jamison, Andrew. 1994. 'Western Science in Perspective and the Search for Alternatives.' In Jean-Jacques Salomon et al., eds., *The Uncertain Quest: Science, Technology and Development* (131-67). Tokyo: United Nations Press.

Jasanoff, Maya. 2005. *Edge of Empire: Lives, Culture and Conquest in the East, 1750-1850.* New York: Knopf.

Jasper, JE and Mas Pirngadie. 1916. *De Inlandsche Kunstnijverheid in Nederlandsch Indië III: De batikunst.* Netherlands: Van Regeeringswege Gedrukt en Uitgegevan Te 'S-Gravenhage Door De Broek & Kunstdrukkerij, Mouton & Co.

Jessup, Helen Ibbitson. 1990. *Court Arts of Indonesia.* New York: The Asia Society Galleries in Association with Harry N Abrams, Inc.

Johns, AH. 2016. '*Surat al-Mu'minun*: A Reading and Reflection.' *Journal of Qur'anic Studies* 18(3): 70-90. https://doi.org/10.3366/jqs.2016.0250.

Jones, Justin. 2012. *Shi'a Islam in Colonial India: Religion, Community and Sectarianism.* Cambridge, UK: Cambridge University Press.

Junod, Benoît et al., eds. *Islamic Art and the Museum: Approaches to Art and Archaeology of the Muslim World in the Twenty-First Century.* London: Saqi Books.

Kafescioğlu, Çiğdem. 2009. *Constantinopolis/Istanbul: Cultural Encounter, Imperial Vision and the Construction of the Ottoman Capital.* University Park, PA: The Pennsylvania State University Press.

Karamustafa, Ahmet T. 1992. 'Cosmographical Diagrams.' In JB Harley and David Woodward, eds., *The History of Cartography*, vol. 2 (71-89). Chicago: The University of Chicago Press.

Kamali, Mohammad Hashim. 1988. 'Have We Neglected the Shariah Law Doctrine of Maslaha?' *Islamic Studies* 27: 287-304.

Kanda, KC. 2005. *Masterpieces of Patriotic Urdu Poetry: Text, Translation, and Transliteration*. New Delhi: Sterling.

Kennedy, Edward S. 1998. *Astronomy and Astrology in the Medieval Islamic World*. Brookfield, Vt.: Ashgate.

Kepler, Johannes. 1604. *Astronomiae Pars Optica*. Francofurti: Apud Claudium Marnium & Haeredes Joannis Aubrii.

Kerlogue, Fiona. 2004. *The Book of Batik: Featuring Selections from the Rudolf G. Smend Collection*. Singapore: Archipelago Press.

_______. 1997. 'Batik Cloths from Jambi, Sumatra.' Unpublished PhD thesis, University of Hull.

Khan, Iqbal Ghani. 1997. 'Scientific Concepts in Abu'l Fazl's *Ain-i Akbari*.' In Irfan Habib, ed., *Akbar and his India* (121-8). New Delhi: Oxford University Press.

Khan, Iqtidar Alam. 2009. 'Tracing Sources of Principles of Mughal Governance: A Critique of Recent Historiography.' *Social Scientist* 37(5-6): 45-54.

Khawaji, S. 'ʿIlm.' In Bernard Lewis et al., eds., 1986, *Encyclopedia of Islam*, vol. 3 (1133-4). Leiden: Brill.

Khemir, Sabiha. 2014. *Nūr: Light in Art and Science from the Islamic World*. Seville: Focus-Abenoga Foundation.

King, David A. 2012a. *Islamic Astronomy and Geography*. Aldershot: Routledge.

_______. 2012b. 'Taḳī al-Dīn.' In P Bearman et al., eds., *Encyclopaedia of Islam, Second Edition*. Available at: <http://dx.doi.org.proxy.library.adelaide.edu.au/10.1163/1573-3912_islam_SIM_7337>. Accessed 9 March 2017.

Knighton, William. 1921. *The Private Life of an Eastern King*. London: Humphrey Milford Oxford University Press.

Knut, Vikør S. 2005. *Between God and Sultan: A History of Islamic Law*. Oxford: Oxford University Press.

Koch, Ebba. 2009. 'Jahangir as Francis Bacon's Ideal of the King as an Observer and Investigator of Nature.' *Journal of the Royal Asiatic Society of Great Britain and Ireland* 19(3): 293-338. https://doi.org/10.1017/S1356186309009699.

Kochhar, RK. 1991. 'The Growth of Modern Astronomy in India, 1651-1960.' *Vistas in Astronomy* 34: 69-105. https://doi.org/10.1016/0083-6656(91)90021-J.

Korn, Lorenz. 2012. 'Intrinsic Goals and External Influence: On Some Factors Affecting Research and Presentation of Islamic Art.' In Benoit Junod et al., eds., *Islamic Art and the Museum: Approaches to Art and Archaeology of the Muslim world in the Twenty-First Century* (84-9). London: Saqi Books.

'K. Ratu Kencana.' 2015. *Geni*. Available at: <www.geni.com/people/K-Ratu-Kencana/6000000014559561542>. Accessed 15 February 2018.

Kuban, Doğan. 2011. *Sinan's Art and Selimiye*. Istanbul: Türkiye Iş Bankası Kültür Yayınları.

_______. 2010. *Ottoman Architecture*. Translated by Adair Mill. Woodbridge, Suffolk: Antique Collectors' Club.

Kuşpinar, Bilal. 1996. *Ismail Ankravi on the Illuminative Philosophy: His Izhu'l Hikem: Its Edition and Analysis in Comparison with Dawwānī's Shawakil al-Hur, Together with the Translation of Suhrawardī's Hayākil al-Nūr*. Kuala Lumpur: ISTAC.

Laarhovan, Ruurdje. 1994. 'The Power of Cloth: The Textile Trade of the Dutch East India Company (VOC) 1600-1780.' Unpublished PhD thesis, Australian National University.

Lahōri, Abdul Hamid. 2010. *Lahōri's Pādshāhnāmah (1592-1638)*. Translated by Hamid Afaq Siddiqi. Delhi: Idarah-i Adabiyat-i Delli.

Laios, Konstantinos, Marilita M Moschos and Androutsos George. 2016. 'Ocular Anatomy in Medieval Arabic Medicine: A Review.' *Italian Journal of Anatomy and Embryology* 121(1): 105-11.

Lavy, Paul. 2012. 'Art as Cultural Bridge.' Seminar presented at *Thinking through Diversity: Bridging Cultural Differences in Asian Traditions*, East-West Center, Honolulu, Hawaii, July 12-19.

Leach, Neil, ed. 1997. *Rethinking Architecture: A Reader in Cultural Theory*. London: Routledge.

Lewis, Geoffrey. 1957. *The Balance of Truth*. London: Allen and Unwin.

Lindberg, David and Ronald Numbers. 1986. *God and Nature: Historical Essays on the Encounter between Christianity and Science*. California: University of California Press.

Livingston, John. 1996. 'Western Science and Educational Reform in the Thought of Shaykh Rifa al-Tahtawi.' *International Journal of Middle East Studies* 28(4): 543-64. https://doi.org/10.1017/S0020743800063820.

Llewellyn-Jones, Rosie. 2014. *The Last King in India: Wajid Ali Shah*. London: Hurst.

_______. 1985. *A Fatal Friendship: The Nawabs, The British, and the City of Lucknow*. Delhi: Oxford University Press.

Llewellyn-Jones, Rosie, ed. 2006. *Lucknow, City of Illusion*. Munich: Prestel.

McMahon, Robert. 2002. 'In Nervous Times, Islamic Art in Museums seen as Cultural Bridge.' *Radio Free Europe/ Radio Liberty (RFE/RL)*. Available at: <http://www.rferl.org/a/1099888.html>. Accessed 21 April 2017.

Mahmoud, Samir. 2011. 'Color and the Mystics: Light, Beauty, and the Spiritual Quest.' In Jonathan Bloom and Sheila Blair, eds., *'And Diverse Are Their Hues': Color in Islamic Art and Culture* (99-119). New Haven: Yale University Press.

Malik, ibn Anas (Imam). 1989. *Al-Muwatta of Imam Malik ibn Anas: The First Formulation of Islamic Law*. Translated by Aisha Abdurrahman Bewley. Granada: Madinah Press of Granada.

Manucci, Niccolao. 1907. *Storia do Mogor or Mogul India 1653-1708*. Translated by William Irvine. London: John Murray.

Marcotte, Roxanne. 2005. 'Reason (*ʿaql*) and Direct Intuition (*Mushāhada*) in the Works of Shihāb al-Dīn al-Suhrawardī (d. 587/1191).' In T Lawson, ed., *Reason and Inspiration in Islam: Theology. Philosophy and Mysticism in Muslim Thought* (221-47). London: IB Tauris with The Institute of Ismaili Studies.

Markel, Stephen and Tushara Bindu Gude, eds. 2010. *India's Fabled City: The Art of Courtly Lucknow*. Los Angeles: Los Angeles County Museum of Art.

Masud, Muhammad Khalid. 1977. *Islamic Legal Philosophy: A Study of Abu Ishaq al-Shatibi's Life and Thoughts*. Isamabad: Islamic Research Institute.

Maxwell, Robyn. 2003a. *Sari to Sarong*. Canberra: National Gallery of Australia.

_______. 2003b. *Textiles of Southeast Asia: Tradition, Trade and Transformation*. Hong Kong: Periplus Editions.

Maybudī, Rashīd al-Dīn. 2015. *The Unveiling of the Mysteries and the Provisions of the Pious* (Kashf al Asrār wa ʿUddat al-Abrār). Translated by William Chittick. Kentucky: Fons Vitae.

Maẓhar, Ismāʿīl. 2014. *Bayn al-ʿilm wa-l-dīn: ṭārīhk al-ṣirāʿ baynahuma fī al-qurūn al-wusṭā*. (Translation of AD White, 1897). Cairo: Hindāwī.

Maẓhar, Ismāʿīl, ed. 1928. *Al-ʿUṣūr* 4: 125-6.

Meisami, Julie Scott. 2001. 'Palaces and Paradises: Palace Description in Medieval Persian Poetry.' In Oleg Grabar and Cynthia Robinson, eds., *Islamic Art and Literature* (21-54). Princeton: Markus Weiner Publishers.

Mengenal Pesantren Kaligrafi Alquran (LEMKA). 2002. *Mengenal Pesantren Kaligrafi Al-Quran LEMKA Sukabumi, Jawa Barat: Mengaji dan Berekreasi di Kampus Seniman Muslim* (Introducing Pesantran Kaligrafi Al-Quran LEMKA, Sukabumi, West Java: Studying and Being Creative at the Muslim Artists' Campus). Java: LEMKA Department of Information and Publicity.

Mestyan, Adam. 2011. 'Arabic Lexicography and European Aesthetics: The Origin of *Fann*.' *Muqarnas* 28(1): 69-100. https://doi.org/10.1163/22118993-90000174.

Meyerhof, M. 1928. *The Book of the Ten Treatises on the Eye, Ascribed to Hunain ibn Ishaq (809-877 AD). The Earliest Existing Systematic Text-book of Ophthalmology*. Cairo: Government Press.

Mihailovic, Konstantin. 1975. *Memoirs of a Janissary*. Translated by Benjamin Stolz. Ann Arbor: University of Michigan.

Miksic, John. 2012. 'Life Among the Ruins: Habitation sites of Trowulan.' In Alexandra Haendel, ed., *Old Myths and New Approaches: Interpreting Ancient Religious Sites in Southeast Asia* (121-33). Clayton: Monash University Publishing.

Millie, Julian. 2008. '"Spiritual Meal" or Ongoing Project? The Dilemma of *Dakwah* Oratory.' In Greg Fealy and Sally White, eds., *Expressing Islam: Religious Life and Politics in Indonesia* (80-94). Singapore: Institute of Southeast Asian Studies.

Mohiuddin, Momin. 1971. *The Chancellery and Persian Epistolography under the Mughals: From Babur to Shahjahan, 1526-1658: A Study on Inshá, Dar al-Insha, and Munshis Based on Original Documents*. Calcutta: Iran Society.

Mohsan, Fání. 1843. *Dabistan, or School of Manners*. Translated by David Shea and Antony Troyer. Paris: Oriental Translation Fund of Great Britain and Ireland.

Monserrate, Fr. 1922. *The Commentary of Father Monserrate on the Journey to the Court of Akbar*. Translated by JS Hoyland and annotated by SN Banerjee. London: Oxford University Press.

Morewedge, Parviz. 2004. 'Knowledge.' In Richard C Martin, ed., *Encyclopedia of Islam and the Muslim World*, vol. 1 (397-402). New York: Macmillan Reference USA.

Murphey, Rhoads. 2008. *Exploring Ottoman Sovereignty: Tradition, Image and Practice in the Ottoman Imperial Household, 1400-1800*. London: Continuum Books.

Al-Muqtaṭaf. 1877a. 'Al-'ulūm al-ṭabī'iyya.' 1(8): 169-71.

_______. 1877b. 'Correspondence from Archimandrite Gabriel Jbāra.' 1(8): 171-4.

_______. 1877c. 'Al-'ulūm al-ṭabī'iyya wa-l-'ulūm al-shar'iyya.' 1(10): 217-20.

Mustopo, Moehamad Habib. 2001. *Kebudayaan Islam di Jawa Timur: Kajian Beberapa Unsur Budaya Masa Peralihan*. Yogyakarta: Penerbit Jendela.

Na'īmā, Mustafa. 1967. *Tārīḫ-i Na'īmā* (Naima Tarihi). Edited by Zuhuri Danisman. Istanbul: Zuhuri Danisman Yayinevi.

Nalbantoğlu, Gülsüm. 1988. 'The Birth of an Aesthetic Discourse in Ottoman Architecture.' *Journal of Fine Arts (METU)* 8(2): 115-22.

Nasr, Seyyed Hossein. 2010. 'Islam and The Problem of Modern Science.' *Islam and Science* 8, 1: 63-75.

_______. 2006. *Islamic Philosophy from its Origin to the Present: Philosophy on the Land of Prophecy.* New York: SUNY.

_______. 1998. *A Young Muslim's Guide to the Modern World*. Lahore Pakistan: Suhail Academy.

_______. 1994. *Ideals and Realities of Islam*. London: The Aquarian Press.

_______. 1993. *An Introduction to Islamic Cosmological Doctrines: Conceptions of Nature and Methods Used for its Study by the Ikhwān al-Ṣafā', Al-Bīrūnī, and Ibn Sīnā*. New York: SUNY.

_______. 1990. *Traditional Islam in the Modern World*. London: Kegan Paul International.

_______. 1976. *Islamic Science: An Illustrated Study*. England: World of Islam Festival Publishing Company Limited.

_______. 1964. *Three Muslim Sages: Avicenna, Suhrawardī, Ibn 'Arabi*. Cambridge, Mass.: Harvard University Press.

Nasr, Seyyed Hossein and Amin Mehdi Razavi, eds. 1996. *The Islamic Intellectual Tradition in Persia*. London: Curzon.

Nasr, Seyyed Hossein et al., eds. 2015. *The Study Qur'ān: A New Translation and Commentary*. New York: Harper Collins.

Nasution, Harun H et al., eds. 2002. *Ensiklopedia Islam Indonesia*. 2nd ed. Jakarta: Djambatan.

Nawawī, al-. 2014. *The Book of Remembrances* (Kitāb al-Adhkār). Translated by MI Waley. London: Turath.

Necipoğlu, Gülru. 1995. *The Topkapi Scroll: Geometry and Ornament in Islamic Architecture: Topkapi Palace Museum Library MS H.1956/Gülru Necipoğlu; with an Essay on the Geometry of the Muqarnas by Mohammad al-Asad*. Santa Monica, CA: Centre for the History of Art and Architecture.

_______. 1991. *Architecture, Ceremonial and Power: The Topkapı Palace in the Fifteenth and Sixteenth Centuries.* Cambridge, Mass.: MIT Press.

_______. 1990. 'Review of Ca'fer Efendi, *Risāle-i Mi'māriyye, An Early Seventeenth-Century Ottoman Treatise on Architecture.*' *Journal of the Society of Architectural Historians* 49(2): 210-13. https://doi.org/10.2307/990479.

_______. 1986. 'Plans and Models in Fifteenth and Sixteenth Century Architectural Practice.' *Journal of the Society of Architectural Historians* 45(3): 224-43. https://doi.org/10.2307/990160.

Newton, Isaac. 1721. *Opticks: Or, a Treatise on the Reflections, Refractions, Inflection and Colours of Light*. 3rd ed. London: printed for William and John Innys at the West End of St. Paul's.

Nizami, Khaliq Ahmad. 1989. *Akbar and Religion.* New Delhi: Idarah-i-Adabiyat-i-Delli.

Norberg, M. 1818. *Gihan Numah. Geographia orientalis ex Turcico in Latinum versa*. Göteborg: Londini Gothorum, literis Berlingianis.

O'Hanlon, Rosalind. 2007. 'Kingdom, Household and Body History: Gender and Imperial Service under Akbar.' *Modern Asian Studies* 41(5): 889-923. https://doi.org/10.1017/S0026749X06002654.

Ôhashi, Yukio. 2008. 'Introduction of Persian Astronomy into India.' *Tarikh-e 'Elm: Iranian Journal for the History of Science* 6: 49-74.

_______. 1997. 'Early History of the Astrolabe in India.' *Indian Journal of History of Science* 32(3): 199-295.

Oldenburg, VT. 1989. *The Making of Colonial Lucknow, 1856-1877*. Delhi: Oxford University Press.

O'Malley, Charles and John Saunders. 1950. *The Illustrations from the Works of Andreas Vesalius of Brussels: With Annotations and Translations, a Discussion of the Plates and their Background, Authorship and Influence, and a Biographical Sketch of Vesalius*. Cleveland: World Publishing.

Osman, Rifat. 1957. *Edirne Sarayı*. Ankara: Türk Tarih Kurumu Basımevi.

Osmanlica Turkce Sozluk. 2017. 'Celebi.' *Osmanlica Turkce Sozluk.* Available at: <http://www.osmanlicaturkce.com/?k=çelebi&t=%40>. Accessed 23 January 2017.

Öz, Tahsin. 1993. 'Edirne Yeni Sarayında Kazı ve Araştırmalar.' In *Edirne: Edirne'nin 600. Fethi Yıldönümü Armağan Kitabi* (217-22). Ankara: Türk Tarih Kurumu Basımevi.

Peckham, John. 1970. *Perspectiva communis*. Translated by David C Lindberg. Madison: University of Wisconsin Press.

Peirce, Leslie. 2004. 'Changing Perceptions of the Ottoman Empire: The Early Centuries.' *Mediterranean Historical Review* 49(1): 6-28.

———. 1993. *The Imperial Harem: Women and Sovereignty in the Ottoman Empire*. Oxford: Oxford University Press.

Pelikan, Jaroslav. 1985. *Jesus Through the Centuries: His Place in the History of Culture*. New York: Harper and Row.

Pemble, John. 1977. *The Raj, the Indian Mutiny and the Kingdom of Oudh, 1801-1859*. Hassocks: The Harvester Press.

Perry, Charles. 1743. *A View of the Levant: In Four Parts*. London: T Woodward.

Pesantren Kaligrafi Alquran Lemka. 2011. *'Aksi-aksi Shoting di Pesantren Kaligrafi Alquran Lemka part 2'* (Filming at Pesantren Kaligrafi Alquran Lemka Part 2). *LEMKA*. Available at: <https://www.youtube.com/watch?v=QQdz6vEuoJI>. Accessed 14 July 2016.

Phillips, Amanda. 2012. 'The Historiography of Ottoman Velvets, 2011-1572: Scholars, Craftsmen, Consumers.' *Journal of Art Historiography* 6: 1-26.

Pingree, David. 2012. *"Ilm al-Hay'a."* In P Bearman et al., eds., *Encyclopaedia of Islam, Second Edition*. Available at: <http://dx.doi.org/10.1163/1573-3912_islam_COM_0365>. Accessed 31 March 2017.

———. 2002. 'Philippe de La Hire at the Court of Jayashimha.' In SM Razaullah Ansari, ed., *History of Oriental Astronomy* (123-31). Netherlands: Springer.

Plato. 2003. *The Republic*. Translated by D Lee. London: Penguin Books.

———. 1977. *Timaeus and Critias*. Translated by D Lee. London: Penguin Books.

Pollock, Sheldon. 2011. 'The Languages of Science in Early Modern India.' In Sheldon Pollock, ed., *Forms of Knowledge in Early Modern Asia, Explorations in the Intellectual History of India and Tibet 1500-1800* (19-48). Durham: Duke University Press. https://doi.org/10.1215/9780822393580-002.

Pormann, PE and Emilie Savage-Smith, eds. 2007. *Medieval Islamic Medicine*. Washington: Georgetown University Press.

Princep, James, ed. 1833. 'VIII. Progress of European Science. Practical Astronomy.' *The Journal of the Asiatic Society of Bengal* 2: 48-56.

Qandahāri, Muhammad Ārif. 1993. *Tārikh-i Akbarī*. Translated by Tasneem Ahmad. New Delhi: Pragati Publications.

Qushayrī, Abu 'l-Qāsim al-. 2007. *Al-Qushayrī's Epistle on Sufism* (Al Risāla al-Qushayriyya fī *'ilm* al-taṣawwuf). Translated by AD Knysh. Reading: Garnet.

Raby, Julian. 1980. '"El Gran Turco": Mehmed the Conqueror as a Patron of the Arts of Christendom.' Unpublished PhD thesis, University of Oxford.

Raby, Julian and Zeren Tanındı. 1993. *Turkish Bookbinding in the Fifteenth Century: The Foundation of an Ottoman Court Style*. Edited by Tim Stanley. London: Azimuth Editions.

Raffles, Thomas Stanford. 1988. *The History of Java*. Singapore: Oxford University Press.

Rahman, A et al. 1982. *Science and Technology in Medieval India — A Bibliography of Source Materials in Sanskrit, Arabic and Persian*. New Delhi: Indian National Science Academy.

Rahman, Fazlur. 1979. *Islam*. 2nd ed. Chicago: University of Chicago Press.

Rajah, Nirajan. 2001. 'Insyirah Al-Sadr: The Art of Sulaiman Esa' in Petronas Gallery.' In *Insyirah: Lukisan Sulaiman Esa dari 1980 hingga 2000* (31-43). Kuala Lumpur: Petronas Gallery.

Rasmussen, Anne K. 2010. *Women, the Recited Qur'an, and Islamic Music in Indonesia*. Berkeley: University of California Press. https://doi.org/10.1525/california/9780520255487.001.0001.

Razavi, Mehdi Amin. 1997. *Suhrawardī and the School of Illumination*. London: Curzon.

Redford, Scott. 2003. 'Thirteenth-Century Rum Seljuq Palaces and Palace Imagery.' *Ars Orientalis* 23: 210-36.

Rettig, Simon. 2016. Press briefing for the exhibition *The Art of the Qur'an*, Freer and Sackler Museum, Washington DC, October 2016-February 2017. Available at: <http://www.asia.si.edu/press/2016/art-of-the-quran.asp>. Accessed 21 April 2017.

Ricklefs, MC. 2012. *Islamisation and Its Opponents in Java: A Political, Social, Cultural and Religious History, c. 1930 to the Present*. Singapore: NUS Press.

———. 2007. *Polarising Javanese Society: Islamic and Other Visions (c. 1830-1930)*. Singapore: NUS Press.

_______. 2001. *A History of Modern Indonesia since c.1200*. Stanford: Stanford University Press

_______. 2006. *Mystic Synthesis in Java: A History of Islamization from the Fourteenth to Early Nineteenth Centuries*. Norwalk: EastBridge Press.

_______. 1998. *The Seen and Unseen Worlds in Java, 1726-1749: History, Literature and Islam in the Court of Pakubuwana II*. St Leonards, NSW: Allen & Unwin.

Riddell, Peter. 2003. *Islam and the Malay-Indonesian World: Transmission and Response*. Singapore: Horizon Books.

Risner, Friedrich. 1572. *Opticae Thesaurus: Alhazeni Arabis Libri Septem Nunc Primum Editi, Eiusdem Liber De Crepusculis Et Nubium Asensionibus*. Item Vitellonis Thuringopoloni Libri X.

Rosenthal, Franz. 2007. *Knowledge Triumphant: The Concept of Knowledge in Medieval Islam*. Leiden: Brill, rev. ed.

_______. 1970. *Knowledge Triumphant: The Concept of Knowledge in Medieval Islam*. Leiden: Brill.

Rosyad, Rifki. 2006. *A Quest for True Islam: A Study of the Islamic Resurgence Movement among the Youth in Bandung, Indonesia*. The Australian National University: ANU Press.

Ruggles, D Fairchild. 2008. *Islamic Gardens and Landscapes*. Philadelphia: University of Pennsylvania Press. https://doi.org/10.9783/9780812207286.

Rupii, nwww. 2015. 'Batik Truntum Motif Kupu-Kupu karya Go Tik Swan.' *Rupipitruntum Blog*. Available at: <http://rupipitruntum.blogspot.com.au/>. Accessed 9 May 2017.

Sabra, Abdelhamid I. 2012. 'Manāẓir, or 'Ilm al-Manāẓir.' In P Bearman et al., eds., *Encyclopaedia of Islam, Second Edition. Available at:* <http://dx.doi.org.proxy.library.adelaide.edu.au/10.1163/1573-3912_islam_SIM_4911>. Accessed 9 March 2017.

_______. 2007. 'The "Commentary" that Saved the Text: The Hazardous Journey of Ibn al-Haytham's Arabic Optics.' *Early Science and Medicine* 12(2): 117-33. https://doi.org/10.1163/157338207X194668.

_______. 2002. *The Optics of Ibn al-Haytham. Edition of the Arabic Text of Books IV-V: On Reflection and Images Seen by Reflection*. Kuwait: The National Council for Culture, Arts and Letters.

_______. 1989. *The Optics of Ibn al-Haytham. Books I-II-III: On Direct Vision*. London: The Warburg Institute.

Şakir-Taş, Aziz Nazmi. 2009. *Adrianopol'den Edirne'ye: Edirne ve Civarında Osmanlı Kültür ve Bilim Muhitinin Oluşumu (XIV-XVI. Yüzyıl)*. Istanbul: Boğaziçi Üniversitesi Yayınevi.

Saliba, George. 1995. *A History of Islamic Astronomy: Planetary Theories During the Golden Age of Islam*. New York: NYU Press.

Santosa, Revianto Budi and Bambang Tri Atmojo. 2007. *Kota Gede: Life Between Walls*. Jakarta: Penerbit PT Gramedia Pustaka Utama.

Sardar, Ziauddin. 2006. *How Do You Know?* London: Pluto Press.

_______. 1989. *Explorations in Islamic Science*. London: Mansel.

Sarton, George. 1947. *Introduction to the History of Science: Science and Learning in the Fourteenth Century*. Baltimore: Williams and Wilkins.

Savage-Smith, Emilie. 2007. 'Anatomical Illustration in Arabic manuscripts.' In Anna Contadini, ed., *Arab Painting: Text and Image in Illustrated Arabic Manuscripts* (147-60). Leiden: Brill. https://doi.org/10.1163/9789004236615_013.

_______. 1995. 'Attitudes Towards Dissection in Medieval Islam.' *Journal for the History of Medicine and Allied Sciences* 50(1): 67-110. https://doi.org/10.1093/jhmas/50.1.67.

Schimmel, Annemarie. 1992. *A Two-Colored Brocade: The Imagery of Persian Poetry*. Chapel Hill: University of North Carolina Press.

Schneider, Cynthia P. 2007. 'Building Cultural Bridges between the US and the Islamic World: Challenges and Possibilities.' *Qatar Conferences*. Available at: <http://www.qatar conferences.org/usislamic2007/doc/building.pdf>. Accessed 21 April 2017.

Scollay, Susan. 2012a. 'An Introduction to Persian Poetry and its Milieu.' In Susan Scollay, ed., *Love and Devotion: From Persia and Beyond* (1-19). Melbourne: Macmillan Art Publishing.

_______. 2012b. 'An Ottoman Garden of Love: The Oxford *Dilsuznama*, the "Book of Compassion".' In Susan Scollay, ed., *Love and Devotion: From Persia and Beyond* (119-33). Melbourne: Macmillan Art Publishing.

Scriver, Peter and Vikram Prakash, eds. 2007. *Colonial Modernities: Building Dwelling and Architecture in British India and Ceylon*. London: Routledge.

Selin, Helaine, ed. 2000. *Astronomy across Cultures: The History of Non-Western Astronomy*. Dordrecht: Springer. https://doi.org/10.1007/978-94-011-4179-6.

Sen, Joydeep. 2016. *Astronomy in India, 1784-1876*. Abingdon: Routledge.

Şen, Tunç. 2017. 'Practicing Astral Magic in Sixteenth-Century Ottoman Istanbul: A Treatise on Talismans Attributed to Ibn Kemāl (d. 1534).' *Magic, Ritual, and Witchcraft* 12(1): 66-88. https://doi.org/10.1353/mrw.2017.0005.

Serdaroğlu, Vildan. 2006. 'When Literature and Architecture Meet: Architectural Images of the Beloved and the Lover in Sixteenth-Century Ottoman Poetry.' *Muqarnas* 23: 273-87. https://doi.org/10.1163/22118993-90000103.

Shah-Nawaz Khan, Nawab Samsam al-Dawla and Abdul Hayy. 1979. *Ma'athir-ul-Umara*. Translated by H Beveridge and Baini Prashad. 2 vols. Patna: Janaki Prakashan (1st ed. 1911).

Sharar, Abdul Halim. 1975. *Lucknow: The Last Phase of an Oriental Culture*. Translated and edited by ES Harcourt and Fakhir Hussain. London: Paul Elek.

Sharma, Sunil. 2011. '"If there is a Paradise on Earth, it is Here": Urban Ethnography in Indo-Persian Poetic and Historic Texts.' In Sheldon Pollock, ed., *Forms of Knowledge in Early Modern Asia, Explorations in the Intellectual History of India and Tibet 1500-1800* (240-56). Durham: Duke University Press. https://doi.org/10.1215/9780822393580-010.

Shields, Christopher. 2007. *Aristotle*. London: Routledge.

Shīrāzī, Mullā Ṣadrā. 2004. *On the Hermeneutics of the Light Verse of the Qur'an* (Tafsīr Āyat al-Nūr). Translated by LP Peerwani. London: ICAS Press.

Sims, Eleanor. 2012. '"Bahram Gur Visits the Lady from Khwarazm in the Blue Pavilion on Wednesday" and Other Similar Representations from Illustrated Manuscripts by Nizami, Hatifi and Mir 'Ali Shir in the Bodleian Library.' In Susan Scollay, ed., *Love and Devotion: From Persia and Beyond* (49-53). Melbourne: Macmillan Art Publishing.

Singh, Surya Narain. 2003. *The Kingdom of Awadh: Its History, Polity and Administration*. New Delhi: Mittal.

Sirojuddin AR, Didin. 2012. *331 Goresan Hitam Putih Kaligrafi Islam: 'Melukis Hidup dengan Amal Saleh'* (331 Black and White Islamic Calligraphies: 'Paint Life with Good Deeds'). Jakarta: LEMKA.

———. 2007. *Koleksi Karya Master Kaligrafi Islam* (Collected Works by Master Islamic Calligraphers). Jakarta: Darul Ulum Press.

———. 2005. *Nuansa Kaligrafi Islam: Kumpulan tulisan sekitar ide-ide pengembangan seni kaligrafi Islam di Indonesia* (Islamic Calligraphy: Collected Writings about the Development of Islamic Calligraphy in Indonesia). Jakarta: Studio Lemka.

———. 2001. 'Seni Menulis Khat dan Metode Pembinaannya Secara Intensif' (The Art of Writing Calligraphy and an Intensive Method for its Teaching). Speech to workshop for Calligraphy Judges in West Kalimantan, Indonesia.

———. 1997. *Khat Naskhi untuk Kebutuhan Primer Baca Tulis* (Naskh Script for Basic Reading and Writing). IAIN Syarif Hidayatullah Jakarta Selatan: Lembaga Kaligrafi AlQuran.

———. 1987. *Seni Kaligrafi Islam*. Jakarta: Multi Kreasi.

Sloterdijk, Peter. 2009. 'Talking to Myself about the Poetics of Space.' *Harvard Design Magazine*. Available at: <http://www.harvarddesignmagazine.org/issues/30/talking-to-myself-about-the-poetics-of-space>. Accessed 23 April 2017.

Smith, Mark A. 2001. *Alhacen's Theory of Visual Perception: A Critical Edition, with English Translation and Commentary, of the First Three Books of Alhacen's* De aspectibus, *the Medieval Latin Version of Ibn al-Haytham's* Kitāb al-Manāẓir. Philadelphia: American Philosophical Society.

Sobti, Manu P and Mohammad Gharipour. 2011. 'The Hues of Paradise: Examining Colour Design Layout in the Persian Garden.' In Jonathon Bloom and Sheila Blair, eds., *'And Diverse Are Their Hues': Color in Islamic Art and Culture* (304-25). New Haven: Yale University Press.

Somogyi, Joseph. 1950. 'Ad-Damiri's Hayat al-hayawan: An Arabic Zoological Lexicon.' *Osiris* 9: 33-43. https://doi.org/10.1086/368522.

Steinmann, A. 1947. 'Batik Designs.' *CIBA Review* 58: 2114.

Stierlin, Henri et al. 2012. *Persian Art and Architecture*. New York: Thames and Hudson.

Stevenson, Angus, ed. 2010. *Oxford English Dictionary*. 3rd ed. Oxford: Oxford University Press.
Storey, CA. 1977. *Persian Literature, A Bio-Bibliographical Survey.* Leiden: The Royal Asiatic Society of Great Britain and Ireland.
Suhrawardī, al-. 1999. *The Philosophy of Illumination* (Ḥikmat al-Ishrāq). Translated by J Walbridge and H Ziai. Utah: Brigham Young University Press.
_______. 1982. *The Mystical and Visionary Treatises of Shihabuddin Yahya Suhrawardī.* Translated by WM Thackston. London: Octagon Press.
_______. 1935. *Three Treatises of Mysticism*. Translated and edited by Otto Spies and SK Khattak. Stuttgart: W. Kohlhammer.
Supomo, S. 1997. 'From Sakti to Shahadah: The Quest for New Meanings in a Changing World Order.' In PG Ridell et al., eds., *Islam: Essays on Scripture, Thought and Society* (219-36). Leiden: Brill.
Suyanto, AN. 2002. *Sejarah Batik Yogyakarta.* Yogyakarta: Rumah Penerbitan Merapi.
Tabrizi, Badi' al-Din Manuchihr al-Tajiri al-. Dated AH 860/1455-56 CE, Edirne. 'Dilsuznāma.' Oxford: Bodleian Library, MS Ouseley 133.
Tagliabue, John. 2005. 'Saudi Vows Millions for a New Wing at the Louvre.' *Chicago Tribune*, 28 July. Available at: <http://articles.chicagotribune.com/2005-07-28/news/0507280188_1_islamic-art-islamic-world-cultures>. Accessed 1 March 2018.
Tahānawī, Muhammad A'lā al-. 1996. *Kashshāf al-iṣṭilāḥāt al-'ulūm wa-l-funūn.* Beirut: Maktabat Lubnān Nāshirūn.
Al-Ṭahṭāwī, Rifā'a. 2003. *Ṭakhlīṣ al-Ibrīz fī talkhīṣ bārīz*. Beirut: Dār al-Anwār.
Tandan, Banmali. 2008. *The Architecture of Lucknow and Oudh, 1722-1856: Its Evolution in an Aesthetic and Social Context.* Cambridge: Zophorus.
_______. 2001. *The Architecture of Lucknow and its Dependencies, 1722-1856: A Descriptive Inventory and an Analysis of Nawabi Types*. New Delhi: Vikas.
Taqī al-Dīn. n.d. 'Nūr hadaqat al-ibsār wa-nawr hadīqat al-anẓār.' Cairo: Dār al-Kutub al-Miṣriyya, 'Ulūm Riyāḍiyya MS 893.
Ṭāshkubrīzāda (Ahmad bin Mustafa). 2002. *Miftāḥ al-sa'āda wa miṣbāḥ al-siyāda fī mawḍū'āt al-'ulūm*. Beirut: Dār al-Kutub al-'Ilmiyya.
_______. 1975. *Al-shaqā'iq al-nu'māniyya fī 'ulamā' al-dawla al-'uthmāniyya*. Beirut: Dār al-Kitāb al-'Arabī.
Taşköprülü-zāde. 1975. *Mevzuat'ül-Ulüm*. Istanbul: Er-tu.
Tavakoli-Targhi, Mohamad. 2011. 'Early Persian Modernity.' In Sheldon Pollock, ed., *Forms of Knowledge in Early Modern Asia, Explorations in the Intellectual History of India and Tibet 1500-1800* (257-87). Durham: Duke University Press.
Tekili, Sevim. 1980. 'The Observational Instruments of Istanbul Observatory.' In M Dizer, ed., *Proceedings of the International Symposium on the Observatories in Islam* (33-43). Istanbul.
Tekin, Gönül. 2004. 'Turkish Literature: Thirteenth to Fifteenth Centuries.' In Halil Inalcık and Günsel Renda, eds., *Ottoman Civilisation*, vol. 2 (497-520). Ankara: Republic of Turkey Ministry of Culture and Tourism.
Thevenot, Jean de. 1687. *The Travels of Monsieur de Thevenot into the Levant in Three Parts, viz. into I. Turkey, II. Persia, III. The East-Indies, Newly Done out of French.* Translated by Archibald Lovell. London: H Clark.
Tillotson, Giles HR. 1989. *The Tradition of Indian Architecture: Continuity, Controversy and Change since 1850*. New Haven and London: Yale University Press.
Tim 7 LEMKA. 2006. *Pak Didin Sirojuddin AR Menabur Ombak Kaligrafi: Catatan Media* (Mr Didin Sirojuddin AR spreads the waves of calligraphy: Media clippings). 6th ed. Jakarta: Studio LEMKA. First printed in 2002.
Tirtaamidjaja, N. 1966. *Batik: Pola dan Tjorak.* Jakarta: Penerbit Djambatan.
Tjandrasasmita, Uka. 1984. *Islamic Antiquities of Sendang Duwur.* Jakarta: Pusat Penelitian Arkeologi Nasional.
Tonna, Jo. 1990. 'The Poetics of Arab-Islamic Architecture.' *Muqarnas* 7: 182-97. https://doi.org/10.2307/1523128.
Totton, Mary-Louise. 2005. 'Cosmopolitan Tastes and Indigenous Designs — Virtual Cloth in a Javanese *candi*.' In Ruth Barnes, ed., *Textiles in Indian Ocean Societies* (105-25). London: Routledge.
Trivedi, Madhu. 2010. *The Making of Awadh Culture.* Chennai: Primus Books.
Truschke, Audrey. 2016. *Culture of Encounters: Sanskrit at the Mughal Court.* New York: Colombia University Press.

Ṭūsī, Naṣīr al-Dīn al-. 1964. *Akhlāq-i Naṣīri* (The Nasirean Ethics). Translated by GM Wickens. London: George Allen & Unwin.

Uda, Raja Fuziah Raja Yun and Abdul Rahma Al-Hamadai. 2000. 'Malay Arts and Crafts: Islamic Inspiration in Creativity.' In Mohd. Taib Osman, ed., *Islamic Civilization in the Malay World* (279-353). Kuala Lumpur: Dewan Bahasa dan Pustaka & The Research Centre for Islamic History, Art and Culture.

University of South Australia. 2008. 'The Islamic Spectrum in Australia — Building Cultural Bridges through Understanding.' *University of South Australia News and Events.* Media release, 30 April. Available at: <http://w3.unisa.edu.au/news/2008/300408.asp>. Accessed 21 April 2017.

Ünver, A Süheyl. 1953. *Edirnede Fatih'in Cihannüma Kasrı.* Istanbul: Ismail Akgün Matbaasi.

_______. n.d. *Süleymaniye Kütüphanesine Hediye Ettiği*, Defter 3, Defter 42, Defter 59.

Utama, Andhika. 2011. 'Terjemahan Teks Serat Sana Sunu.' *Jawa Ampuh Blog.* Available at: <http://jawaampuh.blogspot.com.au/2011/01/terjemahan-teks-serat-sana-sunu.html>. Accessed 22 June 2016.

replace with

Valle, Pietro della. 1892. *The Travels of Pietro della Valle in India.* Translated by G. Havers in 1664 and edited by Edward Grey. London: Hakluyt Society.

Van Hout, Itie, ed. 2001. *Batik: Drawn in Wax.* Amsterdam: Royal Tropical Institute.

Veldhuisen, Harmen C. 1993. *Batik Belanda 1840-1940: Dutch Influence in Batik from Java: History and Stories.* Jakarta: Gaya Favorit Press.

Verma, Som Prakash. 1999a. *Mughal Painter of Flora and Fauna, Ustad Mansur.* New Delhi: Abhinav Publications.

_______. 1999b. 'Portraits of Birds and Animals under Jahangir.' In Som Prakesh Verma, ed., *Flora and Fauna in Mughal Art* (12-24). Mumbai: Marg Publications.

Vesalius, Andres. 1964. *De humani corporis fabrica, libri septem.* Bruxelles: Culture et civilisation.

Voegelin, Eric. 2000. *Plato.* Columbia: University of Missouri Press.

Walbridge, John. 2001. *The Wisdom of the Mystic East.* New York: SUNY.

Watson, CW. 2005. 'Islamic Books and their Publishers: Notes on the Contemporary Indonesian Scene.' *Journal of Islamic Studies* 16(2): 177-210. https://doi.org/10.1093/jis/eti131.

Weintraub, Andrew N., ed. 2011. *Islam and Popular Culture in Indonesia and Malaysia.* New York: Routledge.

Weiss, Sarah. 2006. *Listening to an Earlier Java: Aesthetics, Gender and the Music of Wayang in Central Java.* Leiden: KITLV.

White, Andrew Dixon. 1897/1910. *A History of the Warfare of Science with Theology in Christendom.* New York: D Appleton and Company, vol. I 1897, vol. II 1910.

Wijaya, Made. 2014. *Majapahit Style.* Sanur: Yayasan Beringin Berapi.

Wilson, David B. 2002. 'The Historiography of Science and Religion.' In *Gary Ferngren, Science and Religion: A Historical Introduction* (13-29). Baltimore: Johns Hopkins University Press.

Winship, Frederick M. 2004. 'Islamic Art Emerges as Cultural Bridge.' *United Press Internaitonal Inc. (UPI).* Available at: <http://www. upi.com/Islamic-art-emerges-as-cultural-bridge/11311083505680/>. Accessed 21 April 2017.

Witelo. 1977-83. *Perspectiva.* Translated and edited by Mark A Smith. Warsaw: Polish Academy of Sciences Press.

Wolff, Shane. 2010. 'Three Rules of Curating.' *The Art Life*, 15 October. Available at: <http://theartlife.com.au/2010/three-rules-of-curatorship/>. Accessed 21 April 2017.

Woodward, Hiram W. 1977. 'A Chinese Silk Depicted at Candi Sewu.' In KL Hutterer, ed., *Economic Exchange and Social Interaction in Southeast Asia* (233-43). Ann Arbor: University of Michigan.

Yalcinkaya, Alper. 2011. 'Science as an Ally of Religion: A Muslim Appropriation of "the Conflict Thesis".' *The British Journal for the History of Science* 44(2): 161-81.

Yates, Frances. 2002. *Giordano Bruno and the Hermetic Tradition.* New York: Routledge.

_______. 1987. *Theatre of The World.* Chicago: University of Chicago Press.

Yatim, Othman. 1995. *Islamic Arts.* Kuala Lumpur: Dewan Bahasa dan Pustaka.

Yoltar-Yıldırım, Ayşin. 2012. 'The 1455 Oxford *Dilsuznama* and its Literary Significance in the Ottoman Realm.' In S Bağcı and Z Yasa Yaman, eds., *Tradition, Identity, Synthesis, Cultural Crossings and Art: Studies in Honour of Günsel Renda* (243-8). Ankara: Hacateppe University Press.

Yussof, Sheila Ainon. 2014. 'The Politics, Art and Science of Batik.' *IAIS Malaysia Bulletin on Islam and Contemporary Issues* 20: 14.

Zain, Dzul Haimi Mhd. 2005. 'The Art of Nusantara: The Southeast Frontier of Islam.' In Islamic Arts Museum Malaysia, *The Message and the Monsoon: Islamic Art in Southeast Asia* (16-23). Kuala Lumpur: Islamic Arts Museum of Malaysia.

Ziai, Hossein. 2004. 'Suhrawardī on Knowledge and the Experience of Light.' In M Kapstein, ed., *The Presence of Light: Divine Radiance and Religious Experience* (25-44). Chicago: University of Chicago Press.

Zilfi, Madeline C. 1986. 'The Kadızādelis: Discordant Revivalism in Seventeenth-Century Istanbul.' *Journal of Near Eastern Studies* 45(4): 251-69. https://doi.org/10.1086/373194.

CPSIA information can be obtained
at www.ICGtesting.com
Printed in the USA
LVHW022324300919
632711LV00010B/601/P

9 781925 261752